Originally published as:
The Giant Book of Sports Trivia #2

COMPLETE PLAYER'S GUIDE TO SPORTS TRIVIA

by
Damien Christopher
Illustrated by Eric Peterson

Edited by Steve Diamond and Barry Gold

Revised Edition

Modern Promotions/Publishers
A Division of Unisystems, Inc.
New York, New York 10022

Printed in Canada

Contents

Hockey

1. One of the greatest hockey players of all times had the nickname, "the Flower." Can you name him?

2. True or false: the New York Rangers were the first American team in the NHL?

3. True or false: goalies have always been allowed to pass the puck in the NHL?

4. The Pittsburgh Penguins are the only team in the NHL to paint their home ice surface yellow. True or false?

5. Did Guy Lafleur of the Montreal Canadiens ever win the MVP award in the NHL?

6. Who holds the record for most consecutive **fifty-or-more** goal seasons?

7. Has a team in the NHL ever been defeated 15-0 by another NHL team?

8. What does NHL stand for?

9. The NHL record for ties in one season is 24. Which one of these teams owns that record: New York Rangers, St. Louis Blues, or the Philadelphia Flyers?

10. The Philadelphia Flyers won 36 out of 40 games at home during the 1975-76 season. Did they win the Stanley Cup that season?

11. What is the Stanley Cup?

12. What is the Hart Memorial Trophy in the NHL?

13. What is the Vezina trophy?

14. To whom is the Bill Masterson Trophy awarded in the NHL?

15. To whom is the Art Ross Trophy awarded in the NHL?

16. To whom is the James Norris Memorial Trophy awarded?

17. To whom is the Calder Memorial Trophy awarded in the NHL?

18. What is the name of the trophy awarded to a player for outstanding play during the Stanley Cup playoffs?

19. Is there a trophy given in the NHL that is named after a woman?

20. Did Bobby Clarke ever win the MVP award in the NHL?

21. Can you name the only player ever to win the Hart Trophy (MVP) three consecutive years in the NHL?

22. Only one goalie has ever won the Vezina Trophy five consecutive seasons. Can you name him?

23. Where do the cheerleaders stand in the NHL?

24. What position did Bill Durnan play for the Montreal Canadiens?

25. How many players per team are allowed on the ice in the NHL?

26. From the 1970-71 season through the 1973-74 season one player led the NHL in scoring. Can you name him?

27. In the 1960's Stan Mikita won scoring championships four times. For what team did he play?

28. Can you name the Montreal Canadien player who led the league in scoring 1975-76, 1976-77, and 1977-78?

29. Has anybody ever scored seven goals in a game in the NHL?

30. What player has scored the most goals in one game?

31. Does Phil Esposito hold the record for most assists in a single game in the NHL?

32. Who holds the record for most points in a single NHL game: Phil Esposito, Stan Mikita, Bobby Orr or somebody else?

33. Which one of these players compiled the most penalty minutes during a single game in the NHL: Jim Dorey or Randy Holt?

34. Who holds the record for most shutouts by an NHL goalie: Tony Esposito, Ken Dryden or George Hainsworth?

35. Can you name the player who has chalked up the most penalty minutes in a season in the NHL?

36. Who holds the record for most seasons played in the NYL and for whom did he play?

37. Which one of these goalies holds the record for most shutouts in his career in the NHL: Terry Sawchuk, Tony Esposito or Ken Dryden?

38. Who has won the James Norris Memorial Trophy more times: Bobby Orr or Doug Harvey in the NHL?

39. True or false: Denis Potvin, Bryan Trottier and Mike Bossy, all the Islanders, won the rookie of the year award in the NHL?

40. True or false: the last time a Ranger won the rookie of the year honors in the NHL was in 1953-54, Camille Henry?

41. A goalie won the most valuable player award in the Stanley Cup play-offs two years straight: can you name him?

42. From 1955-56 through 1959-60 one team won the Stanley Cup five consecutive years. Name the team and the coach.

43. True or false: the New York Rangers last won the Stanley Cup in 1960-61 in the NHL?

44. Who is the only NHL player to score five goals in his very first game: Bobby Hull, Phil Esposito or Al Hill?

45. In hockey the team that wins the coin toss take the puck out in all three periods. True or false?

46. True or false: the first artificial ice rink was built in Miami, Florida for an exhibition game between two Canadian teams?

47. Jean Ratelle, Brad Park and Joe Zanussi were traded from the New York Rangers to the Boston Bruins in 1975. Whom did they get in return?

48. True or false: Guy Lapointe is an all-star goalie for the Montreal Canadiens?

49. True or false: in the NHL the Jack Adams trophy is awarded to the losing coach in the Stanley Cup finals?

50. True or false: Phil Esposito has played in more NHL all-star games than any other player?

51.. Glenn Hall played in a record 13 all-star games for a goalie in the NHL with three different teams. Name two out of the three teams he played for.

52. What country has won the most Olympic gold medals in hockey: Russia, Canada or Switzerland?

53. True or false: the longest NHL hockey game lasted almost three hours?

54. True or false: the consecutive games played by a goaltender in the NHL is over 500?

55. During the 1971-72 season in the NHL Ross Lonsberry played in 82 regular season games although the regular season schedule called for only 78 games. How did he manage that?

56. The winningest record ever in the NHL was 60 wins and 8 losses with 12 ties. Who set this record?

57. The New York Rangers set the record for most losses in a single season in the NHL. True or false?

58. True or false: a world championship hockey once ended in a 47-0 score?

59. What famous hockey star moves faster than any other player on skates?

60. Where did the largest crowd ever assemble to see a professional hockey game?

61. Is there a Hockey Hall of Fame?

62. Who won the 1980 Stanley Cup final in hockey?

63. In the 1980 Stanley Cup series, which player scored the most points, Mike Bossy or Bryan Trottier?

64. Who won the 1980 Conn Smythe trophy as most valuable player in the Stanley Cup?

65. During the 1979-80 NHL season which team had the best regular season record, the Islanders, the Flyers or the Canadiens?

66. Which one of these players won the Art Ross trophy for scoring during the 1979-80 season in the NHL, Wayne Gretzky or Marcel Dionne?

67. On January 7, 1980 the Philadelphia Flyers' record of 35 consecutive games without a defeat was halted by whom?

68. Has anybody ever scored more than 800 goals in his career in the NHL?

69. Which one of these teams posted the best record in the NHL during the 1980-81 season: the Islanders, the Flyers or the Canadiens?

70. Who was the top scorer in the NHL in the 1980-81 season, Mike Bossy, Wayne Gretzky or Marcel Dionne?

71. What are the names of the divisions in the Campbell Conference?

72. What are the names of the divisions in the Wales Conference?

73. How many teams are there in the National Hockey League: 17, 21, or 24?

74. Can you name the teams in the Patrick Division in the NHL?

75. Can you name the teams in the Smythe Division in the NHL?

76. Can you name the teams in the Adams Division in the NHL?

77. Can you name the teams in the Norris Division in the NHL?

78. How old was Gordie Howe when he retired from professional hockey?

79. Which one of these players scored the most goals in the NHL during a regular season: Mike Bossy, Wayne Gretzky or Marcel Dionne?

80. Which one of these teams won the Patrick Division in the NHL during the 1980-81 season: the New York Islanders or the Philadelphia Flyers?

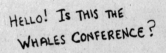

86. Two teams set new Stanley Cup playoff records for penalties in the NHL. Can you name the teams and the records?

87. Who won the 1981 Stanley Cup championship in the NHL?

88. Which one of these Islander players won the 1981 Conn Smythe trophy as the most valuable player in the playoffs: Mike Bossy, Butch Goring or Denis Potvin?

89. Which one of these players scored the most in the 1981 Stanley Cup playoffs: Mike Bossy, Butch Goring, or Steve Payne?

90. Ted Kennedy, who played with the Toronto Maple Leafs in the NHL had a nickname. Can you recall it?

81. Which one of these teams won the Smythe Division during the 1980-81 NHL regular season: the Chicago Black Hawks or the St. Louis Blues?

82. Which one of these teams won the Adams Division in the NHL during the 1980-81 regular season: the Buffalo Sabres or the Boston Bruins?

83. Which one of these teams won the Norris Division in the NHL during the 1980-81 regular season: the Los Angeles Kings or the Montreal Canadiens?

84. For the first time in NHL history three goalies shared the Vezina Trophy. (Goaltenders with the fewest goals allowed in regular season play by one team, all players must play in at least 25 games.) Can you name the team they played for?

85. Can you name the player who set a new NHL record in assists during the 1980-81 season?

91. Can you name the coach who has won more Stanley Cups than any other coach in history? Here's a hint: he coached the Canadiens.

92. Who was known as the "Rocket" in the NHL?

93. True or false: Maurice "The Rocket" Richard had a younger brother called "The Pocket Rocket"?

94. Between what years was the WHA in operation?

95. Can you name the seven teams that were left when the WHA folded in 1979?

96. True or false: Maurice "The Rocket" Richard once coached in the WHA?

97. What team has won the most Stanley Cup finals in NHL competition?

98. Which one of these players has played in the most Stanley Cup victories in the NHL: Henri Richard, Gordie Howe or Bobby Orr?

99. Only four teams have won Stanley Cups since 1968 in the NHL. Can you name them?

100. Can you name the player who played in the most games in his career in the NHL?

101. True or false: Gordie Howe has the record for most consecutive games in the NHL?

102. What great NHL player has the alltime record for assists in his career?

103. Name the player who has scored both 50 or more goals and 100 or more points for six consecutive seasons in the NHL.

104. What is a "hat trick" in hockey?

105. Which one of these players has the record for hat tricks in his career in the NHL: Gordie Howe, Guy Lafleur or Phil Esposito?

106. Which one of these teams holds the record for the longest winning streak without a tie: Boston, Montreal or Chicago?

107. Which one of these teams holds the record for most goals in a regular season by a single line: Islanders, Canadiens or Bruins?

108. What New York Ranger as of 1981 set the WHA record for goals in a single season?

109. What year did the N.Y. Rangers last win the Stanley Cup?

110. In 1947 Billy Taylor of the Detroit Red Wings set a WHL record with 7 assists in a single game. In 1980 a NHL player tied that record: who is he and what team did he play for?

111. The longest a goalie in the NHL has gone without a defeat is 33 games. Can you name him?

112. Has a goalie in the NHL ever had more than 5 consecutive shutouts during the regular season?

113. Who is the only goaltender ever to score a goal in a NHL game?

114. What NHL player was known as the "Golden Jet"?

115. In the 1974-75 season a player scored 50 goals in 50 games in the WHA. Can you name him?

116. Which one of these players did not play for the Montreal Canadiens: Jean Beliveau, Howie Moreng, Maurice Richard, or Henri Richard?

117. Who captained the 1980 U.S. Olympic team in hockey?

118. Who was the goalie for the U.S. Olympic team in hockey in 1980?

119. Who is the only player ever to win a gold medal in the Olympics and to be on the Stanley Cup championship team in ice hockey in the same year?

120. Who won the 1980 Olympic finals in ice hockey in Lake Placid, New York?

125. What is "offsides" in hockey?

126. What is "icing" in hockey?

127. Who has won more Art Ross trophies in the NHL, Phil Esposito or Gordie Howe?

128. In the NHL hooking is a foul that earns a player 5 minutes in the penalty box. True or false?

129. Which one of these players has won the Hart trophy the most times in the NHL, Maurice Richard, Gordie Howe or Phil Esposito?

130. What team did Jean Beliveau play for in the NHL?

121. Who did the U.S. hockey team beat in the finals to win the gold medal in 1980?

122. In 1947 two NHL players were suspended for life for alleged association with gamblers. Who were they and who suspended them?

123. True or false: all NHL hockey rinks are the same size?

124. True or false: 16 out of the 21 NHL teams make the playoffs?

131. For what team did Eddie Shore play in the NHL?

132. Has anybody ever won the Hart, Ross and Lady Byng trophies all in the same year in the NHL?

133. True or false: George Hainsworth, formerly of the Montreal Canadiens, holds the all-time single season shutout by a goalie in the NHL?

134. Who was known as "Boom Boom" in the NHL?

135. Who coached the gold medal winning American Olympics hockey team in 1980?

136. Has a defenseman ever scored 7 points in a single NHL game?

137. Can you name the New York Islander player who holds the NHL record for points in a single season by a rookie?

138. True or false: Bobby Hull and Denis Hull are brothers?

139. Were the first NHL franchises from Canada or the United States?

140. In what years did the U.S. hockey team win gold medals in Olympic competition?

141. Has the United States hockey team ever won the silver medal in Olympic competition?

142. What is a screen shot in hockey?

143. True or false: a hockey puck used in the NHL weighs 10 ounces?

144. True or false: a player may score a goal by batting the puck with his arm or hand only in the NHL?

145. What does it mean when a goalie gloves the puck?

146. True or false: a misconduct penalty is two minutes in the penalty box for the offending player in the NHL?

147. Who was the first team to win three straight Stanley Cups in NHL competition?

148. What do these former NHL goalies have in common: Roy Worters, Charlie Rayner, Al Rollins and Jacques Plante?

149. What position did Doug Harvey play and for what teams in the NHL did he play?

150. When Bobby Orr retired after 12 seasons in the NHL he was second on the all-time goal scoring list for defensemen; who was number one?

WE'RE EITHER GOING TO HAVE TO USE A LIGHTER PUCK, OR GET THICKER ICE.

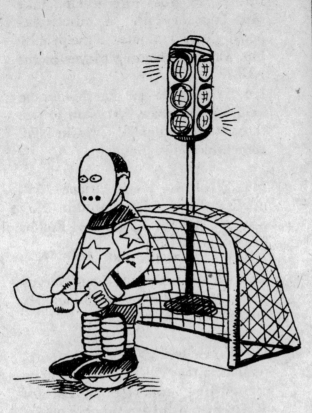

151. From 1969-70 to 1974-75 Bobby Orr led the NHL in assists all but one season. Who beat him out the one season and what year was it?

152. Wayne Gretzky of the Edmonton Oilers set a NHL record in total points for a regular season in 1980-81 with 164. Whose record did he beat out?

153. Of Gordie Howe's 801 career goals scored in the NHL, how many came on penalty shots?

154. True or false: a WHA game was once cancelled on Friday the thirteenth because the Zamboni went through the ice?

155. Can you name the only two players ever to score 50 goals in both the NHL and WHA in one season?

156. The 1934 baseball St. Louis Cardinals were known as the gashouse gang. The same name was given to a NHL team in the 1931-32 season. Can you name the team?

157. The Montreal Canadiens have won the most Stanley Cups in the NHL with 21. What team next to the Canadiens has won the most times?

158. True or false: the New York Rangers once had to use their coach as a goaltender in the Stanley Cup finals?

159. What is the function of the red and green lights behind the net in NHL games?

160. What is the attacking zone in hockey?

161. What is the crease in hockey?

162. Where does forechecking take place in hockey?

163. What is a power play in hockey?

164. What is the line that divides the ice in half in hockey?

165. What is roughing?

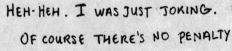

HEH-HEH. I WAS JUST JOKING. OF COURSE THERE'S NO PENALTY.

Answers

1. Guy Lafleur of the Montreal Canadiens. Lafleur means flower in French.

2. False. The Boston Bruins were the first. They entered the league in 1924.

3. False. It wasn't until the 1920-21 season that the goalie was allowed to pass the puck.

4. False. Since the 1949-50 season all NHL rinks have been painted white for viewing ease.

5. Yes. Lafleur won the MVP award in 1977 and in 1978, while leading his team to Stanley Cup victories both of those years.

6. Mike Bossy holds the record with seven consecutive seasons.

7. Yes. On January 23, 1944 the New York Rangers were shut out by the Detroit Red Wings 15-0 for the worst defeat ever in the NHL.

8. National Hockey League.

9. The Philadelphia Flyers set the record with 24 ties during the 1969-70 season.

10. No. The Montreal Canadiens won it in 1975-76. The Flyers had won the previous two Stanley Cup finals (1973-74, 1974-75).

16. The James Norris Trophy is awarded to the NHL best defenseman by vote of the league's writers and broadcasters.

17. The Calder Trophy is awarded to the league's outstanding rookie by vote of the writers and broadcasters in the NHL.

18. The Conn Smythe Trophy is awarded to the most valuable player in the Stanley Cup playoffs by vote of the league Governers.

19. Yes. The Lady Byng Trophy is awarded to the player combining the highest type of sportsmanship and gentlemanly conduct plus a high standard of playing ability. Lady Byng was the wife of the Governor-General of Canada. She presented the trophy to the NHL in 1925.

20. While playing for the Philadelphia Flyers Bobby Clarke won the MVP award three times: 1972-73, 1974-75, and 1975-76, when he had his best season with 119 points.

11. The Stanley Cup was donated by Frederick Arthur, Lord Stanley of Preston and the son of the Earl of Derby, who was the Governor-General of Canada from 1889 to 1893. The award is given to the winner of the NHL play-off at the end of the season.

12. The Hart trophy is awarded to the NHL's most valuable player by vote of the NHL's hockey writers and broadcasters. The trophy is named after Cecil Hart, former manager-coach of the Montreal Canadiens.

13. The Vezina Trophy is awarded to the NHL goalie or goalies for the team which gives up the fewest goals during the regular season. A goalie must play in 25 games to be eligible.

14. The Bill Masterson Trophy is awarded to "the NHL player who exemplifies the qualities of perseverance, sportsmanship and dedication to hocky." It is named after the late Minnesota North Star player.

15. The Art Ross Trophy is awarded to the player who compiles the highest number of points during the regular season. The trophy is named after the former manager-coach of the Boston Bruins.

21. If you said Bobby Orr you are right. Playing for the Boston Bruins, Orr won the award three years straight 1969-70, 1970-71, 1971-72: He had his best season in 1970-71 when he scored 139 points.

22. Jacques Plante of the Montreal Canadiens in the seasons 1955-56 through 1959-60. During that span the Canadiens won the Stanley Cup all five seasons.

23. Trick question! There aren't any cheerleaders in the NHL.

24. Durnan played goalie for the Canadiens and won the Vezina Trophy six times including four straight (1943-44 through 1946-47).

25. Six at a time. The rules used to call for nine, were later changed to seven, then to six.

26. Phil Esposito of the Boston Bruins. During that four season span he scored 560 points, averaging an incredible 140 points a season!

27. Stan Mikita won the scoring championship in the 1963-64 through 1967-68 seasons playing for the Chicago Black Hawks. His best season was the 1966-67 when he scored 97 points in 70 games.

28. Guy Lafleur did that, with his best season in 1976-77, when he scored 136 points.

29. Yes, just once. Joe Malone of the Quebec Bulldogs scored seven times January 31, 1920 playing against the Toronto Pats. Malone led the league in scoring that year with 48 points in 24 games.

30. Joe Malone scored seven goals January 31, 1920.

31. Bill Taylor of the Detroit Redwings and Wayne Gretsky of the Edmonton Oilers, share the record with seven assists.

32. Darryl Sittler of the Maple Leafs holds that record with 10 points (six goals, four assists) against the Boston Bruins February 7, 1976.

33. While playing for the L.A. Kings on March 11, 1979, Randy Holt had 67 penalty minutes.

34. George Hainsworth of the Montreal Canadians with 22 during the 1928-1929 season.

35. Dave Shultz of the Philadelphia Flyers had an incredible 472 minutes in the penalty box during the 1975-76 season while playing for the Stanley Cup winners that season.

36. Gordie Howe, who played 26 seasons for the Detroit Red Wings 1946-47 through 1970-71 and the Hartford Whalers 1979-80.

37. Terry Sawchuk with 103 career shutouts while playing for Detroit, Boston, Toronto, Los Angeles, and the New York Rangers.

38. Doug Harvey of the Montreal Canadiens won the trophy seven times in eight seasons, but the great Bobby Orr won the trophy that goes to the leagues best defenseman eight seasons consecutively from 1967-68 through 1974-75.

39. True. Potvin won it in 1973-74, Trottier in 1975-76 and Bossy won it in 1977-78.

40. False. Steve Vickers won the award in 1972-73 when he scored 53 points in 61 games for the New York Rangers.

41. Bernie Parent of the Philadelphia Flyers. He led them to two championships, 1973-74 and 1974-75.

42. The Montreal Canadiens led by coach Toe Blake completely dominated the NHL during that span.

43. No way. The Chicago Black Hawks won that season. The last time the Rangers won the cup was in the 1939-40 season.

44. Al Hill, of course.

45. False. The puck is dropped at center ice to start a period.

46. False. The first artificial ice rink was built in 1879 at the old Madison Square Garden in New York.

47. Phil Esposito and Carol Vadnais.

48. False. Lapointe is all-star, alright, but he played defense, not goalie, for the Canadiens.

49. False. The Jack Adams Trophy is awarded to the coach of the year by vote of the NHL Broadcasters Association, in honor of long-time Red Wing coach-manager, Jack Adams.

50. False. Gordie Howe has that record with 22 all-star appearances during his fantastic career.

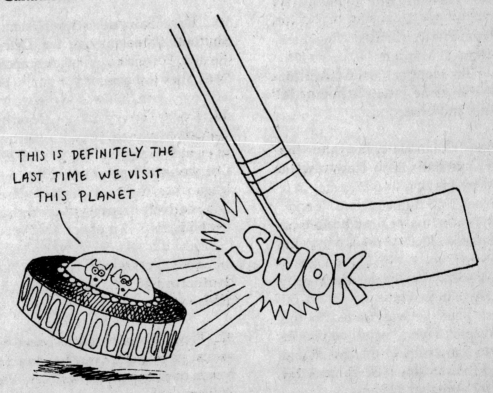

THIS IS DEFINITELY THE LAST TIME WE VISIT THIS PLANET

SWOK

51. From 1955 to 1969 Glenn Hall played with the Red Wings, the Black Hawks and the Blues. Hall won the Vezina trophy three times: 1962-63, 1966-67 with Chicago and 1968-69 with St. Louis.

52. Canada has won the Olympic gold medal a record six times: 1920,-24, -28,-32, -48, -52. They have also won the world title 19 times.

53. True. The Detroit Red Wings beat the Montreal Maroons 1-0 in the 17th minute in Montreal on March 25, 1936. The game lasted 2 hours, 56 minutes, and 30 seconds.

54. True. Glenn Hall playing for the Red Wings and Black Hawks set a record by playing in 502 games in a row from 1955 till he suffered a back injury in a game against Boston on November 7, 1962.

55. Lonsberry started the season with the L.A. Kings where he played 50 games. Then he was traded to the Philadelphia Flyers, who had played only 46 games up to that point. He played the remaining 32 games with them for a total of 82 games.

56. The Montreal Canadiens, of course. They earned a record 132 points and the best record ever in the NHL during the regular 80-game season in 1976-77.

57. False, but if you said the Washington Capitols you are correct. During the 1974-75 season, their first in the NHL, they lost a record 67 games and won only 8. In that season they lost 17 straight.

58. True. On February 12, 1949 Canada beat Denmark 47-0.

59. The fastest speed measured for any player is 29.7 mph for Bobby Hull (Chicago Black Hawks), who also has the highest puck speed. His shots have been measured at speeds up to 118.3 mph.

60. The largest crowd ever to see a pro hockey game gathered in the Montreal Forum on January 7, 1974. There were 19,040 people in attendance.

61. Yes, the Hockey Hall of Fame is in the Canadian National Exhibition Park in West-End, Toronto.

62. The New York Islanders defeated the Philadelphia Flyers 4 games to 2 in the best of seven series.

63. Bryan Trottier of the Islanders led all scorers with 29 points, (12 goals, 17 assists).

64. Bryan Trottier of the world champion Islanders scored 29 points to lead all scorers and his team to victory.

65. The Philadelphia Flyers had the record in the NHL in 1979-80 with a 48-12-20 mark and a total of 116 points.

66. Gretzky of Edmonton and Dionne of Los Angeles tied for the lead in points with 137, but Dionne scored 53 goals compared to Gretzky's 51 and took the trophy.

67. The Minnesota North Stars beat the Flyers 7-1 in Minnesota to end the longest unbeaten streak in the NHL's history. During that streak they won 25 games and tied 10 others.

68. Yes, only one man has done that: Gordie Howe, who scored 801 goals in his career playing for the Detroit Red Wings and the New England Whalers.

69. The New York Islanders with a record of 48-18-14 with 110 points.

70. Wayne Gretzky of Edmonton set a new points record for regular season play with 164 points (55 goals, 109 assists).

71. The Patrick Division and the Smythe Division.

72. The Adams Division and the Norris Division.

73. There are 21 teams in the NHL as of the 1980-81 season.

74. The teams in the Patrick Division are the New York Islanders, Philadelphia, Calgary, New York Rangers and Washington.

75. The teams in the Smythe Division are St. Louis, Chicago, Vancouver, Edmonton, Colorado and Winnipeg.

76. The teams in the Adams Division are Buffalo, Boston, Minnesota, Quebec and Toronto.

77. The teams in the Norris Division in the NHL are Montreal, Los Angeles, Pittsburgh, Hartford and Detroit.

78. When Howe retired in 1980 he was 52 years old. His professional playing career with the NHL and the WHA lasted 32 years.

79. Wayne Gretsky of the Edmonton Oilers by far. He scored 92 goals in the 1981-1982 season.

80. The New York Islanders with a 48-18-14 record with 110 points compared to the Flyers 41-24-15 record with 107 points. The Islanders went on to win the Stanley Cup.

81. The Blues completely dominated the Smythe Division with a 45-18-17 record with 107 points compared to the second place Black Hawks, who had a 31-33-16 record with only 78 points.

82. The Sabres beat out the Bruins with a 39-20-21 record with 99 points compared to Boston's 37-30-13 record with 87 points.

83. In a very close race the Canadiens just beat out the Kings with a 45-22-13 record with 103 points compared to L.A.'s 43-24-13 record with 99 points.

84. Richard Sevigny, Denis Herron and Michel Larocque, who was traded to Toronto during the regular season, all appeared in enough games for the Montreal Canadiens to win the award.

85. Edmonton Oiler Wayne Gretzky assisted on 109 goals during the regular season to break Bobby Orr's record of 102 assists set during the 1970-71 season.

FACE-OFF

86. On April 9, 1981 the New York Rangers and the L.A. Kings set three new playoff records for penalties: 43 penalties in a period broke the 36 achieved in 1980 by the Islanders and the Bruins; and the Rangers' 24 penalties broke the record of 19 set by the Atlanta Flames in 1979. In total there were 267 minutes of penalties, also a record. The Kings won 5-4.

87. For the second straight year the New York Islanders captured the crown defeating the Minnesota North Stars 4 games to 1 in the best of seven series.

88. Butch Goring won for the Islanders. He scored two goals in the final game to wrap it up for the world champions.

89. Mike Bossy of the Islanders set a new scoring record with 35 points (17 goals, 18 assists) in the playoffs. He also set a record for most goals in a season and playoffs with 85.

90. Ted, "Teeder," Kennedy captained the Leafs from 1948 to 1955 and again in 1956-67. He was known as one of the greatest face-off artists ever to play.

91. Toe Blake coached the Montreal Canadiens to eight Stanley Cups in 1956, -57, -58, -59, -60, -65, -66, and 1968; more than any other coach in history.

92. Maurice "The Rocket" Richard, who scored 965 points in his career with the Canadiens and once scored 50 goals in 50 games during the 1944-45 season. Richard was a member of the team that won five straight Stanley Cups (1956-1960).

93. True. Henri Richard, fifteen years younger than his brother, played with the Canadiens from 1955 to 1973 and scored a total of 978 career points.

94. The WHA operated for seven seasons from 1972-73 through 1978-79.

95. The seven teams left were the Quebec Nordiques, the Winnipeg Jets, the New England Whalers, the Edmonton Oilers, the Cincinnati Stingers, the Indianapolis Racers, and the Birmingham Bulls.

96. True. Richard coached for two games and was replaced by Maurice Filion after a 1-1 record with the Quebec Nordiques.

97. The Montreal Canadiens have won 22 finals in 1916, -24, -30-31, -44, -46, -53, -56-60, -65-66, -68-69, -71, -73, -76-79.

98. Henri Richard, who played in 11 Stanley Cup victory games with Montreal.

99. The Montreal Canadiens (1968, -69, -71, -73, -76, -77, -78, -79), the Boston Bruins (1970, -72), the Philadelphia Flyers (1974, -75), and the New York Islanders (1980, -81).

100. Gordie Howe, who played in 1,687 NHL games. During that time he set records in goals, assists, and points scored.

101. False. Gary Unger, playing for Toronto, Detroit, St. Louis, and Atlanta, played in 914 straight games from February 24, 1968 through December 21, 1979 when a shoulder injury put him out of action.

102. Gordie Howe, who played the Detroit Red Wings and Hartford Whalers, scored a record 1,850 points in his career. 1,049 were assists.

103. Guy Lafleur of the Montreal Canadiens accomplished that from 1974-75 through 1979-80.

104. A "hat trick" is any 3-goal effort by a player in one game.

105. Phil Esposito has this record with a total of 32 hat tricks in his 17-year NHL career while playing for Boston, Chicago and the New York Rangers.

106. In the 1929-30 season, the Boston Bruins won 14 consecutive games without a tie.

107. The Montreal Canadien line of Guy Lafleur, Steve Shutt and Jacques Lemaire scored a total of 150 goals in the 1976-77 season for a record.

108. Anders Hedberg, playing for the Winnipeg Jets, scored 83 goals during the 1976-77 regular season.

109. The N.Y. Rangers won the Stanley Cup in 1940.

110. Wayne Gretzky of the Edmonton Oilers assisted on 7 goals against Washington, February 15, 1980.

BUT COACH, WHAT DO YOU MEAN 'MAYBE I SHOULD SIT THIS GAME OUT'?

113. Billy Smith of the New York Islanders against the Colorado Rockies in Denver, November 28, 1979. When the Rockies removed their goaltender during a penalty, a Rockie defenseman's pass skidded down the entire length of the ice into his own goal. Smith of the Islanders was given credit for the goal because he was the last opposing player to touch it.

114. Bobby Hull, who played with the Chicago Black Hawks for 15 seasons. He scored 1,153 career points, 604 of them goals. He was known as the "Golden Jet" because of his fast skating and shooting.

115. Playing for the Winnipeg Jets, Bobby Hull became the first since Maurice Richard to score 50 goals in 50 games. He finished the season with 77 goals in 78 games on 556 shot on goal, also a record.

116. Trick question. They all played for the Canadiens and are the only players to have their numbers retired by the club.

117. Mike Eruzione was the team leader. He scored the winning goal in the 4-3 victory over the Soviet Union.

118. Jim Craig. He played every minute of every game and allowed only 15 goals in seven games for the gold medal winning U.S. team.

111. Gerry Cheevers of the Boston Bruins set that record during the 1971-72 season.

112. Yes. Alex Connell of the Ottawa Senators kept his opponents scoreless over 461 minutes, 29 seconds in the 1927-28 season. Over that period he had six shutouts.

119. Ken Morrow, who now plays with the New York Islanders, played on the gold medal winning U.S. hockey team and on the world champion Islanders in 1980.

120. The U.S. hockey team won the gold medal for only the second time in Olympic history in 1980.

121. The U.S. defeated Finland 4-2 in front of 10,000 people and millions watching on televison.

122. Clarence Campbell suspended Bill Taylor and Don Gallinger March 9, 1947. They were cleared of the charges in 1970 when they were both too old to play.

123. False. 200 feet by 85 feet is recommended, but his isn't always true; Detroit's Olympia Stadium is 200 feet by 83 feet; Boston's Garden is 191 feet by 85 feet and Chicago Stadium is 188 feet by 85 feet.

124. True. Based on the number of points a team has accumulated 16 out of the 21 NHL teams make the Stanley Cup playoffs.

125. If a player enters the attacking zone ahead of the puck or if a player sends a pass from his defensive zone to a teammate whose skates are over the center red line, the referee will call the play offsides.

126. It is an infraction of the rules which calls for a "face off" in the offending team's goal area. It is called when the puck is shot from the defensive side of the middle redline past the opposition goal line without being touched by any player.

127. Trick question! Both have won a record four consecutive Ross trophies: Esposito in 1971, -72, -73, -74 and Howe in 1951, -52, -53, -54.

128. False. Hooking, which is called when a player restrains another with his stick, earns a minor two minute penalty.

129. Gordie Howe has the all-time NHL record with six Hart trophies in his career (1952, -53, -57, -58, -60, -63). Richard has won it just once in 1947 and Esposito has won twice in 1969 and 1974.

130. Jean Beliveau played for the Montreal Canadiens from the 1950-51 season until the 1970-71 season. He won the Hart trophy twice (1956, -64), the Ross trophy once (1956—47 goals, 41 assists) and Conn Smythe trophy once in 1965.

131. Eddie Shore played for the Boston Bruins from the 1926-27 season until part of the 1939-40 season when he was traded to the New York Americans and finished out the season and retired. Shore was a great defenseman who won the Hart trophy four times (1933, -35, -36, -38) and was an all-star seven years.

132. Yes. Stan Mikita, who played for the Chicago Black Hawks had an outstanding 1966-67 season. He scored 97 points (35 goals, 62 assists) in 70 games and won the Hart, Ross, and Lady Byng trophies that year.

133. True. In the 1928-29 season Hainsworth had 22 shutouts in 44 games with an amazing .0198 average. This is the only time in NHL history that anybody has ever averaged under 1.00 per game.

134. Bernie Geoffrian, who played for the Montreal Canadiens (1950-1964) and the New York Rangers (1966-68). He won the Hart trophy in 1961 and led the NHL in scoring twice (1954-55 and 1960-61). In his career he had a total of 822 points (393 goals, 429 assists).

135. Herb Brooks, then head coach at the University of Minnesota and now New York Ranger head coach.

136. Yes. On November 7, 1973 Bobby Orr scored 7 points against the New York Rangers and became the first defenseman ever to do this.

137. Bryan Trottier, who scored 95 in the 1975-76 season and won the Calder Memorial trophy as the league's outstanding rookie.

138. True. Bobby Hull is five years older than younger brother Denis.

139. The first two NHL franchises were the Montreal Canadiens and the Toronto Maple Leafs on November 22, 1917.

140. The United States captured the gold medal in Olympic competition in 1960 and again in the 1980 Olympics with the "miracle team."

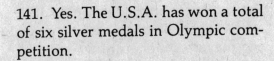

146. False. A misconduct penalty is incurred when a player deliberately injures another player or uses abusive language or commits any other gross action. The penalty can earn the player ten minutes or the remainder of the game in penalty time.

147. If you said the Canadiens, you are wrong. It was the Toronto Maple Leafs, who accomplished that in 1947, -48, -49.

148. They were the only goalies in NHL history to win the Hart trophy; Worters with the N.Y. Americans in 1928-29, Rayner of the N.Y. Rangers in 1949-50, Rollins of the Chicago Black Hawks in 1954-55, and most recently Plante of the Montreal Canadiens in 1961-62.

149. Harvey was an outstanding defenseman who won the Norris trophy seven out of eight seasons in the NHL. During his career he played for the Canadiens, Rangers, Red Wings, and Blues.

150. Red Kelly, who played for Toronto and Detroit, scored a total of 281 goals in his years in the league compared to Orr's 270 goals in his career.

141. Yes. The U.S.A. has won a total of six silver medals in Olympic competition.

142. A screen shot in hockey occurs when a player shoots the puck and the goalie's vision is partially or totally blocked by another player.

143. False. A puck is three inches in diameter, one inch thick and weighs up to 6 ounces.

144. False. However, if an official feels that this was done unintentionally a goal will be a awarded.

145. The term means that the goalie has caught the puck with his glove.

151. In the 1972-73 season Orr had 72 assists, but Phil Esposito had 75 assists that season; enough to beat him out.

152. Phil Esposito scored 76 goals and assisted on 76 others in the 1970-71 season for a total of 152 points. The record held for ten years.

153. In his 26 years of NHL competition Howe scored just two penalty shot goals.

154. True. On October 13, 1972 the Philadelphia Blazers had to cancel their game because before the game the Zamboni machine came out to resurface the ice and ended up going right through it. As the unhappy event took place thousands of fans expressed their displeasure by throwing the souvenir pucks, which they had received when entering the stadium, onto the ice.

155. Only Bobby Hull (five in the NHL, four in the WHA) and Blaine Stoughton (one in the NHL, one in the WHA) have accomplished this feat.

156. The Toronto Maple Leafs were given that name by the Toronto press as they marched to the Stanley Cup that year.

157. The Toronto Maple Leafs have won the Stanley Cup eleven times in the NHL.

158. True. In 1928 the Rangers were forced into using their coach, Lester Patrick, in the goal during an overtime period in which the Rangers scored after 7 minutes and 15 seconds to win 2-1.

159. The red light is turned on by a judge when a goal is scored and the green light indicates that the clock has been stopped and a goal cannot be scored.

160. The area from an opponent's blue line to the goal.

161. The rectangular area marked off in front of each net. Only the goalie is permitted in the crease and an opposing player cannot score when in the crease unless he is pinned there by his opponent.

162. Forechecking is checking the opponent in his own zone.

163. A manpower advantage resulting from a penalty to the opposing team.

164. The center line is called the red line.

165. Minor fisticuffs or shoving. It calls for a minor penalty of two minutes.

Football

GEE COACH, I KNOW YOU SPENT ALL WEEK ON THIS GAME-PLAN, BUT I REALLY THINK WE SHOULD TRY SOMETHING ELSE.

1. When did the National Football League come into existence?

2. True or false: Amos Alonzo Stagg coached college football longer than anybody else?

3. Who is the winningest coach of all time in the National Football League?

4. True or false: a high school coach has won more games than any professional or college coach?

5. Which one of these players set the record for touchdowns for a rookie in the NFL: Earl Campbell, O.J. Simpson or Gale Sayers?

6. What former Kansas City Chief holds the record for helmet kicking?

7. True or false: the most regularly contested series between two college football teams is between Princeton and Harvard?

8. Which one of these college teams holds the record for the most consecutive games without a loss: Washington, Oklahoma or Notre Dame?

9. True or false: a college team once beat another 222 to 0?

10. True or false: a college running back once rushed for more than 500 yards in one game?

11. True or false: There was once an all-American team with a player who was 47 years old in college?

12. Which one of these college players scored the most points in his career: Tony Dorsett, O.J. Simpson or George Rogers?

13. True or false: Lydell Mitchell holds the college football record for points in a season?

14. The most points by a player in a college football game is 44. Can you name him?

15. Glenn Davis, who played for Army, 1943-46, holds the record for touchdowns in a college career with another player. Can you name the other player?

16. Which one of these players scored the most touchdowns in a season in college: Charles White, Lydell Mitchell or Tony Dorsett?

17. True or false: Jim Brown holds the college record for most touchdowns in a single game?

18. Which one of these players holds the record for field goals in a college career: Tony Franklin or Obed Ariri?

19. Who holds the record for field goals in a single season in college football?

20. The record for field goals in a game by a college player is held by three players. What is the record?

21. What is the record for most consecutive field goals made in college football: 10, 12 or 13?

22. True or false: the longest field goal ever made in college is longer than the NFL record?

23. True or false: a college player made 125 consecutive points after touchdowns?

24. Which one of these running backs holds the record for career yards in rushing in college: Jim Brown, Tony Dorsett or Archie Griffin?

25. True or false: Tony Dorsett holds the single season rushing record for college?

26. Can you name the player who holds the modern (after 1938) day college football rushing record for a single game? Here's a hint: he played for Georgia Tech.

27. True or false: Greg Pruitt averaged over nine yards a carry for Oklahoma in 1971?

28. Has there ever been a 99 yard run from scrimmage in college football?

29. True or false: Joe Namath holds the record for passing for the most yards in a college career?

30. Can you name the quarterback who holds the record for most yards gained in one game?

31. True or false: Joe Theismann holds the college record for most touchdowns passed for in a career?

32. Can you name the college quarterback who holds the record for most touchdown passes in a season?

33. The most consecutive complete passes by a college quarterback is?

34. How many yards did the longest pass play from scrimmage go in a game?

35. True or false: Howard Twilley holds the college record for most receptions in a career?

36. True or false: Lynn Swan holds the college record for most reception during a season?

37. True or false: the most receptions in a game in college football by one receiver is 22?

38. True or false: John Jefferson holds the college record for the most passes caught in one game?

39. What college team won two consecutive Cotton Bowls in 1978 and 1979?

40. What college team has scored the most points in a season?

49. Which one of these players has the record for most points in a career in pro football: George Blanda, O.J. Simpson or Jim Brown?

50. True or false: Paul Hornung has the pro football record for scoring the most points in a single season?

YOU FORGOT TO LET GO OF THE BALL AGAIN!

41. What is the record for most touchdown passes caught in a single game: 4, 5 or 6?

42. What college team lost the most fumbles in a game?

43. What is the most interceptions by one player ever recorded in a college game?

44. True or false: the longest punt ever in college football went 91 yards?

45. Has anybody ever returned a punt 100 yards in college football?

46. There have been over 100 players to return kickoffs of 100 yards in college football. Has anybody ever done this twice?

47. Name the player who played in the most AFL and NFL games during his career.

48. Who was the top player chosen in the 1983 draft?

51. Which one of these players holds the record for most points during his rookie season in the NFL: Gale Sayers, Jim Brown or O.J. Simpson?

52. Which one of these players has the pro football record for most points scored in a single game: Gale Sayers, Ernie Nevers or Paul Hornung?

53. Don Hutson has the pro football record of 8 seasons leading the league in scoring. Who did he play for and what was his nickname?

54. Which one of these players scored the most touchdowns in his career: Jim Brown, Lenny Moore or George Blanda?

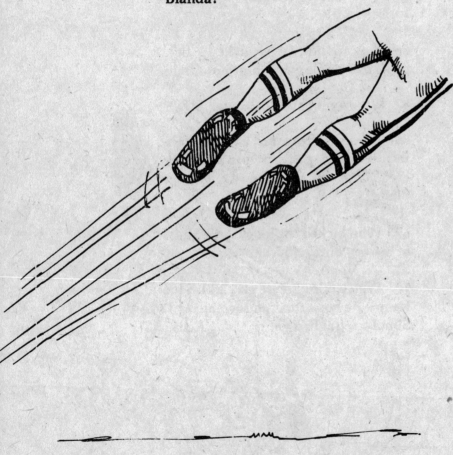

55. Which one of these great players hold the record for most touchdowns in a season: Gale Sayers, O.J. Simpson, Chuck Foreman or Jim Brown.

56. Which one of these players scored more touchdowns in his rookie season: Tony Dorsett, Earl Campbell or John Jefferson?

57. True or false: Dub Jones once scored six touchdowns in a game to tie a NFL record?

58. Which one of these players has the record for the most consecutive games scoring a touchdown: Lenny Moore or O.J. Simpson?

59. Who has led the league in points after touchdowns the most times in pro football?

60. Has a kicker in pro football ever had 10 or more points after touchdowns in a single game? If so, who?

61. Which one of these kickers has the record for most consecutive points after touchdown: Jim Turner, George Blanda or Tommy Davis?

62. What position did Danny Villanueva play in pro football?

63. Can you name the Cleveland Brown kicker who led the league in field goals 5 times during the 1950's?

64. Who has kicked the most field goals in his career, Fred Cox or George Blanda?

65. The most field goals kicked by one player in a single season is 34. Who has that record and what team did he play for?

66. Has anybody ever kicked 7 field goals in a single game in pro football?

67. Who won the 1984 Sugar Bowl?

68. Who has the record for most consecutive field goals in pro football: Fred Cox, Jim Turner or George Blanda?

69. Who kicked the longest field goal in history of pro football?

70. Which one of these players led the league the most times in rushing: O.J. Simpson, Jim Brown, or Leroy Kelly?

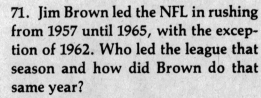

74. Who has the record for the most yards gained in a single season: Jim Brown, O.J. Simpson or Walter Payton?

75. Who broke O.J. Simpson's record for most yards gained in a single game?

76. Which one of these players holds the record for most games rushing over 200 yards: Jim Brown, O.J. Simpson or Walter Payton?

77. Has anybody ever had back to back 200 or more yard rushing games in pro football?

78. Who has had more 100 yard games rushing in pro football: O.J. Simpson, Jim Brown or Franco Harris?

79. Who won the 1984 Orange Bowl?

80. Who won the 1984 Cotton Bowl?

71. Jim Brown led the NFL in rushing from 1957 until 1965, with the exception of 1962. Who led the league that season and how did Brown do that same year?

72. Who has gained the most yards rushing in pro football?

73. Who won the 1984 Rose Bowl?

88. For what pro team and position did Sammy Baugh play?

89. Which one of these quarterbacks holds the NFL record for most completed and most attempted passes in his career: George Blanda, Y.A. Tittle, or Fran Tarkenton?

90. True or false: Fran Tarkenton holds the NFL single season record for most completed and most attempted passes?

81. Has anybody ever run for more than 97 yards from scrimmage in a pro football game?

82. Who had the highest average going in a career based on 700 attempts: O.J. Simpson, Jim Brown or Mercury Morris?

83. Who scored more touchdowns in his professional career, Jim Brown or Jim Taylor?

84. Who was the oldest man ever to play professional football?

85. True or false: in the Dallas Cowboys first year in the NFL, they did not win a single game?

86. Jim Taylor playing for the Green Bay Packers in 1962 set a NFL record with 19 touchdowns rushing. Can you name the two other players who scored 19 touchdowns?

87. Ernie Nevers holds the all-time NFL record for most touchdowns ever scored in a single game with six. True or false: he also pitched in the major leagues?

91. Who holds the NFL record for most consecutive passes completed by a quarterback?

92. Which one of these quarterbacks holds the NFL record for highest percent of completions in a career: Joe Namath, Ken Stabler or Y.A. Tittle?

93. True or false: Y.A. Tittle holds the NFL record for highest percentage of passing a single season based on 100 attempts?

94. True or false: the shortest pass for a touchdown was 2 inches long?

95. The longest touchdown pass from scrimmage was 99 yards. It has been accomplished only four times in NFL history. When was it last done and who was playing?

96. Which one of these quarterbacks has thrown for the most yards in his NFL career: Johnny Unitas, Fran Tarkenton or George Blanda?

97. What pass receiver led the NFL in reception in 1959 and 1960?

98. Joe Namath of the N.Y. Jets set the record for most yards passed for in a season in 1967. This record was broken in 1981. Who now holds the record?

99. Has a NFL quarterback ever passed for more than 500 yards in a single game?

100. Who has thrown for more touchdown passes in his NFL career, Fran Tarkenton or Johnny Unitas?

101. The most touchdown passes in a season is 36 and only two quarterbacks have done that. Who are the two out of the following list: Y.A. Tittle, Sonny Jurgensen, George Blanda or Joe Namath?

102. Joe Kapp tied the record for most touchdown passes in a single game. For what team was he playing at the time?

103. True or false: Johnny Unitas has the record for most consecutive games in which a player threw a touchdown pass?

104. Has a quarterback in the NFL ever gone an entire season without throwing an interception, based on 100 attempts?

105. What is the greatest number of interceptions thrown in a ball game by one quarterback: 5, 7 or 8?

106. What quarterback threw the most interceptions in his NFL career, George Blanda or Fran Tarkenton?

107. True or false: Frank Trepucka has the NFL record for most interceptions in a single season?

108. Has anybody ever led the NFL in pass receptions for 5 consecutive years?

109. Which one of these players holds the NFL record for most receptions in a career: Charley Taylor, Don Maynard or Raymond Berry?

110. Name the player who led the league in rushing from 1978 to 1980.

50

111. Has anybody ever caught more than 100 passes in a single season in the pros?

112. Which one of these receivers has gained the most yards in his career: Don Maynard, Lance Alworth or Raymond Berry?

113. Who won the 1983 Super Bowl?

114. For what team and what position did Charley Hennigan play in his professional career?

115. Has anybody ever gained over 300 yards receiving in a single game in the pros?

116. Which one of these players has the record for most touchdown passes in a season: Don Hutson, Elroy Hirsch or Bill Groman?

117. Who was known as "Crazylegs"?

118. Who was known as "Night Train"?

119. Which one of these players holds the record for interceptions in a season: Dick Lane, Johnny Sample or Spec Sanders?

120. In 1979 Paul Krause broke the career interception record of whom?

121. What is the greatest number of touchdowns on interceptions in a career by a player: 6, 7 or 9?

122. True or false: Sammy Baugh led the league in punting four consecutive seasons?

123. How far did the longest punt go in professional football: 75, 91, or 98 yards?

124. Which punter has the highest lifetime average: Sammy Baugh, Tommy Davis or Yale Lacy?

125. Can you name the all-time leading punt returner in NFL history? Here's a hint: he played for the Denver Broncos.

126. Who is known as "White Shoes" in the NFL?

127. What team did Jack Christiansen play for in the NFL?

128. What was Ron Smith best known for in the NFL?

129. Which team has won the most Super Bowls?

130. Which one of these quarterbacks has the distinction of fumbling the most times in his career: Len Dawson, Randy DiMarzo or Roman Gabriel?

131. Has a pro quarterback ever fumbled 7 times in one game?

132. Has anybody ever returned a fumble for more than 100 yards in the NFL?

133. How far did the longest drop kick field goal travel for 3 points?

134. Has a team in the NFL ever gone undefeated in a regular season and post season play?

135. In the American Conference in the NFL name the teams in the Eastern Division.

136. Name the teams in the Central Division in the American Conference.

137. Name the teams in the Western Division in the American Conference.

138. Name the teams in the Eastern Division in the National Conference.

139. Name the teams in the Central Division in the National Conference.

140. Name the teams in the Western Division in the National Conference.

141. True or False: Dan Fouts broke his own record for passing yardage in the 1982 season?

142. Which one of these teams came in first in the Eastern Division of the AFC in 1983, the Miami Dolphins or the Baltimore Colts?

143. Which one of these teams won the Central Division in the AFC in 1983: Cleveland Browns, Pittsburgh Steelers or the Houston Oilers?

144. Which one of these teams won the Western Division in the AFC in 1983, L.A. Raiders or the San Diego Chargers?

145. Which one of these teams won the Eastern Division in the NFC in 1983, the Dallas Cowboys or the Washington Redskins?

146. Which one of these teams won the Central Division in the NFC in 1983, the Minnesota Vikings or the Detroit Lions?

147. Which one of these teams won the Western Division in the NFC in 1983, the Los Angeles Rams or the San Francisco 49ers?

148. Which one of these teams had the worst record in the NFL in 1983: the Houston Oilers, Tampa Bay Bucs or the N.Y. Giants?

149. Which one of these teams scored the most points in the NFL in the 1983 season: the Washington Redskins, the Dallas Cowboys, or the L.A. Raiders?

150. Which team won the Atlantic Division in the USFL in 1983?

151. Which team won the Central Division in the USFL in 1983?

152. Which team won the Pacific Division in the USFL in 1983?

153. Can you name the running back from the St. Louis Cardinals who gained over 1,000 yards in 1980?

154. Who was the top pass receiver in the USFL?

155. How does the NFL rate quarterbacks for the league statistics?

156. Which running back led the USFL in rushing in 1983?

157. Which quarterback led the USFL in passing for touchdowns in 1983?

158. Can you name the USFL quarterback who threw the most interceptions in 1983?

159. Who led the USFL in scoring in 1983?

160. True or false: the San Diego Chargers had the top three receivers in the AFC in 1980?

161. Which one of these receivers led the NFL in touchdowns in 1980: Steve Largent, John Jefferson or Ahmad Rashad?

162. True or false: Earl Campbell led the NFL in touchdowns scored in 1980?

163. What were the first two teams ever to play in the Super Bowl?

164. Who won Super Bowl II between the Green Bay Packers and the Oakland Raiders?

165. Who won Super Bowl III between the New York Jets and the Baltimore Colts?

166. Who won Super Bowl IV beetween the Minnesota Vikings and the Kansas City Chiefs?

167. Who won Super Bowl V between the Baltimore Colts and the Dallas Cowboys?

168. Who won Super Bowl VI between the Miami Dolphins and the Dallas Cowboys.?

169. Who won Super Bowl VII between the Miami Dolphins and Washington Redskins?

170. Who won Super Bowl VIII between the Minnesota Vikings and the Miami Dolphins?

171. Who won Super Bowl IX between the Minnesota Vikings and the Pittsburgh Steelers?

172. Who won Super Bowl X between the Pittsburgh Steelers and the Dallas Cowboys?

173. Who won Super Bowl XI between the Minnesota Vikings and the Oakland Raiders?

174. Who won Super Bowl XII between the Denver Broncos and the Dallas Cowboys?

175. Which of these teams has won more NFL championships, the Green Bay Packers or the Chicago Bears?

176. What two running backs were known as "Butch Cassidy" and the "Sundance Kid"?

177. Has a rookie quarterback ever led the NFL in passing?

178. Can you name the player who has played in three different Super Bowls with three different teams?

179. Can you name the officiating team and their positions during a pro football game?

180. Was Terry Bradshaw the first player ever to win four Super Bowl championship rings?

181. The MVP award in Super Bowl play has been awarded to a player on the losing club only once. Can you name him and his team?

182. Can you name the only man in both the Football and Baseball Halls of Fame?

183. Has anybody ever played in the Rose Bowl and the World Series?

184. Who keeps the official time during a football game?

185. How many timeouts are teams permitted in football?

186. True or false: the first indoor football game was played in the Houston Astrodome?

187. Jim Brown had an outstanding senior year at Syracuse but did not win the Heisman trophy that year. Who did?

188. Who was the first Heisman Trophy winner and in what year was the trophy first awarded?

189. Which one of these teams won Super Bowl XIII, the Pittsburgh Steelers or the Dallas Cowboys?

190. What is the Grey Cup in football?

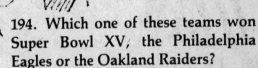

191. Who won the 1979 Grey Cup between the Eskimos and Alouettes?

192. Who won the 1980 Grey Cup between the Tiger-Cats and the Eskimos?

193. Which one of these teams won Super Bowl XIV, the Los Angeles Rams or the Pittsburgh Steelers?

194. Which one of these teams won Super Bowl XV, the Philadelphia Eagles or the Oakland Raiders?

195. What is the Suicide Squad in football?

196. Who has passed for more yards in a game: Dan Fouts or Norm Van Brocklin?

197. Are the footballs the same in the pros and in college?

198. Name the original teams in the old AFL.

199. To whom is the Vince Lombardi Trophy awarded?

200. As of 1981 who is the commissioner of the National Football League?

201. Name the teams in the Big Ten in the NCAA.

202. Name the football teams in the Ivy League.

203. In what Super Bowl were the most points scored?

204. How many NFL franchises are there?

Answers

1. The NFL was founded in Canton, Ohio in 1920. It did not adopt its present name until 1922.

2. True. Stagg, who coached Springfield in 1890-91, Chicago from 1892 to 1932 and College of the Pacific from 1933 to 1946, served as coach for a record 57 years in football.

3. George Halas, who coached the Chicago Bears 1920-29, 1933-42, 1946-55, 1958-67 and won a record total of 325 football games.

4. True. Gordon Wood has guided various high school teams in Texas to a 367-43 record since 1938.

5. In 1965 rookie running back Gale Sayers of the Chicago Bears scored 22 touchdowns for the record for T.D.s by a rookie.

6. Fred "The Hammer" Williamson kicked a football helmet 38 yards at the Palm Springs Hamilton/Avnet competition on January 20, 1980 for the record.

7. False. The most regularly contested series is between Lafayette and Lehigh, who have met a total of 116 times since 1884.

8. The longest unbeaten streak is 63 games (59 won, 4 tied) by Washington from 1907 to 1917. Oklahoma once won 47 straight.

9. True. Georgia Tech beat Cumberland University of Lebanon 222-0 on October 7, 1916. Cumberland did not make one first down. These are some of the records set in that game: most points in a quarter (63), most touchdowns (32), most points after touchdown (30), and largest victory margin.

10. True. Joe Korshalla of West Liberty State rushed for a record 504 yards in 20 carries and scored 71 points against Cedarville College, Ohio on November 19, 1932. He also scored 11 touchdowns, 5 extra points and never carried the ball for less than 22 yards.

11. False. The oldest All-America selection ever was Al Wistert of the University of Michigan. He was selected at age 33 in 1947. Wistert, a tackle, never played high school football.

12. Tony Dorsett, now playing for the Dallas Cowboys in the NFL, scored 356 points for the University of Pittsburgh from 1973 to 1976 for the record.

13. True. Mitchell scored 174 points in 1971 playing for Penn State and went on to play great football in the NFL.

14. Jim McMahon who played for Brigham Young scored 44 points.

15. Tony Dorsett of Pittsburgh, 1973-76 and Glenn Davis hold the record for career touchdowns with 59 each.

16. Lydell Mitchell, the Penn State running back, scored 29 touchdowns for a record in 1971.

17. False. Arnold Boykin of Mississippi scored 7 touchdowns in one game against Mississippi State in 1951.

18. Obed Ariri of Clemson, 1977-1980, had a career record of 60 field goals.

19. Paul Woodside, who had 28 3-pointers playing for West Virginia in 1982.

20. The record for field goals in a college game is 6. It is held jointly by Vince Fusco, Duke (vs. Clemson) 1976; Frank Nester, W. Virginia (vs. Villanova) 1972; Charlie Gogolak, Princeton (vs. Rutgers) 1965.

21. Ish Odoney of Arkansas, 1978-79 and Dale Castro of Maryland, 1979 hold the record with 15 consecutive field goals made in college.

22. True. Joe Williams, Wichita (vs. So. Illinois) 1978; Steve Little, Arkansas (vs. Texas), 1977; and Russell Erxleben, Texas (vs. Rice), 1977. All hold the college record of 67 yards, while the NFL record is 63 yards.

23. True. Vwe von Schamann of Oklahoma made 125 straight from 1976 to 78.

24. Tony Dorsett of the University of Pittsburgh ran for 6,082 yards in his college career from 1973 to 1976.

25. False. Marcus Allen gained 2,342 yards on the ground in 1981 for U.S.C. for the college record.

26. Eddie Lee Ivery rushed for 356 against Air Force in 1978.

27. True. Pruitt averaged 9.35 yards a carry in 1971 for a college football record.

28. Yes. It was first done in 1963 by Kansas running back Gale Sayers against Nebraska and it was last done by Kelsy Finch of Tennessee against Florida in 1977.

29. False. Jim McMahon who played for Brigham Young, 1978-1981, owns that record with 9,536 career yards.

30. Dave Wilson gained 621 yards while playing for Illinois in 1981.

31. False. Jim McMahon of Brigham Young passed for 84 career touchdowns from 1977-81.

32. Jim McMahon of Brigham Young threw for 47 touchdown passes in 1980.

33. Steve Young of Brigham Young threw 22 consecutive passes in 1982.

34. 99 yards was the longest pass play from scrimmage. It has been done six times. The last time was in 1977 when Cris Collinsworth passed to Derrick Gaffney of Florida in a game against Rice.

35. True. Twilley caught 261 passes for Tulsa, 1963-65, for a college record.

36. False. Howard Twilley of Tulsa has that record with 134 receptions for Tulsa in 1965.

37. True. Jay Miller of Brigham Young caught 22 passes in a game against New Mexico in 1973.

38. False. Jay Miller of Brigham Young holds the record.

39. Notre Dame defeated Texas 38-10 in 1978 and Houston 35-34 in 1979.

40. Nebraska scored 624 points in 1983.

41. Tim Delaney caught 6 touchdown passes in a game against New Mexico while playing for San Diego State in 1969.

42. Wichita State lost 10 fumbles in 1963 against Florida State.

43. 5 interceptions in one game is the record. It was last accomplished by Dan Rebech of Miami, Ohio against Western Michigan in a game in 1972.

44. False. Pat Brady of Nevada-Reno, kicked a 99 yard punt against Loyola, California in 1950.

45. Yes. It has been done seven times. The last time was in 1968 when Richie Luzzi of Clemson returned a missed field goal 100 yards against Georgia.

46. Yes. Ottis Anderson, who played for Miami, ran back two 100 yard kickoffs for touchdowns in the 1978 season.

47. George Blanda, who played with Chicago, 1949-58; Baltimore, 1950; AFL: Houston, 1960-66; Oakland, 1967-75, played in a record 340 games over a 26 year span.

48. John Elway of Stanford was chosen number 1 by Baltimore Colts.

49. George Blanda by far. In his 26 year career Blanda has 2,002 points on 9 touchdowns, 943 PATS and 335 field goals.

50. True. In the 1960 season Hornung, playing for the Green Bay Packers, scored 15 touchdowns, 41 PATS and 15 field goals for a record total of 176 points.

HEY, I'VE SCORED 150 POINTS, SO WHAT DO YOU MEAN, 'THE NEW GUY IS A REAL SCORING MACHINE'?

57. True. Dub Jones of the Cleveland Browns scored six times, 4 running, 2 on passes, against the Chicago Bears November 25, 1951.

58. Lenny Moore of the Baltimore Colts scored in 18 straight games from 1963 till 1965 for a record. Simpson scored in every game for the Bills during the 1975 season (14 consecutive).

59. George Blanda with 8 seasons leading the league 1956, 1961-62, 1967-69, 72, 74. He also has the lifetime record for pats with 943.

60. Nobody has ever had 10 PATS in one game, but three players have had 9. The last was Charlie Gogolak playing for Washington against the N.Y. Giants November 27, 1966.

51. Gale Sayers set the rookie point scoring record in the 1965 season with 22 touchdowns for 132 total points.

52. Ernie Nevers of the Chicago Cardinals scored 40 points (6 T.D.s, 4 PAT) against the Chicago Bears on November 28, 1929. Sayers once scored 36 points in a game (6 T.D.s) in 1965 and Hornung once scored 33 points (4 T.D.s, 6 PAT, 1 FG) in 1961.

53. The "Alabama Antelope" played for the Green Bay Packers from 1935 until 1945 and was an All-Pro nine times. His best season was in 1942 when he scored 138 points.

54. Jim Brown, of course, with a record 126 T.D.s (106 r, 20 p) for the Cleveland Browns from 1957 till 1965.

55. It's close but O.J. Simpson owns this record with 23 touchdowns for Buffalo in 1975. Sayers and Foreman scored 22 each and Brown scored 21 in his best season.

56. Trick question! They all scored 13 touchdowns in their rookie year: Dorsett in 1977, and Campbell and Jefferson in 1978.

61. Tommy Davis of the San Francisco 49ers kicked 234 straight from 1959 until 1965. He also has the record for highest percentage in a career with a 99.43 mark on 348 out of 350 from 1959 until 1969.

62. Villanueva was a place kicker with the L.A. Rams, 1960-64, and Dallas, 1965-67. He has the record for most points after a touchdown with no misses in a season with 56.

63. Lou Groza, who also played tackle for the Browns, led the NFL in field goals 1950, 1952-54, 1957 for a record and was the Sporting News player of the year in 1954.

64. George Blanda holds the record with 335 career field goals. Cox had 282 career field goals with the Vikings from 1963 until 1977.

65. Jim Turner of the Super Bowl champion New York Jets set a record in 1968 by kicking 34 field goals.

66. Yes. Jim Bakken of St. Louis kicked 7 field goals against Pittsburgh on September 24, 1967 for a record. He also kicked 6 in a game against Atlanta in 1973.

67. Auburn defeated Michigan 9-7.

68. Fred Cox of the Minnesota Vikings holds the record with 31 consecutive field goals from 1968 until 1970.

69. Tom Dempsey of the New Orleans Saints kicked a 63 yard field for a record against the Detroit Lions on November 8, 1970 to win the game 19-17. Dempsey was born with only half a right foot and part of his right arm. He wore a special shoe for place kicking.

70. Jim Brown led the league a record 8 times for the Cleveland Browns, 1957-61, 1963-65. Simpson led the league 4 times and Kelly led the league 2 times.

C'MON KID, IT'S ONLY THE SECOND KICK YOU'VE MISSED IN TEN YEARS.

71. In 1962 Jim Taylor of the Green Bay Packers won the rushing title by gaining 1,474 yards to beat out runner-up, Jim Brown.

72. Jim Brown of the Cleveland Browns gained 12,312 yards rushing from 1957-65. He is known as the greatest running back in the history of the game.

73. UCLA defeated Illinois 45 to 9.

74. O.J. Simpson broke Jim Brown's record of 1,863 yards rushing (1963) by gaining 2,003 yards in the 1973 season. Walter Payton, in his best year, 1977, gained 1,852 yards for the Chicago Bears.

75. In a game in 1976 Simpson broke his own record of 250 yards in one game by rushing for 273 yards against Detroit. On November 20, 1977, Walter Payton of the Chicago Bears broke Simpson's record with 275 yards rushing against the Minnesota Vikings.

76. O.J. Simpson has the record with six 200 yard + games. Brown had four and Payton has had two.

77. Yes. O.J. Simpson of the Buffalo Bills had two, in 1973 and in 1976.

78. Jim Brown by far. From 1957 until his retirement in 1965 Brown had 58 100 or more yard games compared to second place O.J. Simpson, who had 42.

79. Miami defeated Nebaska 31 to 30.

80. Georgia defeated Texas 10 to 9.

HERE'S MY FAVORITE RECORD

I THINK YOU GUYS WILL IMPROVE!

COWBOYS 49

COWBOY 31

0-11-1

85. True. In 1960, their first year, the best they could do was tie one game while losing 11 others.

86. Earl Campbell of the Houston Oilers in 1979 and Chuck Munsie of the San Diego Chargers in 1981.

87. True. Nevers pitched for the St. Louis Browns from 1925 until 1927. In 1927 he gave up two of Babe Ruth's 60 homeruns that year.

88. Sammy Baugh played for the Washington Redskins from 1937 until 1952. He led the NFL in passing a record six times (1937, 40, 43, 45, 47, 49) and led the NFL in punting four times (1940-43). Baugh quarterbacked his team to two world championships; in 1937 and 1942. He also set the all-time punt average record, 51.0 yards per kick.

89. Fran Tarkenton, who played for the Minnesota Vikings, 1961-66, 72-78, and for the N.Y. Giants, 1967-71, completed a record 3,686 passes out of a record 6,467 attempts.

90. False. In 1981, Dan Fouts completed 360 passes out of 609 attempts for the San Diego Chargers.

81. Tony Dorsett ran for 99 yards against the Minnesota Vikings on January 3, 1983.

82. Jim Brown with an average of 5.22 yards per carry. Mercury Morris, who played for Miami, 1969-75 and San Diego 1976, is second with an average gain of 5.14 yards per carry.

83. Jim Brown of the Cleveland Browns holds the record with 106 career touchdowns while Jim Taylor is second on the all-time list with 83.

84. George Blanda, who played a record 26 years, retired when he was 48 years old!

97. Raymond Berry playing for the Baltimore Colts.

98. In 1967 Namath passed for 4,007 yards for a record that held until Dan Fouts of the San Diego Chargers passed for 4,802 yards in the 1981 season.

99. Yes. Norm Van Brocklin of the L.A. Rams passed for 554 yards against the N.Y. Yanks on September 28, 1951.

100. Fran Tarkenton threw a total of 342 touchdowns in his career with the Vikings and Giants to beat out Johnny Unitas, who had 290 career T.D.s for the Baltimore Colts and the San Diego Chargers.

91. Ken Anderson of the Cincinnati Bengals completed 20 straight against the Houston Oilers on January 2, 1983.

92. Ken Stabler of the Oakland Raiders and Houston Oilers, has completed almost 60 percent of his passes in his career for an NFL record.

93. False. Sammy Baugh of the Washington Redskins completed 129 passes out of 182 attempts for a record 70.3 percent in the 1945 season.

94. True. On October 9, 1960 Eddie Lebaron of the Dallas Cowboys hit Rich Bielski with a touchdown pass against the Washington Redskins. The ball was 2 inches from the goal line at the start of the play.

95. Sonny Jurgensen passed to Gerry Allen of the Washington Redskins on September 15, 1968 for 99 yards against the Chicago Bears for the longest pass play in the history of the NFL.

96. Fran Tarkenton has this record with a total of 47,003 yards gained in his NFL career. Unitas is second with 40,239 in his.

101. George Blanda and Y.A. Tittle. Blanda did it in 1961 playing for Houston and Tittle did it for New York in 1963.

102. Kapp threw 7 T.D.s playing for the Minnesota Vikings against the Baltimore Colts on September 28, 1969 to tie the record held by four others.

103. True. Between 1956 and 1960, Unitas threw four touchdowns in 47 consecutive games for the Baltimore Colts.

104. No. Joe Ferguson of the Buffalo Bills came the closest with only 1 interception during the 1976 season on 151 attempts.

105. Jim Hardy of the Chicago Cardinals threw 8 interceptions out of 39 attempts against the Philadelphia Eagles September 24, 1950. He should have kept the ball on the ground!

106. George Blanda threw 277 interceptions for a NFL record compared to 266 by Tarkenton.

107. False. Tripucka is second on that list with 34 in 1960 for Denver. George Blanda has the single season record with 42 in 1962 with Houston.

108. Yes. Don Hutson of the Green Bay Packers led the NFL from 1941 until 1945 for a record. He also holds the record for most seasons leading the league lifetime with 8, 1936-37, 1939, 1941-45.

109. Charley Taylor of the Washington Redskins caught a total of 649 passes in his career, 1964-75, 77 for the all-time record.

110. Earl Campbell of the Houston Oilers led the league 3 consecutive years.

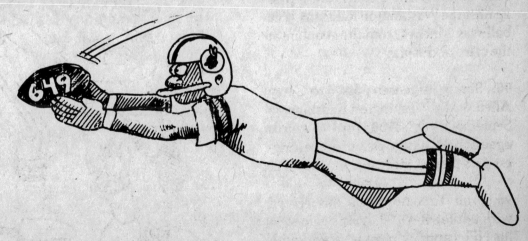

116. Trick question! They all share the record of 17 T.D.s in a season. Hutson did it with Green Bay in 1942, Hirsch with L.A. in 1951 and Groman with Houston in 1961.

111. Lionel Taylor of Denver caught 100 passes in 1961, but Charley Hennigan of Houston caught 101 passes in 1964 for the record.

112. Don Maynard gained 11,834 career yards for the all-time record followed by Alworth with 10,266 and Berry with 9,275.

113. Washington defeated Miami with a score of 27 to 17.

114. Charley Hennigan, an end, played for the Houston Oilers from 1960 to 1966 and set the record for most yards gained receiving in a single season with 1,746 in 1961. He had another great year in 1964 when he gained 1,546 yards. He once gained 272 yards in a game against Boston on October 13, 1961.

115. Yes. Jim Benton gained 303 yards while playing for Cleveland against Detroit in a game in 1945 and Cloyce Box of Detroit gained 302 yards against Baltimore in 1950.

117. Elroy "Crazylegs" Hirsch, who played with the Chicago Rockets (AAFC) 1946-48, and the Los Angeles Rams 1949-57, caught a career total of 343 passes for 6,249 yards, made 53 touchdowns and was an all-pro in 1951.

118. Dick "Night Train" Lane, whom Vince Lombardi called the best cornerback he has ever seen. He led the league in interceptions 2 years, 1952 with the Rams and 1954 with the Chicago Cardinals and was an all pro 1956, 60-63.

119. Dick "Night Train" Lane, who intercepted 14 passes for L.A. in 1952. Sanders once intercepted 13 for the N.Y. Yanks in 1950.

120. Emlen Tunnell of the N.Y. Giants 1948-58 and Green Bay Packers. He had a career total of 79 interceptions. Krause had 81 after the 1979 season and 164. The Packers defeated the Raiders.

121. Ken Houston has the record of 9 during his career with Houston, 1967-72 and Washington 1973-78.

122. True. As well as being a premier quarterback Baugh was an ace punter and led the league from 1940 through 1943 with the Washington Redskins.

123. Steve O'Neal of the N.Y. Jets kicked a 98 yard punt against the Denver Broncos on September 21, 1969.

124. Sammy Baugh, with a 45.10 average from 1937 till 1952 with the Redskins, followed by Davis, 44.68 and Lacy, 44.29.

125. Rick Upchurch, who has been playing with the Broncos since 1975, has, as of the 1979 season, gained 2,288 yards. In 1976 he ran back 2 punts in one game and 4 in that season for touchdowns, both records.

126. Billy "White Shoes" Johnson, who played with the Houston Oilers from 1974 till 1980. Now playing in the Canadian football league, Johnson holds the record for lifetime punt average: 13.4 yards per carry. He is also an outstanding receiver.

127. Jack Christiansen played for the Detroit Lions from 1951 through 1958. He holds the record for touchdowns returning punts in a career with 8. In 1953 he led the NFL in interceptions with 12. He tied for lead in 1957 with 10. He was an all-pro 1952, 53, 55-57 and a member of the Pro Football Hall of Fame 1969.

128. Ron Smith, who played for Chicago 1965, 1970-72, Atlanta 1966-67, L.A. 1968-69, San Diego 1973 and Oakland 1974, was known best for returning punts and kickoffs in his career. He has the record for most yards gained lifetime returning kickoffs, 6,922. He led the AFC in punt return average in 1973 with a 13.0 mark, lettered in track at Wisconsin. As a sprinter Smith ran the 100 yard dash in 9.4 seconds.

129. Pittsburg Steelers have won the most Super Bowls with four victories.

130. Roman Gabriel of the Rams, 1962-72, and Eagles 1973-77 fumbled a record 105 times in his career. He once recovered his own fumble four times in one game.

137. San Diego Chargers, Oakland Raiders, Denver Broncos, Kansas City Chiefs and Seattle Seahawks.

138. The Philadelphia Eagles, Dallas Cowboys, Washington Redskins, St. Louis Cardinals, and New York Giants.

139. Minnesota Vikings, Detroit Lions, Chicago Bears, Green Bay Packers, and Tampa Bay Buccaneers.

140. The Atlanta Falcons, Los Angeles Rams, San Francisco 49ers and New Orleans Saints.

131. Yes. Len Dawson, playing for the Chiefs of Kansas City in the old AFL, fumbled 7 times against the Chargers in a game on November 15, 1964 for a record.

132. Jack Tatum of the Oakland Raiders picked up a fumble in the end zone against the Packers on September 24, 1972 and ran it back 104 yards for a touchdown.

133. 50 yards was the longest by two players, Pete Henry in 1922 and Paddy Driscoll of the Chicago Cardinals did it twice, once in 1924 and again in 1925. Driscoll also has the record of 4 drop kick field goals in one game in 1925.

134. Yes. Only one team, the Miami Dolphins won 17 consecutive games including Super Bowl VII in 1972. (Super Bowl VII took place in 1973.)

135. The Buffalo Bills, New England Patriots, Miami Dolphins, Baltimore Colts, and New York Jets.

136. The Cleveland Browns, Houston Oilers, Pittsburgh Steelers, and Cincinnati Bengals.

141. True. With the extended 16 game schedule, Fouts threw for 4,802 yards that year.

142. The Dolphins came in first with a 12-4-0 mark beating out the Patriots who had an 8-8-0 record.

143. The Steelers won the division posting a 10-6-0 record.

144. The Raiders won the division with a 12-4-0 record.

145. The Redskins won the division with a 14-2-0 record.

146. The Lions won with a 9-7-0 mark.

147. San Francisco won its division with a 10-6-0 record.

148. The Bucs and Oilers tied for this distinction with a 2-14-0 record.

149. The Redskins by far, they scored 541 points to the Dallas Cowboys' 479.

150. Philadelphia Stars captured the Crown with a 15-3-0 record.

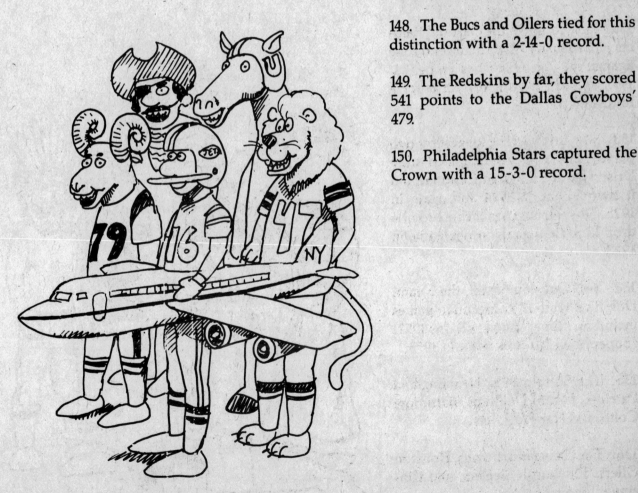

151. The Michigan Panthers won the division with a 12-6-0 mark.

152. The Oakland Invaders with a 9-9-0 record.

153. O.J. Anderson, who was the third leading rusher in the NFL in 1980. He gained 1,352 yards on 301 carries for a 4.5 average and scored 9 touchdowns.

154. Trumaine Johnson of the Chicago Blitz caught 81 passes in 1983.

155. The standings are based on percentage of completions, percentage of touchdowns, percentage of interceptions and average gain per attempt.

156. Herchel Walker of the New Jersey Generals rushed for 1,812 yards.

157. Bobby Hebert of the Michigan Panthers throwing for 27 touchdowns.

158. Fred Besana of the Oakland Invaders threw for 28 interceptions.

159. David Trout of the Philadelphia Stars led the league with 121 points.

160. True. Kellin Winslow led the AFC and NFL in receptions with 89 followed by John Jefferson (82) and Charlie Joiner (71) also of the Chargers. They all gained over 1,000 yards for a record.

161. John Jefferson of the San Diego Chargers led the NFL with 13 T.D. passes caught and also led the NFL in yards by a receiver with 1,340.

162. False. Campbell led the NFL in T.D.s by rushing but rookie sensation Billy Sims scored 16 T.D.s to lead the NFL. He rushed for 13 (tying Campbell) and caught 3 others for a total of 96 points.

163. The Green Bay Packers beat the Kansas City Chiefs 35 to 10. Bart Starr was chosen as the MVP. He completed 16 out of 23 for 250 yards and two touchdowns. Max McGee was the star receiver with 7 catches for 138 yards and two touchdowns for the Packers.

164. The Packers defeated the Raiders 33 to 14. Bart Starr won the MVP as he completed 13 of 24 passes for 202 yards and one touchdown. Don Chandler kicked four field goals for the Pack. It was the last game for Vince Lombardi as the Packer coach, who coached them for 9 years during which he won six Western Conference championships, five NFL championships and two Super Bowls.

165. This was the biggest upset in Super Bowl history with the Jets beating by a score of 16 to 7 a team which had lost only one game all year. Joe Namath was the game's MVP. He completed 17 of 28 passes for 206 yards. Matt Snell rushed for a total of 121 yards and a touchdown and Jim Turner kicked three field goals.

166. Len Dawson of the Chiefs hit on 12 of 17 passes including a 46 yard touchdown pass to Otis Taylor to lead them to victory in Super Bowl IV with a 23 to 7 score. Jan Stenerud kicked three field goals. The Chiefs defense played superbly and Dawson was awarded the MVP.

167. In one of the most exciting Super Bowls ever played Jim O'Brien of the Colts kicked a 32 yard field goal with five seconds remaining to defeat the Cowboys 16 to 13.

168. The Cowboys ran all over the Dolphins for 252 yards and the game, 24 to 3. Roger Staubach was the game's MVP. He completed 12 of 19 passes for 119 yards and two touchdowns.

169. The Dolphins beat the Redskins 14 to 7. All the Miami scoring took place in the first half when the Bob Griese hit Howard Twilley with a 28 yard touchdown pass in the first quarter. In the second quarter Billy Kilmer of the Skins threw an interception; Miami drove down to the one yard line where Jim Kiick ran it in. The Redskins scored when a misplayed field goal attempt was turned into a fumble by Garo Yepremian. The Redskins' Mike Bass picked it up and ran 49 yards for the score.

170. The Dolphins defeated the Vikings 24 to 7 behind a strong defense and the running of Larry Csonka, who gained 145 yards on 33 carries and two touchdowns.

171. The Steelers beat the Vikings 16 to 6 behind the running of Franco Harris, who gained 158 yards on 34 carries and one touchdown. It was the third Super Bowl the Vikings played in without a victory.

172. In a very close game the Steelers beat the Cowboys for their second consecutive Super Bowl title 21 to 17 behind the play of Terry Bradshaw, who threw two T.D.s and Lynn Swann, who caught four passes for 161 yards.

173. Again the Vikings were beaten in the Super Bowl, this time by the Raiders, who scored 32 to 14 behind Clarence Davis' running (137 yards) and four key receptions made by the game's MVP, Fred Biletnikoff. Oakland cornerback Willie Brown intercepted a Tarkenton pass and ran it back 75 yards for a score.

174. The Cowboys defeated the Broncos 27 to 10 behind a balanced offense, which included a 29 yard touchdown pass from running back Robert Newhouse to Golden Richards, and great defensive play by Harvey Martin and Randy White, who were both named MVPs.

175. The Packers, who have won more championships than any other team with 11. The Bears are second with 8.

176. Miami Dolphin running backs Larry Csonka ("Butch Cassidy") and Jim Kiick ("Sundance Kid"), who played together when the Dolphins won two consecutive Super Bowls.

177. Yes. Greg Cook of the 1969 Cincinnati Bengals was the last rookie to lead the leagues in passing. Shortly thereafter he developed sore arm and dropped out of pro football.

178. Preston Pearson, who has played in Super Bowls with Baltimore, Pittsburgh and Dallas.

179. A referee, umpire, head linesman, lines judge, back judge, side judge and field judge. The referee is in charge of the crew.

180. No. Marv Fleming, a tight end who played with Green Bay and Miami, won two rings each in their Super Bowl victories.

181. Chuck Howley of the Dallas Cowboys was given the award even though his team lost 16 to 13 to the Baltimore Colts.

182. Cal Hubbard who played football with Green Bay, New York and Pittsburgh as a lineman. He is also in the Baseball Hall of Fame where he made it as an umpire.

183. Yes. Two men: Jackie Jensen, who played for California in the 1949 Rose Bowl and in the 1951 World Series with the Yankees and Chuck Essegian, who also played with California in the Rose Bowl and with the Los Angeles Dodgers in the 1959 World Series.

184. The time is kept by the scoreboard operator and the line judge.

185. Both pro and college teams are allowed 3 timeouts per half. They are usually used toward the end of each half for strategic purposes.

186. False. The first indoor game was played in Madison Squre Garden in New York in 1902. Syracuse beat Philadelphia 6-0.

187. Notre Dame quarterback, Paul Hornung won it and was also the number one draft pick in the pros by the Packers of Green Bay.

188. Jay Berwanger of the University of Chicago won the award in 1935. He gained 4,108 yards in three varsity seasons and was the number one draft pick by the Philadelphia Eagles but didn't sign.

189. In a very close game the Steelers defeated the Cowboys 35-31 with Terry Bradshaw leading the way with 17 out of 30 passes completed for 318 yards and four touchdonws. He also received the Most Valuable Player award.

190. The Grey Cup is the Canadian Football League championship game.

191. The Edmonton Eskimos beat the Montreal Alouettes 17-9 to win the championship Grey Cup.

192. The Edmonton Eskimos won their third consecutive Grey Cup by defeating the Hamilton Tiger-Cats 48-10.

193. The Steelers won their fourth Super Bowl with a 31-19 win over the Rams. Terry Bradshaw was named the game's MVP with a 14 out of 21 passing day with 309 yards and 2 touchdowns.

194. The Raiders defeated the Eagles 27-10 behind MVP Jim Plunkett. Plunkett had 13 completions out of 21 attempts for 261 yards and 3 touchdowns, including a Super Bowl record 80 yard touchdown pass to Kenny King.

195. It's another name for special teams of players from both teams, who run full speed at one another, one trying to block, the other trying to get to the ball handler.

196. Norm Van Brocklin holds the single game passing record with 554 yards for the L.A. Rams, September 28, 1951.

197. No. The NFL uses a leather ball without stripes and in college the ball always has white stripes and may be rubber.

198. Boston Patriots, Buffalo Bills, Denver Broncos, Houston Oilers, Dallas Texans, New York Titans, Oakland Raiders and Los Angeles Chargers.

199. Since Super Bowl V the Vince Lombardi Trophy is given to the NFL champions.

200. Currently Pete Rozelle is the NFL's commissioner.

201. Ohio State, Illinois, Indiana, Iowa, Wisconsin, Michigan, Michigan State, Minnesota, Purdue and Northwestern.

202. Yale, Princeton, Harvard, Brown, Dartmouth, Cornell, Columbia and Pennsylvania.

203. Super Bowl XIII was the highest scoring with the Pittsburgh Steelers beating the Dallas Cowboys 35-31.

204. There are 28 teams in the NFL. Of the 27 NFL cities only New York has two teams, the Jets and the Giants.

Summer Olympics

9. In what Olympic competition did Jerry West, Walt Bellamy, Jerry Lucas and Oscar Robertson play?

10. Did Bill Russell play in the Olympics?

1. As of the 1976 Olympics what country has won the most medals: the U.S.A., the U.S.S.R. or Great Britain?

2. How many different sports were in the 1976 Olympic games?

3. Where were the first modern Olympic games held?

4. True or false: between 1956 and 1972 one man won the gold medal in the Olympics every year?

5. True or false: since the archery event was reinstated in the Olympics Americans have won the gold medal in both the men's and women's competitions every year?

6. True or false: the United States has won the gold medal in basketball in all Olympic games?

7. Is there women's basketball in Olympic competition?

8. In the 1976 Olympics the U.S.A had something to prove in basketball after their disputed loss to the Russians in 1972. Whom did they play in the finals and what was the outcome?

11. Has an American ever won a gold medal in the light flyweight division in boxing in the Olympics?

12. In 1924 Fidel LaBarba won the gold medal in boxing in the flyweight division. It wasn't until 1976 that another American took the gold in boxing in the Olympics in that division. Can you name him?

13. True or false: only one person has won the Olympic flyweight boxing gold medal twice?

14. True or false: Charles Mooney of the U.S.A. won the Olympic boxing gold medal in the bantamweight division in 1976?

15. Who won the 1976 Olympic gold medal in the lightweight boxing division?

16. True of false: a Cuban won the 1976 boxing Olympic gold medal in the light welterweight division?

17. Has anybody ever won the light welterweight gold medal in Olympic competition twice?

18. Can you name the last boxer to win three gold medals in the Olympics?

19. What brothers' team of boxers both won gold medals in the same year of Olympic competition?

20. Floyd Patterson of the U.S.A. won an Olympic gold medal in boxing. In what year and in what division did he do it?

YOU DIDN'T TELL
ME THERE WAS
A WATERFALLLLLL

21. Has anybody ever taken two gold medals in the middleweight division in the Olympics?

22. Muhammud Ali won an Olympic gold medal in boxing. In what year and what division did he do it?

23. In the 1952 Olympics Hayes Edward Sanders won the gold medal in the heavyweight division in boxing because of a disqualification. Who was disqualified?

24. Who won the 1964 Olympic gold medal in boxing's heavyweight division?

25. Who won the 1968 Olympic gold medal in the heavyweight division in boxing?

26. In the 1972 and 1976 Olympics Romania had a heavyweight in the finals in the boxing event. Did either of them win the title?

27. When was the canoeing event introduced to Olympic competition?

28. Do women compete in canoeing in the Olympics?

29. Where were the 1960 summer Olympic games held?

30. Did any Americans win any gold medals in any of the canoeing events in the 1976 summer Olympics?

31. True or false: cycling has been an Olympic event since the first modern day games took place in 1896?

32. What cycling events were held in Olympic competition in 1976?

33. In what Olympic event did Alwin Schockemohle compete?

34. Can you name any of the events in the Olympic equestrian competition?

35. When was the equestrian event first introduced into the Olympics?

36. What is the greatest number of gold medals won by one rider in the equestrian events in Olympic competition?

37. Did the U.S.A. win any gold medals in the equestrian event in the 1976 summer Olympics?

38. Was fencing one of the original events in the 1896 Olympic games held in Greece?

39. Is there a women's fencing competition in the Olympics?

40. Christian d'Oiola won two gold medals in Olympics. In which event did he win them and which country did he represent?

41. Can you name the Italian who won a record five gold medals in fencing in one Olympiad?

42. What is the greatest number of gold medals won in the fencing events in Olympic competition?

43. When is the last time an American won a medal in fencing in the Olympics?

44. Is there men's gymnastics competition in the Olympics?

45. Where were the 1968 summer Olympic games held?

46. Can you name the country which broke Japan's streak of 5 consecutive team championships in Gymnastics?

47. In what event did Nikolai Andrianov compete in the 1976 Olympics?

48. Boris Shakhlin dominated the 1960 Olympics in men's gymnastics. How many medals did he win?

49. When was women's gymnastics first introduced to Olympic competition?

50. Who was the first female gymnast to be awarded a perfect 10 score in the Olympics: Nelli Kim, Olga Korbut or Nadia Comaneci?

51. Can you name the six gymnastics events featured in Olympic competition for women?

52. Nelli Kim won the 1976 gold medal in the floor exercise at Montreal. One of her teammates had won the same event in 1972. Can you name her?

53. In what event did Larissa Semyonovna Latynina compete in the Olympics?

54. Which one of these countries has won the combined exercise for women in every Olympiad: Rumania, U.S.S.R. or Czechoslovakia?

55. True or false: American women have won only two medals in gymnastics since its introduction to the Olympics?

56. True or false: men and women both do their floor exercises to music in the Olympics?

57. True or false: gymnastics was a part of the Olympic held in Greece?

58. Where were the 1956 Olympic games held?

59. When was handball first introduced into Olympic competition?

60. Is there women's handball in Olympic competition?

68. Has anybody ever won the modern pentathlon individual gold medal twice in Olympic competition?

69. How many events are there in the Olympic rowing competition?

70. Where were the 1932 Olympic games held?

61. Which one of these countries has won the gold medal the most often in Olympic field hockey: Pakistan, India or Great Britain?

62. True or false: the United States women's field hockey team won the gold medal at the 1972 and 1976 Olympics?

63. How many weight divisions are there in Judo in the Olympics?

64. In the 1976 Olympics which country won more gold medals in the Judo event: Japan, U.S.S.R. or Korea?

65. Did any Americans win any medals in the Judo competition in the 1976 Olympics?

66. Name the five events which comprise the Olympic modern pentathlon.

67. Since 1952 either Hungary or the U.S.S.R. has won the team modern pentathlon event in the Olympics except for 1976. Who won it that year?

74. **How many shooting events are there in Olympic competition?**

75. **The fastest times in all eight rowing events for men were recorded in one Olympiad. Which one was it?**

76. **Did any Americans win any gold medals in the shooting events at the 1976 games held in Montreal?**

77. **Soccer is a very big and competitive event in the Olympics. Which one of these countries has won the most titles: U.S.S.R., Hungary or Great Britain?**

78. **Which one of these scores was the biggest defeat in Olympic history in soccer: 9-0, 12-2 or 18-1?**

79. **Which country won the 1976 Olympic gold medal in soccer: Poland, Great Britain or East Germany?**

80. **True or false: the United States has won only one medal in soccer and that came in the 1956 games by default?**

71. **Which one of these countries dominated the rowing events for men at the 1976 Olympics: the U.S.S.R., the U.S.A. or East Germany?**

72. **Is there rowing for women in the Olympics?**

73. **Did any women from the U.S.A. take home any medals in the rowing competition at the 1976 Olympics?**

89. Can you name another Olympic champion who also became Tarzan in the movies?

90. Can you name the only woman to win two diving championships in two successive Olympics?

HOLLYWOOD, JAMES

GIMME A BREAK

81. In what Olympic sport did American Brian Goodell participate?

82. True or false: Mark Spitz holds the Olympic record for most medals won by a swimmer in an Olympic career?

83. True or false: Shirley Babashoff is the only woman ever to win the Olympic trap shooting event?

84. An American set world records at 100 and 200 meters at the 1976 Olympic games in the back stroke swimming event. Can you name him?

85. Has anybody ever won the 100 and 200 meter back stroke events in two consecutive Olympics?

86. Only one person has ever won seven gold medals in any Olympic games. Can you name him? Here's a hint. He is a swimmer.

87. Where were the 1904 Olympic games held?

88. Can you name the man who was named in 1950 by an Associated Press poll "the greatest swimmer of the past 50 years"?

91. True or false: the United States men's swim team has won every 400-meter medley relay title in every Olympiad since its introduction?

92. In what events did Michael Burton win gold medals in the 1968 Olympic games?

93. In the 800 meter freestyle relay event, what country has dominated: the United States, Japan or Australia?

94. In what swimming event did Klaus DiBiasi of Italy dominate in Olympic competition?

95. Has there ever been a perfect dive (10.0) in Olympic competition?

96. True or false: since 1920 the U.S.A. has won the gold medal every year in the Olympic springboard diving event?

97. Kornelia Ender tied a record at the 1976 Olympic games. In what event did she do it and for what country?

98. Who were the other two women to win 4 Olympic gold medals in swimming?

99. Shane Gould won five medals in the 1972 games. In what competition did she do it and for what country?

100. Where were the 1940 Olympic games held?

101. Which country has dominated the 400 meter free-style relay event for women in Olympic competition: the United States, Australia or the U.S.S.R.?

102. Since the introduction of the 400 meter medley relay for women in Olympic swimming in 1960, the U.S.A. has won every year except 1976. Who won then?

103. **Until 1980 only the United States and Germany had won the springboard diving event. Who won the event in 1980?**

104. When is the last time an American woman won the platform diving event in Olympic competition?

105. Which one of these countries has won the Olympic water polo event the most often: the United States, Great Britain or Hungary?

106. Where was the Olympiad of 1912 held?

107. True or false: track and field have been Olympic events since 1912?

108. Who holds the Olympic record for the 100 meter sprint in track, Bob Hayes or Jimmy Hines?

109. In the first modern day Olympics in 1896 the 100 meter sprint was won by Thomas E. Burke of the U.S.A. True or false: his original time has been lowered by more than two seconds?

110. For what country did Hasely Crawford run in the 1976 Olympics?

111. True or false: except for the 1976 games an American runner has always won a medal in the men's 100 meter race since 1896?

112. Why were so many great times achieved at the 1968 games at Mexico City?

113. Who was the last man to double in the 100 and 200 meter sprints in the Olympic games?

114. Did Jesse Owens ever win the gold medal in the 100 meter race at the Olympic games of 1936?

115. Who was the last American to win the men's 200 meter sprint in the Olympic games, John Carlos or Tommie Smith?

116. Has there ever been a double winner in the Olympics in the men's 400 meter race?

117. True or false: in the 1968 Olympic games held in Mexico City the U.S.A. placed one, two and three in the men's 400 meter race?

118. What Cuban runner was known as "the Horse" at the 1976 Olympic games?

119. Peter Snell of New Zealand won the 800 meter gold medal in the 1960 and 1964 Olympic games. Had that ever been done before?

120. Can you name the American runner who won a gold medal in the Olympic games and ran with a golf cap on his head?

121. Did Jim Ryun, former mile record holder, ever win an Olympic gold medal?

122. Can you name the former men's mile record holder who won the 1,500 meter race in the 1976 Olympics? Hint: He's from New Zealand.

123. Can you name the runner who won the men's Olympic 5,000 and 10,000 meter races in both 1972 and 1976?

124. In what event did Frank Shorter win the gold medal in the 1972 Olympics?

125. Has anybody ever won the men's marathon event in the Olympic twice?

126. Which one of these countries has dominated the men's 400 meter relay race in Olympic competition: the U.S.S.R., Great Britain or the United States?

127. Which United States 400 meter relay team holds the Olympic record for this event: 1968, 1972, or 1976?

128. Which country has won the most gold medals in the men's Olympic 1,600 meter relay race: the United States, Kenya or Jamaica?

129. Can you name the American who won the men's 110 meter hurdles at the 1968 Olympic games held in Mexico City?

130. Can you name the runner who broke Willie Davanport's record in the 110 meter hurdles event?

131. Has anybody ever retained the 110 meter hurdle title in the history of the Olympics?

132. Can you name the American who holds the Olympic record in the 400 meter hurdles?

133. Has any runner ever won the men's 400 meter hurdle event two successive Olympics?

134. True or false: an American has never won the men's 3,000 meter Olympic steeplechase event?

135. True or false: an American has won the men's 20,000 meter road walk every year it has been held in the Olympics?

136. True or false: there is a track and field event that is over 30 miles long in Olympic competition?

137. What is the "Fosbury Flop"?

138. Can you name the American who won the Olympic bronze medal in the high jump in 1972 and 1976?

139. Can you name the American pole vaulter who won the gold medal at the 1968 Olympics?

140. In what event did Bob Beamon compete and how did he do?

141. In what Olympic event did Ralph Boston compete?

142. Four people have won the men's triple jump in Olympic competition. Has anybody ever won three times?

143. Has an American ever won the gold medal in the men's shotput event in two consecutive Olympics?

144. Can you name the American who dominated the Olympic discus throw from 1956 till 1968?

145. When is the last time an American won the men's hammer throw in Olympic competition?

146. True or false: an American has never won the gold medal in the men's javelin throw in Olympic competition?

147. Can you name the events in the Olympic men's decathlon?

148. Who is the only man ever to win the decathlon event two times in the history of the Olympics?

149. Which of these people did not win the decathlon in the Olympic Games: Jim Thorpe, Glenn Morris, or Milton Campbell?

150. Who won the 1976 Olympic decathlon?

HOW MANY TIMES DO I HAVE TO TELL YOU — NO SHOTPUTTING UNTIL I GIVE THE SIGNAL !

151. In what Olympic event did Rafer Johnson compete and how did he do?

152. Bill Toomey won a gold medal in the 1968 Olympics in what event?

153. In what Olympic event did Wilma Rudolph compete and how did she do?

154. Can you name the woman who won the 1964 and 1968 gold medals in the 100 meter dash?

155. Which one of these countries has won the gold medal the greatest number of times in the women's 400 meter relay race: East Germany, West Germany or the United States?

156. Has the United States men's volleyball team ever won a medal in Olympic competition?

157. Which one of these countries has won the women's volleyball gold medal the most times: the U.S.S.R, Japan or Korea?

158. Did any United States weight lifters win any medals in the 1976 games at Montreal?

159. Can you name the great Russian super heavyweight who won the gold medal in the 1972 and 1976 Olympics in weight lifting?

160. Can you name the two wrestling events in the Olympics?

163. True or false: the longest competitive span of any Olympic competitor is 40 years?

164. Has a man over 65 years old ever won a gold medal in the Olympic games?

165. In what Olympiad did the greatest number of athletes compete?

166. True or false: Over half a million people were present at a single Olympic event?

167. In what Olympic event did Dan Gable participate and how did he do?

168. True or false: there was once a wrestling match that lasted over 11 hours in the Olympic games?

169. Has an Olympic wrestler ever weighed 420 pounds and won a medal?

170. Has any Olympic wrestler ever won a total of three Olympic titles?

161. True or false: the youngest girl ever to win a gold medal in Olympic competition was only 16 years old?

162. True or false: the youngest male ever to win a gold medal in the Olympic games was not more than 10 years old?

171. Did any American wrestlers win a gold medal at the 1976 games?

172. Can you name the events that make up Olympic yachting?

173. Did the United States win any gold medals in the yachting events at the 1976 Olympics?

174. True or false? Ken Norton won the bronze medal in the light heavyweight boxing division in the 1972 Olympics?

175. Where were the 1948 Olympic games held?

176. In what Olympic events did Harrison Dillard compete and how did he do?

177. True or false: in the first Olympic games of 776 B.C. there was only one event?

178. True or false: the last time an American team won a gold medal in the men's gymnastics competition was in 1956?

OKAY, HE'S STARTING TO FADE, KID. LAST ROUND HE THREW YOU MUCH FARTHER.

COACH

3. In Athens, Greece in 1896. There were entrants representing 13 countries, 9 different sporting events and only 311 competitors, all male!

4. True. In 1972 John C. Williams and Doreen Wilbur of the U.S.A. took the gold and Darrell Pace and Luann Ryon won the gold for the U.S.A. in 1976.

5. False. Archery was not reinstated as an Olympic event until the 1972 games. Previously, the event was held in 1900, 1904, 1908 and 1920.

6. False. In a very controversial game the U.S.S.R. defeated the U.S.A. 51-50. The defeat marked the first loss in basketball the U.S.A. has ever suffered in Olympic competition. They have won 8 gold medals and 77 out of 78 games.

Answers

1. The United States by far with 1,512 (628 gold, 473½ silver, 410½ bronze) compared to Russia's 692 and Great Britain's 527.

2. There are 21 different sports.
   1. Archery
   2. Basketball
   3. Boxing
   4. Canoeing
   5. Cycling
   6. Horsemanship
   7. Fencing
   8. Field Hockey
   9. Gymnastics
   10. Handball
   11. Judo
   12. Modern Pentathlon
   13. Rowing
   14. Shooting
   15. Soccer
   16. Swimming
   17. Track
   18. Volleyball
   19. Weightlifting
   20. Wrestling
   21. Yachting

7. Yes. When introduced in the 1976 games the Russians defeated the American women in the finals with Bulgaria taking the bronze.

8. The U.S.A. rolled to the finals except for a close game against Puerto Rico and beat Yugoslavia 95-74 to win the gold. The U.S. team included now NBA players Phil Ford, Adrian Dantley, Scott May and Mitchell Kupchak.

9. They played on the 1960 Olympic team which beat the Russians in the basketball final that year to win the gold medal.

10. Yes, he did. In 1956 Russell played on the gold medal winning U.S.A. team along with K.C. Jones. Bill Russell went on to greatness in the N.B.A. with the Boston Celtics as the premier center in the league for many years.

11. No. Since the light flyweight division was introduced in the 1968 Olympics only one American has won a medal. He was Harlan Marbley, who won a bronze medal in 1968.

12. Leo Randolph defeated Ramon Duvalon of Cuba in the 1976 Olympics to win the gold.

13. False. Since its introduction in 1904 nobody has won the flyweight boxing gold medal in the Olympics twice.

14. False. Mooney won the silver medal in 1976. Not since 1904 has an American won the gold medal in the bantamweight division. He was Oliver L. Kirk.

15. Howard Davis defeated a tough Romanian opponent Simion Cutov to win the gold medal. It was only the second gold medal that the U.S.A. has won in the lightweight division since 1924.

16. False. Sugar Ray Leonard defeated Andres Aldama of Cuba to win the gold medal. Leonard, as of this writing, now holds the welterweight and junior middleweight titles in professional boxing.

17. Yes. Jerzy Kulej of Poland won the gold in the light-welterweight division twice in 1964 and 1968 to become the only person ever to do so.

18. Teofilo Stevenson won the Heavyweight division in 1972, '76, '80.

19. Michael and Leon Spinks both won gold medals in the 1976 Olympics. Michael won the middleweight title and Leon won the light-heavyweight title. This was the only time a brother team ever accomplished that in the Olympics.

20. Floyd Patterson won the middleweight gold medal in the 1952 Olympic games at Helsinki. He went on to become heavyweight champion of the world.

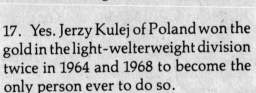

21. Yes. Harry W. Mallin of Great Britain won the Olympic middleweight title twice in 1920 and 1924.

22. Ali, then 18 year old Cassius Clay, defeated Zbigniew Pretrykowski of Poland in the 1960 Olympics to win the light-heavyweight gold medal.

23. Sanders, of the U.S.A., was awarded the gold medal because Ingemar Johansson did not show for the finals. Johansson went on to win the heavyweight title of the world in 1959.

24. Joe Frazier of the U.S.A. beat Hans Huber of Germany for the gold. He went on to win the heavyweight title of the world. This made Frazier the first man to win both the Olympic and professional heavyweight titles.

25. George Foreman of the U.S.A. defeated Russia's Ionas Tschepulis in the finals to win the gold medal. He went on to win the heavyweight title in the pros in 1973 by destroying Joe Frazier in two rounds.

26. No. A Cuban named Teofilo Stevenson won the gold medal both years to become the only heavyweight ever to do so.

27. The canoeing events were first introduced in the 1936 Olympic games held in Berlin. The competitions were the 1,000 meter singles and doubles in kayaking and the 1,000 meter singles and doubles in the Canadien event.

28. Yes. Since 1948 when the women's 500 meter singles kayak event was run in the Olympics. The 500 meter kayak doubles event was introduced in the 1960 Olympics.

29. The XVII Olympiad was held in Rome. Awards were widely spread, with 23 countries winning at least one medal.

30. Out of the eight canoeing events for men and two events for women there were no American winners. The canoeing events were dominated by the Soviets, who scored six golds.

31. True. Cycling was one of the 9 original events held in Greece in 1896. There was only one cycling event, the individual road race, won by A. Konstantinidis of Greece.

32. 1,000 meter sprint; 1,000 meter time trial; 4,000 meter individual pursuit; 4,000 meter team pursuit; individual road race and the road team time trial.

33. Alwin Schockemohle of Germany won the individual equestrian Grand Prix gold medal on "Warwick Rex" in 1976. He also won 3 team medals in 1960, 1968, and 1976.

34. The individual and team Grand Prix (Jumping), individual and team Grand Prix (Dressage) and the individual and team three day event.

35. The Grand Prix (Jumping) event was the only equestrian sport featured in the 1900 Olympic games held in Paris, where it was first introduced. The event was won by Aime Haegeman of Belgium.

36. Hans Winkler of Germany won a record five gold medals in the Olympic equestrian event in his career. He is the only person to do so.

37. Yes. Led by individual three-day event gold medalist, Edmund Coffin, the U.S.A. also won the team gold medal in the same event.

38. Yes. The foil and sabre individual fencing events were featured in 1896. Later the team foil and sabre and individual and team epee events were added.

39. Yes. Women compete in the individual and team foil events. The women's individual was first introduced in 1924 and the team event in 1960. The Russian women have dominated the team foil event, winning every year except 1964 when they came in second to Hungary.

40. D'Oriola of France won two gold medals in the individual foil event and a gold and silver medal in the team event in 1952 and 1956.

41. Nedo Nadi won a record 5 gold medals in fencing at the 1920 Olympic games held in Antwerp.

42. The most medals won in an Olympic career in fencing is 13 (6 gold, 5 silver, 2 bronze) by Edoardo Mangiarotti of Italy in the foil and epee events from 1936 to 1960.

43. The last American to win a medal was Albert Axelrod of New York. He brought home a bronze medal won in the foil event in the 1960 games held in Rome.

44. Yes. Introduced in 1896 as one of the original sports at the Grecian games, it has grown in popularity all over the world. Some of the world's finest athletes compete in gymnastics.

45. The XIX Olympiad was held in Mexico City. 5,531 competitors from 112 nations battled at nearly 7½ thousand feet above sea level.

46. In 1980 Russia stopped Japan's streak.

47. Andrianov of the U.S.S.R. won medals in seven out of the men's eight gymnastic events held in the 1976 games in Montreal. He also won two medals at the 1972 Olympic games.

48. Shakhlin, of the U.S.S.R., won one bronze, two silver, and four gold medals for a total of seven in the 1960 games held in Rome.

49. Gymnastics for women was introduced in the 1952 Olympiad. There were five events, three of which were won by the U.S.S.R. and the other two by Hungary.

50. Fourteen year old Nadia Comaneci of Rumania was the first gymnast to be awarded a perfect score in the 1976 Olympic games held in Montreal.

51. The six events are: combined exercise (team and individual), horse vault, asymmetrical, balance beam and floor exercises.

52. Olga Korbut, who, in the 1972 Olympics, won 3 gold medals and a silver medal.

53. Latynina, who now coaches the U.S.S.R. women's gymnastics team, won a total of 18 Olympic medals (9 gold, 5 silver and 4 bronze), more than any other Olympic competitor.

54. Since the team event was introduced in 1960, the U.S.S.R. has won every year.

55. False. Since the Olympic gymnastics event for women started, the U.S.A. has not produced a single gold medal winner.

56. False. Only the women use music because their programs are based more on grace than the men's. The men's programs have more flips and jumps than the women's.

57. True. A very primitive form of gymnastics was performed in the ancient games (886 B.C. to 393 A.D.) Gymnastics events have been a part of modern Olympic competition since its beginning in 1896.

58. The 1956 games were held in Melbourne, Australia. The equestrian events had to be held separately in Stockholm because of horse quarantine laws in Australia. The swimming competition was dominated by the Australians, who won 8 out of 13 events.

59. Handball was introduced into the 1972 games held in Munich. There is only one event, the team handball event, which was won by Yugoslavia in 1972 and by the U.S.S.R. in 1976.

60. Yes. It was first introduced in 1976 for women and the U.S.S.R. won the gold medal with East Germany winning the silver and Hungary the bronze.

61. India has won the most golds with 7, including 6 in a row (1932-1956). Pakistan has won 2 times and Great Britain has won once.

62. False. As of the 1976 Olympics there was no women's field hockey in the Olympics.

63. There are seven weight divisions: 60 kg. (up to 132½ lbs), 65 kg (up to 143¼ lbs.), 71 kg (up to 156½ lbs.), 78 kg (up to 171¾ lbs.), 86 kg (up to 189½ lbs.), 95 kg (up to 209¼ lbs.), and over 95 kg.

64. The Japanese won 3 gold medals, the U.S.S.R. won 2, and the Koreans did not win a gold medal at the 1976 games held in Montreal.

65. Yes. Allen Coage was the only one. He won a bronze medal in the over 93 kg (205) category for the U.S.A.

66. Riding (800 m course), fencing (epee), shooting (pistol 25 m), swimming (300 m freestyle), and cross-country running (4,000 m).

67. Great Britain won the gold medal, beating out Czechoslovakia and Hungary. This is a three-man team event.

68. Yes. Lars Hall of Sweden won the event in 1952 and again in 1956 to become the only person ever to do so.

69. There are eight events: single and double sculls, quadruple sculls, coxless pairs, coxed pairs, coxless fours, coxed fours and eights.

70. The X Olympiad was held in Los Angeles where every single record in the track and field event was improved except for the long jump. The Japanese brought home five gold medals in the swimming events.

71. The East Germans won five gold medals out of a possible eight. The U.S.S.R. won one gold, while the U.S.A. was shut out in this event.

72. Women's rowing was introduced into Olympic competition in 1976 with six events over 1,000 meters: single and double sculls, coxless pairs, coxed quadruple sculls, coxed four and eights.

73. Joan Lind of the U.S.A. won the silver medal in the single sculls event and the United States women's eights team won a bronze medal.

74. There are: free pistol (50 m), small-bore rifle—prone position, small-bore rifle—three positions (prone, kneeling, standing), rapid-fire pistol, Olympic trap shooting, skeet shooting and running game target, for a total of seven events.

75. The 1976 Olympics held at Montreal produced the fastest recorded times in the eight rowing events. Since water conditions vary from one Olympiad to another the scores are regarded as the fastest times not Olympic records.

76. Lanny Bassham of the U.S.A. won the 1976 small-bore rifle—three positions event with fellow American Margaret Murdock coming in second in the same event. Donald Haldeman also for the U.S.A. won the gold medal in the Olympic trap shooting event with a 190 out of 200 score.

77. The only country to have won three times is Hungary. They won in 1952, 1964 and 1968. Great Britain won in 1908 and 1912 and in the unofficial tournament of 1900.

78. Great Britain defeated a not so tough Denmark team 18-1 in the the 1912 soccer final to win the gold medal.

79. East Germany defeated a tough Poland, who had won the title in 1972, to win the gold medal in 1976 in Montreal.

80. False. Soccer, a relatively new sport to the United States, has never been a medal winning sport for the U.S.A. since its introduction in 1908.

86. Mark Spitz of the U.S.A. won 7 gold medals at the 1972 games in Munich. He also set Olympic records in every one of those events at the time.

87. The 1904 games were held as a side show to the World's Fair in St. Louis. There was a rather small turnout. Because of the distance and expense of travel only seven European and five other countries showed up. There was a scandal in the Marathon race over the finish of Lorz, an American. It seems he got a ride in a car midway through the race and naturally finished first. He was caught and expelled from the games.

81. Goodell, a swimmer, won gold medals in the 400 and 1,500 meters free-style events in 1976. He established Olympic records in both events.

82. True. Spitz of the United States has won a total of 11 medals, including 9 gold. Here is a list of his gold medals.

100 meter free-style   1972
200 meter free-style   1972
100 meter butterfly 1972
200 meter butterfly 1972
4 x 100 meter free-style 1968 + 1972
4 x 200 meter free-style 1968 + 1972
4 x 100 meter medley relay 1972

83. False. Babashoff of the U.S.A. is one of only three women who have won eight Olympic medals in swimming, including two golds.

84. John Naber did that for the U.S.A. with times of 55.49 in the 100 and 159.19 in the 200 meter event. Both times are Olympic records.

85. The 200 meter event was first held in 1900 but not again until 1964 so not many people have had the chance, but Roland Matthes of the German Democratic Republic accomplished that in both 1968 and 1972.

88. Johnny Weissmuller of the U.S.A. He set world records in the 100 and 400 meter free-style events in the 1924 Olympic games. At the 1928 games he won the 100 meter again and was the anchorman of the winning 800 meter relay team. Later he starred as Tarzan in the movies.

89. Buster Crabbe, who won the 400 meter free-style for the United States in 1932 at Los Angeles. Then, like Weissmuller, he became the tree-climbing, vine-swinging Tarzan in the movies.

90. Mrs. Pat McCormick of Long Beach, California won two diving titles (springboard and platform) in the 1952 Olympics and again in the 1956 games at Melbourne.

91. True. Since the introduction of the 400 meter medley relay in 1960, the U.S.A. has swept this event. The order of strokes in a medley relay are: back stroke, breast stroke, butterfly, free-style.

92. Burton of the United States coubled in the 400 meter and 1,500 meter freestyle. He also won a gold medal in the 1972 games, again in the 1,500 meter free-style.

93. Since the introduction of this event in 1908 Australia has won the title twice, Japan twice and the United States a record 10 times. The U.S.A. has dominated this event in every Olympiad since 1948 with the exception of 1956 when Australia won and the U.S.A. took second place.

94. Dibiasi won a total of 5 medals (3 golds, 2 silver) in four games from 1964 to 1976. He is the only diver ever in Olympic competition to win gold medals in three successive games (1968, 1972, 1976) in the highboard event.

95. No. but in the U.S. Olympic trials Michael Finneran scored a 10.0 accorded by all the judges for a backward 1½ somersault 2½ twist free dive from the 10-meter board. He did not win an Olympic medal.

96. False. In 1972 Vladimir Vasin of the Soviet Union won the event to put a hole in the otherwise American dominated sport.

97. Ender of Germany became one of only 3 women to win 4 Olympic gold medals in swimming.

98. Pat McCormick of the U.S.A. won four gold medals in the highboard and springboard diving double in 1952 and 1956 and Dawn Fraser (later Mrs. Gary Ware) of Australia won golds in the 1956, 60, 64, 100 meter freestyle event and a gold in the 400 meter free-style relay in 1956.

99. Shane Gould of Australia won a bronze, a silver, and three gold medals in the swimming event in the 1972 Olympic games held in Munich.

100. The 1940 and 1944 Olympics were cancelled because of World War II. The games were resumed in 1948.

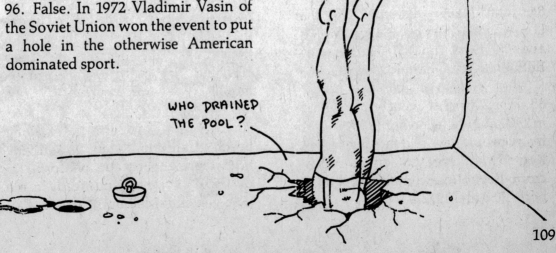

WHO DRAINED THE POOL?

106. The 1912 games were held in Stockholm. The star of these games was American Indian Jim Thorpe, who won both the pentathlon and decathlon. He was later discovered to have played professional baseball and his gold medals were awarded to the runners-up. Thorpe was reinstated as an amateur in 1973 twenty years after his death.

107. False. Track and field have been a part of the modern Olympics since 1896 when the games were started again.

108. Both recorded times of 9.9 seconds but Hayes' time was wind assisted and therefore does not count. Hines' time was accomplished in the finals of the 1968 event held in Mexico City. Hayes recorded a 10.0 in the final in 1964 to win in Tokyo.

109. True. Burke's time in the finals was 12.0 and the record now is 9.9. It was set by Jimmy Hines in the 1968 games.

110. Crawford of Trinidad won the 100 meter sprint in a time of 10.06 seconds beating Don Quarrie of Jamaica and defending champion Valeriy Borzov of the U.S.S.R.

101. Since its introduction in 1912 the United States has won this event a record 10 times. Australia has won it just once and the Soviet Union has yet to win.

102. The East Germans, who won the silver medal in the same event in 1972, captured the title four years later from the defending U.S.A. team with a lead of over 6 seconds.

103. With the United States not participating in the 1980 Summer Olympics the U.S.S.R. won the event for the first time.

104. In 1964 Lesley Bush won the event beating out defending champion Ingrid Engel (formerly Ingrid Kramer) by just over one point. That was the last time an American won it.

105. Hungary has won this event six times since its introduction: in 1908, in 1932, 1936, 1952, 1964, and 1976. Great Britain has won three times and the U.S.A. has never won.

111. False. Every year except 1928 when Canadian Percy Williams won it with Jack London of Great Britain second and Georg Lammers of Germany third.

112. The high altitude helped sprinters because of reduced air resistance, while participants in events which lasted longer than three minutes were unable to beat times achieved in 1948.

113. Valeriy Borzov of the U.S.S.R. won the 1972 100 and 200 meter sprints with times of 10.14 and 20.00 respectively.

114. Yes. Owens of the U.S.A. won four gold medals including the 100 and 200 meters, the 400 meter relay and the long jump.

115. Tommie Smith was the last U.S. runner to win the 200 meter race with an Olympic record time of 19.8 seconds. John Carlos won the bronze medal in that same race not far behind with a time of 20.0.

116. No. Alberto Juantorena of Cuba won the 1976 gold medal in this event to break a string of U.S. victories since 1956.

117. True. Lee Evans set the Olympic record with a time of 43.8 seconds beating out G. Lawrence James, who had a time of 43.9 and fellow American Ronald Freeman won the bronze medal with a time of 44.4.

118. Alberto Juantorena, who won the gold medal in the 400 and 800 meter races in Montreal.

119. Twice before. Douglas Lowe of Great Britain won the 1924 and 1928 races and Malvin G. Whitfield of the United States won the gold at the 1948 and 1952 games.

120. Dave Wottle, who won the 1972 Olympic gold medal in the 800 meter race and ran wearing a golf cap for good luck.

OKAY, YOU CAN RUN WITH THE HAT ON, BUT YOU HAVE TO LEAVE THE CLUBS HERE!

121. No. A favorite to win the 1,500 meter event in the 1972, Ryun fell down in the trial and was eliminated. In 1968 Ryun won the silver medal in the 1,500 while Kenya's great runner Kip Keino won the gold in a record time of 3:34.9.

122. John Walker, who ran a 3:39.2 1500 to beat out Ivo Van Damme of Belgium and Paul Wellmann of Germany.

123. Lasse Viren of Finland set this mark to become the only man ever to do so. He set Olympic records in both events in 1972.

124. Shorter won the gold medal in the marathon event for the U.S.A. and in the 1976 games he won the silver medal in the same event.

125. Yes. Abebe Bikila of Ethiopia is the only runner in the history of the Olympics to retain his marathon title with victories in the 1960 and 1964 games.

126. The U.S.A. has won this event 12 of the 14 times it has been run since 1912. Besides the U.S.A. only Germany in 1960 and Great Britain in 1912 have won golds in the 400 meter relay race.

127. The 1972 team of Larry Black, Bob Taylor, Gerald Tinker and Eddie Hart hold the record with a time of 38.19 compared to the 1968 team's time of 38.20. The 1972 victory was especially rewarding to Eddie Hart, a co-holder of the 100 meter record (9.9 seconds), because he was disqualified from the 100 meter final for missing the time trials. Russia's Valeriy Borzov won the 100 meter in a time of 10.14, a time Hart probably could have beaten.

128. The U.S.A. again dominated this event with 10 titles in 14 Olympiads. Kenya won once in 1972 and Jamaica once in 1952.

129. Willie Davenport won the gold medal in the 110 meter hurdle event and set a record while doing so. He came back 8 years later and won a bronze medal in the 1976 in Montreal.

130. If you said Rod Milburn you are right! In the 1972 Olympic games he ran a 13.24 to break Willie's 13.3 mark.

131. Yes. American Lee Calhoun, who first won it in 1956, when he set a record of 13.5 that stood until 1968. He won again in 1960 to become the only man ever to retain the hurdles title.

132. Edison Moses, who holds the current world record in this event, set the Olympic record of 47.64 in the 1976 games, thereby bettering silver medalist Michael Shine of the U.S.A. by more than one second in the same race.

133. Yes. Glenn Davis of the United States set the Olympic record in winning the 1956 event and four years later in 1960 he broke his own record to win again. He is the only runner to accomplish this feat.

134. False. Horace Ashenfelter of the U.S.A. was the only American ever to do so. He won the gold medal in 1952 beating out Russian Vladimir Kazantsev by more than six seconds to win it.

I'M STUCK!

135. False. Since its introduction in 1956 not a single medal has been won by an American. The 1976 gold medalist was Daniel Bautista of Mexico with a record time of 1h 24:40.6.

138. Dwight Stones, who jumped 7'3" in both Olympiads to win two bronze medals.

136. True. The 50,000 meter (31 miles, 120 yards) road walk was held from 1932 until 1972. The last person to win it was Bernd Kannenberg of Germany with a time of 3h 56:11.6 Larry Young of the U.S.A. came in third in 1968 and 1972.

139. Bob Seagren won it in 1968 with a vault of 17' 8½". He came back in 1972 and won the silver medal for the U.S.A. with the same jump.

137. In the 1968 Olympics Dick Fosbury, unlike any other high jumper in history, jumped over the high bar backwards and won the event with a jump of 7' 4½". Fosbury, an American, set the Olympic record with that jump which became known as the "Fosbury Flop."

140. Beamon of the U.S.A. broke the long jump record by more than 2 feet in an event where records are usually set in inches with a leap of 29' 2½". This record will probably last into the twenty first century. It also won him a gold medal in the 1968 games in Mexico City.

141. Ralph Boston of the United States was the 1960 Olympic long jump gold medalist. In 1964 he came back and won the silver medal and in 1968 won the bronze in the same event.

142. Viktor Saneyev of the U.S.S.R. is the only Olympian to win the triple jump three times (1968, 1972, 1976.)

143. W. Parry O'Brien won the 1952 and 1956 gold medals in the shotput for the U.S.A. He also won the 1960 silver medal in the same event.

144. Al Oerter. During that span he won four gold medals and broke his own Olympic record every year he competed.

145. Harold Connolly was the last American to win the hammer throw. He won in the 1956 games in Melbourne with a throw of 207 feet, 3½ inches.

146. Since the introduction of the javelin throw only one U.S.A. athlete has won this event. In the 1952 games at Helsinki Cyrus C. Young won the gold medal with a toss of 242 feet, ½ inch.

147. 100 meter sprints, long jump, shot put, high jump, 400 meter race, 110 meter hurdles, discus, pole vault, javelin and 1,500 meter race. The decathlon event takes place over a two day period.

148. Bob Mathias of the United States won the 1948 and 1952 gold medals in the decathlon event, becoming the only person in the history of the event to win it twice.

149. They all won it! Jim Thorpe won the 1912 decathlon but was disqualified because of the then amateur rules. He has been reinstated by the A.A.U. of the U.S.A. as an amateur athlete. Glenn Morris won it in 1936 for the U.S.A. Milton Campbell, who won the gold in 1956, won the silver medal in the 1952 games.

150. Bruce Jenner of the United States won the 1976 gold medal in Montreal and broke the Olympic and world record in the process with a total of 8,618 points. He broke the record of the U.S.S.R.'s Nikolai Avilov, 8,454 points amassed in the 1972 games.

151. Rafer Johnson of the United States won the 1960 decathlon event in Rome with 8,001 points defeating Yang Chuan-Kwang, a very tough athlete from Taiwan. Even though Yang won seven of the ten events Johnson won because he piled up so many points in his three specialties: the shot put, discus throw, and javelin throw.

152. Bill Toomey of the U.S.A. won the decathlon event with 8,193 points. He beat second place Hans-Joachim Walde of Germany who scored 8,111 points. Toomey was 29 years old when he won this event, at an age usually considered too old for the grueling two day decathlon.

153. American Wilma Rudolph took almost a half second off the Olympic record and won the 100 meter dash for a gold medal with a time of 11.0. She also won gold medals in the 200 meter dash and was a member of the winning 400 meter relay team.

154. American Wyomia Tyus did that beating out fellow Americans Edith Maguire in 1964 and Barbara Ferrell in 1968. She also tied the Olympic record of 11.0 in 1968 in Mexico City.

155. East Germany won in 1976, West Germany won in 1972 and the United States has won a total of five times in 1932, 1936, 1952, 1960 and 1968.

156. The United States has been shut out in this event. Since the introduction of volleyball in 1964 Russia has won twice (1964, 1968) and Japan (1972) and Poland (1976) once each.

157. Korea has never won the gold medal while Japan and Russia have either come in first or second since the introduction of volleyball in 1964. Japan won in 1964 and 1976 and the U.S.S.R. won in 1968 and 1972.

158. Yes. Only one, Lee James, won the silver medal in the middle heavyweight division with a lift of 799 lbs. (snatch and jerk) to receive the only U.S.A. weight lifting medal in the 1976 games.

159. Vassili Alexeev has won the gold both years the super heavyweight event has been held. In 1976 he had a total of 970 lbs. in the snatch and jerk compared to the 892¾ lbs. total of Gerd Bonk of the German Democratic Republic.

160. The two wrestling events are the freestyle and the Greco-Roman.

161. False. Marjorie Gestring of the United States won the 1936 women's springboard event when she was 13 years, 9 months old.

162. True. A French boy whose name was not recorded coxed the Netherlands coxed pair in 1900. He substituted for Dr. Hermanus Brockman who coxed in the heats but was too heavy. The boy, who may have been as young as seven took over and they won the gold medal.

163. True. Dr. Ivan Osiier of Denmark competed as a fencer in the 1908, 1912, 1920, 1924, 1928, 1932 and 1948 Olympics. He won silver medals in 1908 and 1912. Magnus Konow of Norway also competed for a span of 40 years from 1908-1920 and 1936-1948 in yachting.

164. Yes. Oscar G. Swahn was a member of the gold medal winning Running Deer shooting team in 1912. He was 65 years, 258 days old.

165. The 1972 games at Munich had the most competitors with a record 7,147 athletes from 122 countries.

166. True. There were an estimated 500,000 to 1,500,000 spectators watching the marathon race through Tokyo, Japan on October 21, 1964.

167. Dab Gable of the U.S.A. won the 1972 freestyle lightweight wrestling gold medal in Munich after a great career in college where he posted a 293-6 amateur record.

168. True. Martin Klein of the U.S.S.R. and Alfred Asikainen of Finland wrestled for 11 hours, 40 minutes in the Greco-Roman middleweight "A" event in the 1912 games at Stockholm. Klein won.

169. Chris Taylor of the U.S.A. stood 6 feet, 5 inches and weighed 420 pounds. He won the super heavyweight bronze medal in the 1972 games in Munich.

170. There have been three. The last was Aleksandr Medved of the U.S.S.R., who won the freestyle light-heavyweight title in the 1964 games, the freestyle heavyweight in 1968 and the freestyle super-heavyweight gold medal in the 1972 games.

171. Only one. John Peterson was the only U.S. wrestler to win a gold medal at the 1976 games. He won the middleweight division freestyle title. In 1972 he won the silver medal in the same weight class.

172. The soling class, star class, Flying Dutchman class, 470 class, Finn class, and Tornado class.

173. No. The U.S. did not win any gold medals, but did win silver medals in the Tornado class and the soling class in 1976 at Montreal.

174. False. Norton, who has fought unsuccessfully for the heavyweight title of the world several times, never competed in the Olympics.

175. The 1948 games were held in London where 4,099 competitors and 59 countries competed. Fanny Blankers-Koen, mother of two children, won four gold medals. Bob Mathias at the age of seventeen won the decathlon and Willi Grut of Sweden won the modern pentathlon.

176. Dillard of the United States won the 100 meter dash and was a member of the 400 meter relay gold medal team at the 1948 games.

177. True. Coroebus, cook from Elis, won a foot race of about 200 yards and became the first Olympic winner. The race was the only event in the first Olympiad in Greece.

178. Absolutely false. Since the introduction of the team competition in 1936 the U.S. has never won even a single medal.

Winter Olympics

1. Overall which one of these countries has won the most medals in the history of the winter Olympics: the United States, the U.S.S.R. or Norway?

2. What country won the ice hockey title at the 1980 winter Olympics in Lake Placid?

3. Who did the United States beat in the ice hockey finals in 1980 to win the gold medal?

4. Who coached the U.S. ice hockey team to victory in the 1980 winter Olympics?

5. True or false: Eric Heiden won every speed skating event in the men's division in the 1980 winter Olympics?

6. True or false: Eric Heiden has a sister who won a medal in the 1980 winter Olympics in Lake Placid?

7. Can you name the seven events that make up the winter Olympics?

8. In what winter Olympic event did Ingemar Stenmark compete and how did he do?

9. Did Phil Mahre win any medals at the 1980 winter Olympics?

10. American women have done quite well in the figure skating event in the winter Olympics in recent years. Did the U.S.A. have any medal winner in 1980?

11. What is the greatest number of medals ever won by one person in winter Olympic competition: 5, 7 or 9?

12. In what event did Sheila Young compete at the 1976 winter Olympics?

13. Which one of these women did not win a gold medal in figure skating: Peggy Fleming, Janet Lynn or Dorothy Hamill?

14. What has Sonja Henie done that no other woman has come close to in winter Olympic history?

15. Where and when were the first winter Olympic games held?

16. In what event did Jean-Claude Killy compete at the winter Olympic games of 1968?

17. Where were the 1964 winter Olympics games held?

18. The United States hockey team won the 1960 and 1980 winter Olympics gold medal. Between those titles one country has dominated this Olympic sport. Can you name the country?

19. Can you name the American who won the men's figure skating title two consecutive games?

20. True or false: the largest crowd ever to see a winter Olympic event was present at the ski jumping competition in 1952?

Answers

1. Norway has totalled the most medals with 155 compared to Russia's 140 and the United States' 108, but Russia has the lead in gold medals with 61 to Norway's 51.

2. The Miracle U.S.A. hockey team won the gold medal beating out silver medal winner U.S.S.R. and bronze medal winner Sweden.

3. The United States defeated Finland 4-2 to win the gold medal. The U.S. last won in 1960.

4. Former Minnesota University coach Herb Brooks, who, as of this writing, is now the head coach of the New York Rangers.

5. True. Heiden of the United States won five gold medals in the 500 meter; 1,000 meter; 1,500 meter; 5,000 meter and 10,000 meter races.

6. True. Beth Heiden, Eric's sister, won the bronze medal in the 3,000 meter race.

7. Nordic skiing, Alpine skiing, figure skating, speed skating, bobsled, toboganning and ice hockey.

8. Stenmark of Sweden won the gold medal in the slalom and giant slalom in the 1980 winter games at Lake Placid.

9. Phil Mahre of the United States surprised everybody by winning a silver medal in the slalom event in Lake Placid in 1980.

10. Linda Fratianne won the silver medal at Lake Placid in 1980. She was the only U.S. woman to win a figure skating medal in 1980.

11. Sixten Jernberg of Sweden has won a total of 9 medals — 4 gold, 3 silver and 2 bronze — more than any other athlete in winter Olympic history.

12. Sheila Young of the U.S.A. won a gold, a silver and a bronze medal at Innsbruck in the speed skating competition. She was also the world cycling champion.

13. Janet Lynn is the only one not to win the gold medal. She won the bronze medal in the 1972 games in Sapporo, Japan.

14. She won three consecutive figure skating titles in 1928, 1932 and 1936. Nobody has won even twice besides Norwegian Henie.

15. The first winter Olympics were held in Chamonix-Mont Blanc, France in 1924. Sixteen nations sent teams to the games. Clas Thunberg of Finland won 3 gold, 1 silver and 1 bronze medal and Thorleif Hug of Norway won 3 golds and bronze for Nordic Skiing.

16. Killy of France won all three events in the Alpine skiing competition at the 1968 games held in Grenoble, France.

17. The 1964 games were held in Innsbruck, Austria. The U.S.S.R. romped through these games with 25 medals. The U.S.A won 6. The star of the games was Russia's Lydia Skoblikova, who won four golds in speed skating.

18. The U.S.S.R. has won every Olympic hockey title except for 1960 and 1980 since they first won in the 1956 games.

19. Dick Button, who is a skating commentator on television, won the 1948 and 1952 gold medals rather easily for the United States.

20. True. 150,000 spectators gathered to watch the ski jumping competition at the 1952 games in Oslo, Norway.

Basketball

1. Who invented the modern day game of basketball and in what country?

2. True or false: A man once sank over 2,000 consecutive free throws?

3. True or false: A man once sank over 12,000 baskets in a 24 hour period?

4. The longest field goal ever made in a game was 86 feet by a high school player, a college player, or an NBA player?

5. Where is the tallest basketball player from, United States, Russia, or China?

6. Who is the tallest NBA player of all time?

7. What is the largest crowd ever to see a basketball game in person, 50,000, 75,000, or 100,000?

8. Who founded the Harlem Globetrotters?

9. Has the U.S.A. basketball team ever lost in the Olympics?

10. True or false: A team is awarded two points for a free throw?

11. Is Wilt Chamberlain over 7 feet tall?

12. True or false: Elgin Baylor played his entire career for the Boston Celtics?

13. In the NBA there is only one "Dr. J." Who is he?

14. Can you name the four teams who joined the NBA from the ABA when the ABA dissolved?

15. For whom did John Havlicek play in his career in the NBA?

16. True or false: Bob Pettit scored more points in his career than did Hal Greer?

17. True or false: the circumference of an NBA basketball is 30 inches?

18. After whom is the basketball hall of fame named?

19. Can you name the great Los Angeles Laker guard who scored over 25,000 points in his career?

20. Can you name the only three positions in basketball?

21. Besides Wilt Chamberlain has anybody ever won the rookie of the year and the most valuable player awards in the same season?

22. What is the nickname of NBA great, Elvin Hayes?

23. What former NBA player was known as "Clyde?"

24. Define a conversion in basketball.

25. Bob McAdoo won the MVP in the NBA in the 1974-75 season. For what team did he play?

26. For what teams did Bob Cousy play in his NBA career?

27. Did Bob Cousy ever win the MVP award in the NBA?

28. For what team did Bob Pettit play in the NBA?

29. Did Bob Pettit ever win the MVP award in the NBA?

30. What former NBA great was known as the "Big O?"

31. Did Oscar Robertson ever win the MVP award in the NBA?

32. True or false: Wilt Chamberlain was the first player to score 20,000 points in the NBA?

33. What happens if an NBA team fails to bring the ball across the mid court line in less than ten seconds?

34. Has anybody ever won the Most Valuable Player award six times in the NBA?

35. How many times did Wilt Chamberlain win the MVP award in the NBA?

36. With what team did Bill Russell play his NBA career?

37. Did Bill Russell ever win the MVP award in the NBA?

38. What former NBA player was known as "Earl the Pearl?"

39. The Sullivan award is given every year to the amateur athlete of the year. A basketball player from UCLA won the award in 1973. Can you name him?

40. What team has won the most NBA championships?

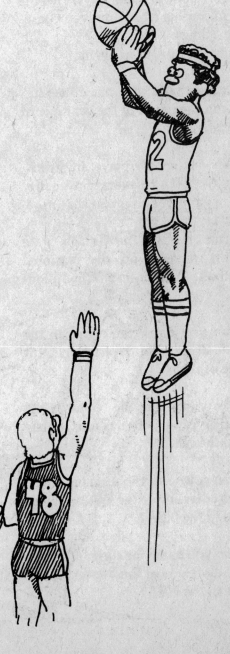

49. Which one of these teams won the Atlantic division in the NBA in the 1982-83 season, the Philadelphia 76ers or the Boston Celtics?

50. Which one of these teams won the Central division in the NBA in the 1982-83 season, the Chicago Bulls or the Milwaukee Bucks?

41. Which one of these players led the NBA in scoring a record seven consecutive times: Elgin Baylor, Wilt Chamberlain or Julius Erving?

42. True or false: not one coach has ever won the coach of the year award in the NBA two times?

43. Who is the only player in the history of the NBA to average over fifty points a game for a regular season?

44. True or false: the Golden State Warriors never won the National Basketball Association Championship?

45. Can you name the teams in the Atlantic division in the Eastern Conference of the NBA?

46. Can you name the teams in the Central division in the Eastern Conference of the NBA?

47. Can you name the six teams in the Midwest division of the Western Conference in the NBA?

48. Can you name the six teams in the Pacific divisions of the Western Conference in the NBA?

51. Which one of these teams won the Midwest division in the NBA in the **1982-83 season**, the San Antonio Spurs or the Houston Rockets?

52. Which one of these teams won the Pacific division in the NBA in the **1982-83** season: the Los Angeles Lakers or the Phoenix Suns?

53. Can you name the 1982-83 scoring champion in the NBA? Here's a hint: he played for Denver.

54. Can you name the Philadelphia 76ers who led the NBA in rebounding for the 1982-83 season?

55. Can you name the player who led the NBA in total assists for the 1982-83 season?

56. Which one of these players did not average over 25 points a game in the 1980-81 NBA season: Kareem Abdul-Jabbar, Julius Erving or George Gervin?

57. Who won the NCAA finals in basketball in 1984?

58. What Boston Celtic player is known as "the Bird" in the NBA?

59. Can you name the Boston Celtic center who won the most valuable player award in the NBA for the 1972-73 season?

60. For what team and in what position did George Mikan play in the NBA?

61. What is the Podoloff Cup in the NBA?

62. Who won the first most valuable player award in the NBA?

63. What great player in the NBA is known as "the Ice Man?"

64. Has Moses Malone ever won the MVP award in the NBA?

65. The Los Angeles Lakers won the 1971-72 NBA championship. The L.A. Lakers used to be the Minneapolis Lakers. Did they win any NBA titles in Minneapolis?

66. Kareem Abdul-Jabbar now plays for the Los Angeles Lakers. For what other NBA team has he played?

67. Who did Paul Arizin play for in his NBA career?

68. Wilt Chamberlain won seven scoring titles in a row from 1959-60 until 1965-66. Can you name the player who broke his string in 1966-67 and won the title?

69. Who won the 1982-83 NBA Championship?

70. Whom did Bill Fitch replace as coach on the Celtics?

71. True or false: the Houston Rockets played against the Boston Celtics in the NBA finals and had a losing record during the regular season?

72. In 1969 the MVP and Rookie of the Year was the same, can you name him?

73. For what NBA team did Joe Fulks play?

74. What former NBA star was known as "Hondo?"

75. What NBA team did Neil Johnston play for?

76. What former NBA star was known as "Easy Ed?"

77. Did Rick Barry ever play in the ABA?

78. True or false: Julius Erving has never averaged over 30 points a game in his NBA career?

79. Before he became known as Kareem Abdul-Jabbar, what was this player's name and why did he change it?

80. In 1970-71 Dave Cowens of the Boston Celtics shared the rookie of the year award with a player from the Portland Trailblazers. Can you name the other player?

81. Only one New York Knick has ever won the most valuable player award in the NBA. Can you name him?

82. Can you name the only two players ever to win the most valuable player award three consecutive seasons?

83. Who won the first rookie of the year award in the NBA?

84. Which one of these players never won the rookie of the year award: Elgin Baylor, Wilt Chamberlain or Woody Sauldsbury?

85. Ernie DeGregorio won the rookie of the year award for the 1973-74 season. For what team did he play?

86. The record for most points scored in a single game in the NBA is 100 by one person. Who did it and for what team?

87. True or false: the NBA record for most field goals in one game by one player is held by Bob McAdoo?

88. Which one of these players holds the record for most rebounds in one game in the NBA: Bill Walton, Wilt Chamberlain or Bill Russell?

89. On March 14, 1963 Guy Rodgers tied the single game NBA assist record with 28 in a game against St. Louis. Whose record did he tie?

90. True or false: Rick Barry holds the NBA record for most free throws made in a single game?

91. True or false: Wilt Chamberlain holds the NBA record for most free throws missed in a single game?

92. True or false: Julius Erving holds the NBA record for most consecutive points in a single game?

93. True or false: Bob Pettit holds the NBA record for most consecutive free throws made in a single game?

94. Which one of these players holds the NBA record for the highest field goal percentage in a season: Wilt Chamberlain, Jerry West or Kareem Abdul-Jabbar?

95. Does the same person hold the record for free throws attempted and free throws made in a single season?

96. How many teams did Jerry West play for during his great career in the NBA?

97. Which one of these players holds the record for highest free throw percentage during a regular season: Walt Frazier, Ernie Di Gregorio or Rick Barry?

98. Which one of these players holds the NBA record for free throw percentage lifetime: Ernie De Gregorio, Rick Barry or Kevin Porter?

99. Which one of these players holds the NBA record for most rebounds in a season: Bill Russel, Wilt Chamberlain or Moses Malone?

100. True or false: Bob Cousy holds the single season NBA record for assists?

109. Which player has played the most games in his NBA career?

110. True or false: Hal Greer holds the NBA record for most personal fouls in a career?

101. Has anybody ever scored over 30,000 points in a career in the NBA?

102. Who has a higher lifetime scoring average in the NBA: Oscar Robertson or Wilt Chamberlain?

103. True or false: Wilt Chamberlain holds the NBA record for most field goals attempted in a career?

104. Does John Havlicek hold the NBA record for most field goals made in his career?

105. Who holds the NBA record for highest field goal percentage during his career, Wilt Chamberlain or Kareem Abdul-Jabbar?

106. Which one of these great NBA stars holds the record for most free throws made in his career: Wilt Chamberlain, Jerry West or Oscar Robertson?

107. What player holds the record for most rebounds in his career in the NBA?

108. Who had more assists in his career in the NBA: Oscar Robertson or Bob Cousy?

111. For what teamd did Vern Mikkelsen play in his NBA career?

112. True or false: the Golden State Warriors once lost a basketball game by more than 60 points?

113. Which one of these teams has the NBA record for most wins in a season: Boston Celtics, Los Angeles Lakers or the Philadelphia 76ers?

114. Can you name one player from the first team all-NBA squad in 1946-47?

115. What NBA teams did Dolph Schayes play for in his career?

116. Who won the first coach of the year award in the NBA?

117. Did Red Auerbach ever win the coach of the year award?

118. When was the ABA started and when did it shut down?

119. Which team won more ABA titles, the Indiana Pacers or the New York Nets?

120. True or false: former New York Knick guard Bill Bradley was a Rhodes Scholar?

128. Who coached those great UCLA teams?

129. Can you name the college that won the NCAA finals in 1976 with a perfect season without a defeat?

130. How many games does each of the 22 NBA teams play during the regular season?

121. Can you name the only player ever to win three most valuable player awards in the ABA?

122. Can you name the NBA player who won the scoring championship 7 consecutive years?

123. Has a college basketball player ever scored 100 points in a single game?

124. Who won the NCAA 1982-83 championship?

125. Which college holds the record for most consecutive victories?

126. Oscar Robertson from the University of Cincinnati won the first two college player of the year awards in 1959 and 1960. Has anybody ever won three of these awards?

127. Since 1964 what college team has won more NCAA Division 1 basketball championships than any other school?

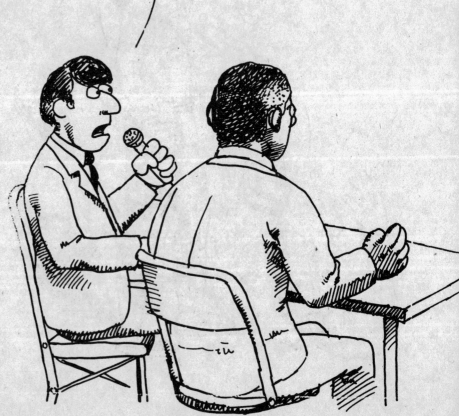

IT SOUNDS LIKE A CLICHÉ, BUT THIS KID IS REALLY BURNING UP THE NET !

131. True or false: The Philadelphia 76ers hold the NBA record for the longest losing streak in the history of the game?

132. Who won the 1980 NBA championship?

133. Which one of these teams holds the record for the worst won-lost record in NBA history: the Detroit Pistons, the Dallas Mavericks, or the Philadelphia 76ers?

134. Who has played more minutes in his NBA career: John Havlicek, Wilt Chamberlain or Elvin Hayes?

135. True or false: Wilt Chamberlain played his entire career with the Los Angeles Lakers?

136. Alvin Adams won the rookie of the year award in the 1975-76 season for what team?

137. In 1978 Guy Rodgers and Bob Cousy's single game assist record of 28 was broken by whom?

138. Who was called "the Stilt" in the NBA?

139. How many different ways of scoring are there in the NBA?

140. Can you name the first player chosen in the 1982-83 NBA draft?

141. Can you name the teams Lew Alcindor and Kareem Abdul-Jabbar played for during the 1970-71 season?

142. True or false: Bill Russell won the rookie of the year award in the 1956-57 season?

143. What is the distance from the basket to the free throw line?

144. True or false: a college player once scored 150 points in a basketball game?

145. True or false: Bill Russell was the first player to grab 1,000 rebounds in an NBA season?

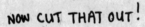

NOW CUT THAT OUT!

Answers

1. The game was invented by Dr. James Naismith (1861-1939) at the Y.M.C.A. College at Springfield, Massachussetts in December, 1891 for the purpose of having an indoor sport during the winter months. The first public game was held on March 11, 1892. It is now played all over the world.

2. True. Ted St. Martin from Jacksonville, Florida sank an incredible 2,036 consecutive free throws on June 25, 1977. That's a record which will be hard to break.

3. True. Fred Newman of San Jose, California sank 12,874 baskets out of 13,116 attempts for a 98.15 percent on May 31-June 1, 1975. He also sank 88 straight free throws WHILE BLINDFOLDED in 1978.

4. Barry Hutchings, 15, of Sutherlin High School made a shot from 86 feet away in a game on March 22, 1976 in Sutherlin, Oregon. Another high school player from Illinois, Larry Slinkard, once sank a shot from 88 feet in practice in 1953.

5. The tallest basketball player of all time is Mu Tieh-Chu from China, who played against a Japanese all-star team in 1978. He measured 7 feet, 9¾ inches. The tallest woman is Iuliana Semenova of the U.S.S.R. She is 7 feet, 2 inches tall and weights 281 pounds.

6. The tallest NBA player of all time is Tom Budason who stood 7 feet, 4 inches tall.

7. The Harlem Globetrotters played before a crowd of 75,000 in the Olympic Stadium, West Berlin, Germany in 1951. The largest crowd ever to see a game indoors assembled on January 20, 1968 when 52,693 screaming spectators watched the University of Houston play U.C.L.A. in the Astrodome.

8. Abe Saperstein (1903-1966) from Chicago. The Globetrotters played their first game in 1927. Since then they have travelled over 6 million miles, have visited 94 countries on 6 continents and have been seen by 80 million spectators. They have won over 12,000 games while losing fewer than 350, but most of these games were not meant to be competitive.

9. Only once since 1936. In 1972 in a much disputed final game against Russia they lost 51-50. They regained the Olympic title in the 1976 games without losing a single game.

10. False. A team is awarded one point for every scoring free throw.

NEEDS A LITTLE AIR —

THUNK

11. Yes. Wilt Chamberlain, who is considered by many to be the greatest basketball player of all time, is 7 feet, 1 inch tall.

12. False. Elgin Baylor played his entire 14 year career for the Minneapolis and Los Angeles Lakers. He averaged almost 25 points a game in his rookie year and kept getting better. Baylor averaged over 27 in his career despite injuries.

13. Julius Erving, currently of the Philadelphia 76ers, is knows as "Doctor J." In his 10 professional seasons (five in the ABA) he has averaged around 26 points a game. He is best known for his amazing jumping ability and for his ability to score on anybody from anywhere.

14. The four teams which joined the NBA are the New York Nets, the San Antonio Spurs, the Indiana Pacers and the Denver Nuggets. They all joined in 1977.

15. John Havlicek played for the Boston Celtics for 16 seasons. He averaged almost 21 points a game and scored 26,395 career points, a Celtic record.

16. False. Hal Greer scored 21,586 points in his 15 year career compared to Bob Pettit's 20,880 points in his 11 year career.

17. True. An NBA basketball is 30 inches in circumference and weighs between 20 and 22 ounces.

18. The basketball hall of fame is named after James Naismith, who founded the game. Located in Springfield, Massachusetts, it is called the Naismith Memorial Basketball Hall of Fame. It was established in 1959 to acknowledge the great contributions to the game by players, coaches and teams.

19. The fourth all time leading scorer in the NBA's history, Jerry West, who scored 25,192 career points in fourteen seasons of play. He averaged over 27 points a game and was said to have one of the best jump shots the game has ever seen.

20. There are five players on the court for each team at one time: one center, two forwards and two guards.

21. Baltimore Bullet Wes Unseld led the previous year's last place team to a first place finish in the Eastern division in the NBA. He was second only to Chamberlain in rebounds with an average of over 18 a game and won both awards.

22. Elvin Hayes is known as the "Big E." In his 13 year career he has averaged over 23 points a game and is in the top ten in all time scoring in the NBA with the Bullets.

23. Former New York Knick and Cleveland Cavalier Walt Frazier, who averaged almost 19 points a game in twelve seasons in the NBA. He played on two New York Knick championship teams (1969-70, 1972-73). Frazier was known as Clyde because he was so cool on and off the court.

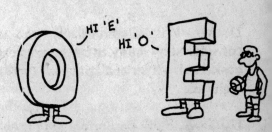

24. A conversion is a successful free throw or the making of a bonus shot.

25. Bob McAdoo won the MVP award playing for the Buffalo Braves, where he averaged 34.5 points a game and scored 2,831 points in that season.

26. Bob Cousy played with the Boston Celtics from the 1950-51 season until the 1962-63 season and had a very brief 7 game stint with the Cincinnati Royals in the 1969-70 season. He averaged 18.4 points a game and played on six NBA championship Celtic teams.

27. Bob Cousy won the MVP award in the 1956-57 season by leading the league in assists and averaged 20.6 points a game for the world champion Celtics.

28. Bob Pettit played for the Milwaukee-St. Louis Hawks from the 1954-55 season till the 1964-65 season. He averaged 26.4 points a game while scoring 20,880 points lifetime. Pettit played on 11 all-star teams and had a lifetime total of 12,851 rebounds. He also scored more than 50 points in a game six times and now is a member of the hall of fame.

29. Bob Pettit won the MVP award twice. He won the first time in 1956 when he averaged 25.7 points a game and the second in 1959 when he averaged 29.2 points a game. In 1956 he led the NBA in rebounds and 1959 he was second in rebounds.

30. Oscar Robertson, who played his career with the Cincinnati Royals and the Milwaukee Bucks from the 1960-61 season until the 1973-74 season. He averaged 25.7 points a game and scored 26,710 lifetime points. He is also the all time leader in career assists with 9,887.

31. Oscar Robertson won the award for his great play in the 1963-64 season, when he averaged 31.4 points a game, second in the league, and averaged 11 assists a game. He was the NBA's MVP of the all-star game that season as well.

32. False. Bob Pettit of the Hawks was the first to do so in the 1964-65 season, his last year as a player. He ended up with 20,880.

33. If a team fails to bring the ball across midcourt in 10 seconds they automatically lose possession of the ball.

34. Kareem Abdul Jabbar has won the MVP award a record six times. He won the MVP award three times with the Milwaukee Bucks (1971, 1972, 1974) and three times with the Los Angeles Lakers (1976, 1977, 1980): more than any other player in NBA history.

35. Wilt Chamberlain won the MVP award four times in his career. In 1960, his rookie season, 1966, 1967 and 1968. His best MVP season was his rookie year when he averaged 37.6 points a game and scored 2,707 points.

36. Bill Russell played his NBA career with the Boston Celtics from the 1956-57 season until the 1968-69 season. He averaged 15.1 points a game and scored 14,522 career points. He was known for his great defensive play and played on 11 championship teams in 13 seasons with the Celtics.

37. Russell won the award five times in his thirteen seasons, 1958, 1961, 1962, and 1965. The Celtics won the NBA championship in every one of those seasons except 1958.

38. Earl Monroe, who played thirteen seasons in the NBA with the Baltimore Bullets and the New York Knicks. He averaged 18.8 points a game. His best season was in 1968-69 when he scored 2,065 points averaging 25.8 per game.

39. Bill Walton, who led UCLA to the College National Championship that year. He went on to lead the Portland Trailblazers to the NBA title in 1977. Walton won the NBA MVP award in 1978.

40. The Boston Celtics, who have won fourteen times including eight straight, 1959 till 1966. Over the years such great players as Bill Russell, Bob Cousy, John Havlicek, Jo Jo White, Dave Cowens, Sam Jones, Tom Hein- sohn, and Bill Sharman have played for this dynasty.

41. Wilt Chamberlain did that for the 76ers and the Warriors with an average of 39.6 points a game over seven consecutive seasons (1960-1966).

42. False. Bill Fitch currently of the Boston Celtics won it in 1980 by coaching the Celtics to the best record in basketball after a last place finish the year before. He also won in 1976 while coaching the Cleveland Cavaliers to a first place finish in the Central division after a sub .500 year.

43. Wilt Chamberlain, who averaged 50.4 points a game in the 1961-62 season playing for the Philadelphia Warriors. He also scored a record 4,029 points in that season.

49. Philadelphia won the division with a 65-17 record.

50. Milwaukee Bucks won the division with a 51-31 record.

44. False. The Golden State Warriors won the 1975 final beating the Washington Bullets 4 games to none. They were led by forward Rick Barry, who averaged 30.6 points a game, second in the league.

45. The New York Knicks, the Philadelphia 76ers, the Boston Celtics, the Washington Bullets and the New Jersey Nets.

46. The Chicago Bulls, the Milwaukee Bucks, the Indiana Pacers, the Atlanta Hawks, the Cleveland Cavaliers and the Detroit Pistons.

47. The Houston Rockets, the Kansas City Kings, the San Antonio Spurs, the Denver Nuggets, the Dallas Mavericks and the Utah Jazz.

48. The Seattle Supersonics, the Golden State Warriors, the Portland Trailblazers, the Phoenix Suns, the Los Angeles Lakers and the San Diego Clippers.

55. E. Johnson of the Los Angeles Lakers accumulated 829 assists for the season.

56. Julius Erving averaged 24.6 points a game with the 76ers in the 1980-81 season.

57. The Georgetown Hoyas defeated the Houston Cougars 84-75.

58. Larry Bird of the Celtics established himself as one of the premier players in the league. He won the rookie of the year award in 1980 and helped Boston to post the best record in 1980 and 1981 in the NBA.

59. Dave Cowens, who averaged 20.5 points a game for the Celtics that year (68-14.) They were beaten in the semi-finals by the N.Y. Knicks.

60. George Mikan was the first real superstar in the NBA playing center for the Minneapolis Lakers. In Mikan's career which started with Chicago in the N.L. in 1946 ended in 1956 with the Lakers, he averaged 22.6 points and scored a career 11,764 points.

51. San Antonio Spurs won the division with a 53-29 record.

52. Los Angeles Lakers won the division with a 58-24 record.

53. Alex English of the Denver Nuggets averaging 28.4 points a game and scored 2,326 points in the regular season.

54. Moses Malone had 1,194 rebounds and averaged 15.3.

61. The Podoloff Cup is named after Maurice Podoloff, the first president of the league. It is the most valuable player award given to the outstanding player in the league.

62. The first MVP award given in the NBA in the 1955-56 season went to Bob Pettit of St. Louis. He averaged 25.7 points a game to lead the league. He also led in rebounding with a 16.2 average and was the MVP in the all-star game. All this happened during his second season.

63. The very talented 6 foot, 7 inch guard George Gervin of the San Antonio Spurs. He has won three consecutive scoring titles (1977-78 through 1979-80) and has averaged over 25 points a game since becoming a professional in 1972.

64. Yes, three times. The last in 1982-83 with the Philadelphia 76ers.

65. From the 1948-49 season until the 1953-54 season the Minneapolis Lakers won the NBA title five out of six seasons led by their big center, George Mikan.

66. Jabbar started his career with the Milwaukee Bucks in the 1969-70 season and was the rookie of the year with a 28.8 scoring average. He played with the Bucks until the 1974-75 season before becoming a Laker. Jabbar won three MVP awards with the Bucks (1970-71, 1971-72, 1973-74.)

67. Arizin played 10 years with the Philadelphia Warriors (1950-51 till 1961-62). He averaged 22.8 points a game and won the scoring championship in 1951-52 with a 25.4 average and in 1956-57 with 25.6. Arizin was known for having one of the best jump shots ever in the NBA.

68. Second year man Rick Barry of the San Francisco Warriors stunned the NBA and won the scoring title with a 35.6 average in 1966-67 beating out Oscar Robertson (30.5) and Wilt Chamberlain (24.1).

69. The Philadelphia 76ers defeated the Los Angeles Lakers 4 games to 0.

70. Bill Fitch replaced Dave Cowens who was the player-coach. When Fitch took over they were a last place team in 1978-79. He led them to the best record in the NBA in both 1979-80 and 1980-81 and the title in the latter year.

75. Neil Johnston played eight seasons, from 1952 through 1959, with the Philadelphia Warriors. He scored 10,123 points and had an average of 19.4 points per game. Johnston won the scoring title three times and was a first team all-star four times.

76. Ed Macauley. He played for the Bombers in his rookie season (1949-50) and averaged 16.1 per game. Then he played with the Celtics and never averaged under 17.5 points a game. Macauley, a center, had his best game against the great George Mikan scoring 46 points. He ended his career with the St. Louis Hawks and scored a life-time 11,234 points. He played on seven all-star teams.

77. From 1968 till 1972 Rick Barry played for Oakland, Washington and New York of the ABA. A great shooter, Barry averaged over 25 points per game in his professional career and over 90 percent in the freethrow department.

71. True. With a 40-42 record during the regular season they just made the playoffs. With the great play of the whole Rocket team, especially that of Moses Malone, they became the first team in the history of the NBA to enter the finals with a regular season losing record.

72. Wes Unseld of the Baltimore Bullets.

73. Jumpin' Joe Fulks played eight seasons for the Philadelphia Warriors (1946-47 to 1953-54.) He was one of the first great scorers in the NBA. In one game Fulks scored 63 points and at that time many teams didn't score 63 points in a whole ball game. He finished his career with 8,003 points and a 16.4 points per game average.

74. John Havlicek of the Boston Celtics, who played 16 seasons and averaged 20.8 points per game. He played both forward and guard and could run with anybody in the league. He retired when he was 38 years old in 1978 and was one of the best the NBA ever saw.

78. True. Since coming to the NBA from the ABA Erving has never averaged higher than 26.9 points per game (1979-80) in the NBA. Playing for the Virginia Squires in the ABA he once averaged 31.9 points a game in the 1972-73 season.

79. Jabbar was known as Lew Alcindor before he took his Muslim name in 1971. He joined the Milwaukee Bucks after his great college career at UCLA where he was a three time all American. He has been the premier center in the NBA since then, averaging almost 29 points a game and has won the MVP award a record six times.

80. In 1970-71 Dave Cowens shared the rookie of the year award with Geoff Petrie who averaged 24.8 points per game in his first season. An injury cut his career short in 1976. His career totals look like this: six seasons in the NBA, 9,732 total points, 21.8 per game point average and 446 games played.

81. New York Knick center Willis Reed won the most valuable player award for his great play and leadership in the 1969-70 championship season. He averaged 21.7 points per game and also won the MVP in the all-star game.

82. Bill Russell of the Boston Celtics won the MVP award three straight seasons: 1960-61, 1961-62 and 1962-63. Wilt Chamberlain was the other with three consecutive MVP winning seasons: 1965-66, 1967-68 and 1969-70.

83. Don "Monk" Meineke won the first rookie of the year award in the NBA in the 1952-53 season. Monk averaged 10.7 points a game with Fort Wayne and scored 725 points in 68 games. He finished his career in 1958 with Cincinnati. His rookie season proved to be his best year.

84. Trick question. They all won the rookie of the year award. Elgin Baylor won in 1958-59 with Minneapolis, Wilt Chamberlain won it in 1959-60 with Philadelphia and Woody Saulds-bury won it in 1957-58 with Philadelphia.

85. Ernie Di Gregorio won the award with the Buffalo Braves averaging 15.2 points a game and won the assist title averaging 8.2 per game.

86. Wilt Chamberlain scored 100 points against the New York Knicks in Hershey, Pennsylvania on March 2, 1962 with the old Philadelphia Warriors.

87. False. The record for most field goals attempted (63) and made (36) in one game is held by Wilt Chamberlain of the Philadelphia Warriors when he scored 100 points on March 2, 1962 against the Knicks.

88. Wilt Chamberlain of the old Philadelphia Warriors set the NBA record for rebounds with 55 against the Boston Celtics on November 24, 1960.

89. Boston Celtic great Bob Cousy, who assisted on 28 baskets against Minneapolis at Boston on February 27, 1959. Cousy led the NBA in assists eight consecutive seasons (1953-60).

90. False. Wilt Chamberlain, one of the worst free throw shooters in the NBA made 28 out of 34 (another record) in the same game in which he scored 100 points on March 2, 1962 against the Knicks.

91. True. Chamberlain missed 22 free throws in a game with the 76ers in 1967 against Seattle. He also holds the record for most missed in a season (528) and in a playoff game (17). Opposing teams often fouled him on purpose rather than let him get close to the basket.

92. False. Larry Costello, playing for Syracuse, scored 32 consecutive points against the Boston Celtics on December 8, 1961 for the record.

93. True. On November 22, 1961 Bob Pettit made 19 consecutive free throws against the Boston Celtics and set an NBA record while playing for St. Louis.

94. Wilt Chamberlain holds the record for the highest field goal percentage in a season with a .727 mark set in the 1972-73 season with the Los Angeles Lakers.

95. No. Wilt Chamberlain attempted 1,363 free throws in the 1961-62 season and made 835 of them, but Jerry West set the record in the 1965-66 season with the Los Angeles Lakers when he made 840 to break Wilt's record.

96. Jerry West started in 1960-61 with the Los Angeles Lakers and played his entire career with them until his retirement after the 1973-74 season. West averaged 27 points a game and scored 25,192 points in his career with L.A.

97. Ernie Di Gregorio set the record in the 1976-77 season with the Buffalo Braves with a .945 free throw percentage.

98. Rick Barry holds this record shooting with an unusual underhand set shot from the free throw line. Playing for San Francisco and Golden State, 1965-67, 1972-78 and Houston 1978-80, Barry has averaged over 90 percent from the free throw line in his career.

99. Wilt Chamberlain set the record of 2,149 rebounds in the 1960-61 season playing for the Philadelphia Warriors.

100. False. In the 1978-79 season Kevin Porter of the Detroit Pistons set the NBA record for most assists in a season averaging 13.4 a game for a total of 1,099.

SOMETHING'S NOT RIGHT HERE.

101. Only one person, Wilt Chamberlain, who scored 31,419 points with the Philadelphia Warriors, the San Francisco Warriors, the Philadelphia 76ers and the Los Angeles Lakers, 1960-73.

102. Oscar Robertson averaged 25.7 points per game in his career from 1960 till 1974. Chamberlain, on the other hand, averaged an NBA record 30.1 points a game from 1960 till 1973.

103. False. John Havlicek of the Boston Celtics attempted an NBA record 23,930 field goals making 10,513 in his career from 1963 till 1978.

104. No. Wilt Chamberlain holds this record with a career total of 12,681 field goals made from 1960 till 1973.

105. Kareem Abdul Jabbar holds this NBA record hitting on 56 percent of his field goal attempts in his career with Milwaukee and Los Angeles, 1970-81. There is a good chance that a few more of Wilt's records will fall to this man before the end of his career.

106. If you said Oscar Robertson, you are right! The Big O has made 7,694 free throws in his fantastic career with Cincinnati and Milwaukee from 1961 till 1974.

107. Wilt Chamberlain also holds this record with 23,924 rebounds from 1960 til 1973. He led the NBA five times in rebounding during his spectacular career.

108. When Bob Cousy retired he held the NBA record for assists with 6,949. When Oscar Robertson retired he held the NBA record for assists with 9,887.

109. John Havlicek holds this record with 1,270 games from 1963-78.

110. True. Greer accumulated 3,885 personal fouls with Syracuse and Philadelphia from 1959 till 1972.

111. His full name is Arild Verner Agerskov Mikkelsen. He played forward with the Minneapolis Lakers and was known for his tough, aggressive play. He fouled out of a record 127 NBA games, served as Laker captain six seasons and played on four title teams. An all-star four times, Mikkelsen scored over 10,000 points and averaged 14.4 points in his career from 1950 till 1959.

112. True. The world champion Los Angeles Lakers beat the Golden State Warriors 162-99 on March 19, 1972. It was the most one-sided contest in the history of the NBA.

113. The 1971-72 Los Angeles Lakers won a record 69 games while losing only 13. At one span they won 33 in a row and went on to win the NBA title that season.

114. The 1946-47 NBA first team consisted of Joe Fulks-Philadelphia, Bob Feerick-Washington, Stan Miasek-Detroit, Bones McKinney-Washington and Max Zaslofsky-Chicago. This was the first year of the NBA.

115. Dolph Schayes played for the Syracuse Nationals from 1948 until 1963, then with the Warriors for one season. He scored 19,247 career points and averaged 18.2 a game. He was one of the last two hand set shooters, and he was deadly with it.

116. The first coach of the year award was given in 1963 to Harry Gallatin of St. Louis. He led his team to a 48-32 record when only one season earlier they were 29-51.

117. Auerback won the award in 1965 when his team, the Boston Celtics posted a 62-18 record and were world champions. Under his direction the Celtics won nine NBA titles in 10 seasons.

118. The ABA started in 1967 with George Mikan named commissioner. They used a red, white and blue basketball and adopted the three point field goal for shots from 25 feet or more. The league closed after the 1975-76 season and four teams, San Antonio, New York, Indiana and Denver were absorbed into the NBA.

119. The Indiana Pacers won three ABA titles, 1970, 1972 and 1973 while the Nets won two, 1974 and 1976.

120. True. Bill Bradley, a three-time all-American at Princeton, spent two years at England's Oxford University as a Rhodes Scholar before playing in the NBA with the Knicks. Bradley is currently a U.S. Senator from New Jersey.

121. Julius Erving of the New York Nets won the MVP award the last three ABA seasons (1974, 75, 76). He shared the award with George McGinnis Indiana in 1975. Erving also holds the ABA record for highest scoring average in a career with a 28.7 per game mark.

122. Wilt Chamberlain won the scoring championship from 1959-60 to 1965-66.

123. In a game in 1954 Frank Selvy of Furman scored 100 points against Newbury. Selvy went on to the NBA where he played with several teams scoring a career 6,120 points and averaging 10.8 per game. He retired at the end of the 1964-65 season with the Lakers.

124. North Carolina State defeated Houston by the score of 54-52.

125. The Bruins at UCLA ran up a string of 88 victories in a row until they lost to Notre Dame 71-70 in 1974. It was the longest winning streak in college basketball history.

126. Bill Walton of UCLA won a record three player of the year awards in college. Other two time winners are Jerry Lucas, 1961-62 at Ohio State, and Lew Alcindor, 1967, 69 while at UCLA.

127. UCLA, of course. They won 10 championships in 12 years: 1964, 65, 67, 68, 69, 70, 71, 72, 73, and 1975. With such players as Gail Goodrich, Walt Hazzard, Lew Alcindor, Lucius Allen, Lynn Shackleford, Sidney Wicks, Keith Wilkes, Henry Bibby and Richard Washington.

128. John Wooden, the Wizard of Westwood, led them to 10 titles in 12 years. He also won college coach of the year award six times, 1964, 1967, 69, 70, 72, and 73.

129. The University of Indiana won 32 straight games in 1975-76, including the NCAA championship against Michigan. They were led by Kent Benson, Scott May, Tom Abernethy, Bobby Wilkerson and Quinn Buckner.

130. The regular season in the NBA consists of an 82 game schedule.

131. True. From January 9, 1973 until February 11, 1973 the Philadelphia 76ers lost an NBA record 20 consecutive games.

132. The Los Angeles Lakers beat the Philadelphia 76ers 4 games to 2 in the best of seven series. Playing without Jabbar in the final game Ervin "Magic" Johnson picked up the slack and scored 42 and grabbed 15 rebounds in the victory. Johnson won the MVP for that series.

133. The Philadelphia 76ers posted the worst record in the history of the NBA with a 9-73 record for a percentage of .110 in the 1972-73 season.

134. Elvin Hayes has played the most minutes with a total of 49,006 through the 1982-83 season.

135. False. Chamberlain, who has set more records than any other player ever to play in the NBA, started in 1959 with the Philadelphia Warriors, who moved to San Francisco in 1962. He was acquired during the 1964-65 season by the Philadelphia 76ers. Chamberlain was traded to the Los Angeles Lakers in 1968. He played with the Lakers until he retired in 1973.

IT'S MAGIC!

136. Alvin Adams won the award playing for the Phoenix Suns. He averaged 19 points per game and in his six years with the club he has averaged over 17 points a game.

137. Kevin Porter of the New Jersey Nets assisted on 29 baskets in a game against the Houston Rockets to beat out Rodgers and Cousy by one in a game on February 24, 1978 in New Jersey.

138. Wilt "the Stilt" Chamberlain, who played with several teams in his NBA career, was probably the greatest basketball player of all time. He retired in 1973 and still holds more records than any other player ever to play the game.

139. There are three different ways of scoring in the NBA: a 3-point field goal, 2-point field goal and a 1-point free throw.

140. Ralph Sampson was chosen first by the Houston Rockets.

141. Trick Question! That was the year Alcindor changed his name, they are one person.

142. False. Russell played in only 48 games. His rookie season averaged 14.7 points per game. Maurice Stokes of the Cincinnati Royals beat him out with a 16.8 points per game average in 67 games.

143. The distance from the basket to the free throw line is 15 feet.

144. True. Clarence Francis of Rio Grande College (small school) scored 150 points in a game in 1954. The college is located in Rio Grande, Ohio.

145. False. Dolph Schayes of the Syracuse Nationals was the first player to have 1,000 rebounds in a season and the first player ever to score 15,000 points in a career.

Tennis

1. True or false: Chris Evert Lloyd has never won the U.S. Open singles title?

2. Who won the 1981 men's singles finals at Wimbledon?

3. Has Bjorn Borg ever won the men's singles finals at Wimbledon?

4. Which one of these players won the women's 1981 singles title at Wimbledon: Chris Evert Lloyd, Hana Mandlikova, or Martina Navratilova?

5. Who was the youngest singles winner in the history of the U.S. Open tournament?

6. Who was the youngest player ever to compete in the Wightman Cup tournament, Chris Evert Lloyd or Andrea Jaeger?

7. Who won the men's singles title at the U.S. Open in 1981?

8. Can you name the woman who won both the 1978 and 1979 singles title at Wimbledon?

9. Has Jimmy Connors ever won the U.S. Open singles title?

10. Who won the 1981 women's singles title at the U.S. Open?

I LIKE ROCK AND ROLL MUSIC — ESPECIALLY THE SONG "BJORN TO RUN."

11. True or false: tennis was originated with a group of American Indians in the thirteenth century?

12. True or false: the largest crowd ever to attend a tennis match assembled in Texas in the United States?

13. What is the Grand Slam in tennis?

14. True or false: Bill Tilden was the first tennis player ever to win the grand slam?

15. Who was the first player ever to win the grand slam of tennis?

16. Can you name the only person in the history of the game ever to win the grand slam twice in his career?

17. Who was first woman ever to win the grand slam of tennis? Here's a hint: it was in 1953.

18. Can you name the woman who won the grand slam in tennis in 1970?

19. Which country has won more Davis Cups, the United States or Australia?

20. Which one of these countries won the 1980 Davis Cup: the United States, Czechoslovakia or Sweden?

29. Can you name the woman who holds the all-time record for singles titles at Wimbledon?

30. True or false: Chris Evert Lloyd was the youngest woman ever to win the Wimbledon singles title?

21. Was Tennis ever an Olympic sport?

22. Which one of these women has won the most titles in the Australian Championships: Chris Evert Lloyd, Margaret Court or Billie Jean King?

23. Which of these men holds the record for singles titles at the Australian Championships: Bjorn Borg, Roy Emerson or Rod Laver?

24. Which one of these women holds the record for most tennis titles won in the French Open: Margaret Court, Billie Jean King or Chris Evert?

25. Which one of these men holds the record for most singles titles at the French Open: Henri Cochet, Stan Smith or Bjorn Borg?

26. True or false: the first Wimbledon tournament was played in 1931?

27. True or false: a man has played in 36 Wimbledon tournaments?

28. True or false: Billie Jean King holds the record for most titles at Wimbledon?

31. True or false: one player won a total of 500,000 dollars for a single match?

32. In 1982 who won the most money: Jimmy Connors, John McEnroe or Ivan Lendl?

33. In 1982 who won the most money: Martina Navratilova, Tracy Austin or Pam Shriver?

34. True or false: a singles match once lasted 105 hours?

35. Who has the fastest serve ever recorded in the history of tennis?

36. Which one of these countries has the most victories in the Wightman Cup: the United States, Great Britain or Australia?

37. What country did the Doherty brothers come from and what tennis records do they hold?

38. Can you name the woman who won 125 straight matches on clay courts in the 1970's?

39. Can you name the American player who won a record 13 Davis Cup challenge singles matches in a row?

40. Can you name the woman who won every set she played for six years?

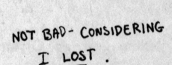

NOT BAD - CONSIDERING
I LOST .

41. Can you name the female player who lost 4 consecutive championship matches in the U.S. Open?

42. What is a fault in tennis?

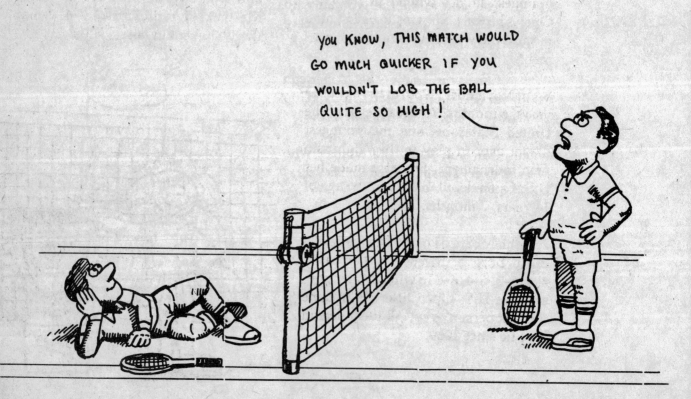

YOU KNOW, THIS MATCH WOULD GO MUCH QUICKER IF YOU WOULDN'T LOB THE BALL QUITE SO HIGH !

Answers

1. False. In 1982, Chris Evert Lloyd won her sixth U.S. Open title.

2. In a very exciting match which included two tie breakers John McEnroe defeated Bjorn Borg 4-6, 7-6, 7-6, 6-4 to win the $50,760 dollar first prize.

3. Yes. If you know anything about Wimbledon in recent years you will associate it with Bjorn Borg, who has won the Wimbledon title five consecutive times, 1976-80. Before losing in 1981 to McEnroe, Borg was supreme at this event.

4. Chris Evert Lloyd defeated Hana Mandlikova pretty handily 6-2, 6-2 and won the $45,684 dollar first prize. It was her third victory at Wimbledon in her career.

5. In 1979 Tracy Austin became the youngest singles winner in the U.S. Open's history. She was 16 years, nine months old when she won the tournament.

6. In November, 1980, at the age of 15 years, 6 months, Andrea Jaeger of the United States became the youngest player ever to play in the Wightman Cup tournament. She also made her U.S. Open debut in 1979 at the age of 14 years, 3 months.

7. John McEnroe of the U.S. defeated Bjorn Borg of Sweden rather easily 4-6, 6-2, 6-4, 6-3 to win his third consecutive U.S. Open title. He became the first person to successively defend his title since 1969.

8. Martina Navratilova of Czechoslovakia won both the 1978 and 1979 singles titles at Wimbledon. She has been a dominant female player in recent years, especially on fast surfaces. In tournament play she has a winning percentage of over 81%.

9. Jimmy Connors has won the U.S. Open singles title five times. His latest victory was in 1983.

10. Tracy Austin rallied from behind and won two tie breakers to defeat Martina Navratilova 1-6, 7-6, 7-6 at the 1981 event in Forest Hills.

11. False. The game of tennis is generally recognized as originating in England as mentioned in an English magazine, *Sporting Magazine*, on September 29, 1793. It was called "field tennis." The game was later called lawn tennis and clubs were formed in the 1800's.

12. The most people, 30,472, ever to attend a tennis match gathered at the Houston Astrodome on September 20, 1973, when Billie Jean King beat Bobby Riggs in the so-called "Tennis Match of the Century" in straight sets.

13. The grand slam in tennis consists of all four of the world's major championship titles: the U.S. Open, Wimbledon, the Australian Championship and the French Championship.

14. False. One of the greatest tennis players of all time, Bill Tilden never won the grand slam.

15. The first player to win the grand slam was Don Budge, who won the Wimbledon, U.S. Open, Australian and French titles in 1938 to become the first ever to do so in the history of the game.

16. Rod Laver of Australia was the only player in the history of tennis to win the grand slam twice and the second person in history to win it at all. He won it first in 1962 as an amateur and again in 1969 as a professional.

17. The first woman ever to win the gran slam was Maureen Connolly of the United States. She won it in 1953 and had she not been injured would have had a good chance of repeating in 1954.

18. The second woman to win the grand slam was Margaret Court of Australia who won in 1970. There haven't been any winners since then.

19. Since the introduction of the Davis Cup in 1900 the United States leads the Australians 26 to 24. Winning the 1978 and 1979 titles the U.S. took the lead.

20. Czechoslovakia defeated Italy to win the Davis Cup. It marked the first time in the history of the tournament that an Eastern European country has won the championship.

NICE SERVE! —

21. Yes. Lawn tennis was an Olympic sport in the first eight games. The winner of the most medals was Max Decugis of France. He won four gold, one silver and one bronze for a total of six medals. The most won by a woman was five by Kitty McKane of Great Britain.

22. Margaret Court of Australia won the greatest number of Australian titles with 22 between 1960 and 1973. She also holds the record for singles titles at this event with 10 over the same period.

23. The most singles titles won at this event is six by Roy Emerson, who accomplished this feat between 1961 and 1967. Borg has never won this event.

24. Margaret Court of Australia holds the French Open titles record with a total of 13, including a record five singles titles between 1962 and 1973.

25. Henri Cochet held the record with four singles titles between 1926 and 1932 until Bjorn Borg broke it in 1980 when he won his fifth French Open singles title. He won his titles between 1974 and 1980.

26. False. The first Wimbledon tournament was played in 1877. Professionals first played in the tournament in 1968.

27. True. Arthur Gore of the U.K. made 36 appearances between 1888 and 1927. He became the oldest singles winner ever at the age of 41 in 1909. Jean Borotia of France appeared in 35 Wimbledons between 1922 and 1964.

28. True. Since 1961 Billie Jean King has won a record 20 Wimbledon titles, including six singles titles, 10 in doubles and four in mixed doubles. Her 1979 doubles victory with Martina Navratilova broke the deadlock with Elizabeth Ryan with 19 titles each.

29. The record for singles titles by a woman at Wimbledon is eight by Helen Wills Moody. She won her first Wimbledon victory in 1927 and her last in 1938. She is from the United States.

30. False. The youngest champion ever was Charlotte "Lottie" Dod, who was 15 years, 9 months old when she won the Wimbledon in 1887. Dod, from Great Britain, went to win five Wimbledon titles in her career.

31. True, a record $500,000 was won by Jimmy Connors, of the United States, when he beat John Newcombe, of Australia, in a challenge match at Caesars Palace Hotel, Las Vegas, Nevada, April 26, 1975.

32. Ivan Lendl led the money list with a total of $1,628,850.

33. Martina Navratilova led the list with a total of $1,475,055.

34. True, the longest recorded singles match non-stop was 105 hours by Ricky Tolston and Jeff Sutton at Bill Faye Park, Kingston, North Carolina, on May 7-11, 1979.

35. The fastest serve ever recorded was by Bill Tilden, clocked at 163.6 miles per hour. Some players consider the 1948 Wimbledon Champion Robert Falkenburg as the fastest server ever.

36. Since it was first held in 1923, the United States has won 43 times, next is Great Britain which has 10 victories.

37. Laurence and Reginald Doherty of Great Britain have combined to win 8 doubles titles at Wimbledon and separately they have a total of 9 singles titles at Wimbledon. Reginald winning 4, (1897-1900) and Laurence winning 5 (1902-1906).

38. Chris Evert Lloyd won 125 straight on clay starting in 1973 and ending in 1979 when Tracy Austin beat her 6-4, 2-6, 7-6 in the semifinals of the Italian Open in Rome. Only eight of the 125 matches went to three sets.

39. Bill Tilden started this string of 13 consecutive victories in 1920 against Australia and lasted until the first match of the 1926 final against France. In his career Tilden won 25 of 30 Davis Cup singles matches between 1920 and 1930.

40. Unbelievable, but true. Helen Wills Moody won every set she played from 1927 until 1933 when she lost the middle set of her final round victory over Dorothy Round at Wimbledon. During that span she won five Wimbledon titles. She also won the U.S. Open four times and the French Open four times.

41. Evonne Goolagong lost 4 consecutive championship matches 1973-76.

42. A fault is a serve not properly placed into the correct court. A double fault occurs when there are two improper serves in a row and the point is given to the receiver.

Track & Field

1. True or false: the record for the mile run was broken three times in 10 days in 1981?

2. Can you name the American runner who holds the world record in the 110 meter hurdles? Here's a hint: his nickname is "Skeets."

3. Does Renaldo Nehemiah also hold the record in the 50 yard high hurdles?

4. What American runner holds the record in the 400 meter hurdles event?

5. Can you name the runner who has won four Boston Marathons and four New York City Marathons?

6. Can you name the winner of the 1980 New York City Marathon in the men's event?

7. True or false: the hurdles used in the 110 and 400 meter races are the same height?

8. Can you name the two American runners who share the world record in the 100 yard dash?

9. A track star from the United States set the long jump record in the 1968 Olympic Games. Can you name him?

10. True or false: former football great O.J. Simpson is a member of the 440 yard relay team that still holds the record?

11. Who was the first track runner ever to break the four minute barrier in the mile run?

12. Can you name the former track star from the United States who set six world records in one day?

13. Which one of these runners holds the world record in the 1,500 meter run: Sebastian Coe, Steve Ovett or John Walker?

14. True or false: Dave Roberts of the U.S. holds the world record in the pole vault event?

15. Which country set the women's world record in the 400 meter relay in 1983?

16. Which one of these runners holds the world record in the 100 meter dash: Bob Hayes or Calvin Smith?

17. True or false: a former Dallas Cowboy wide receiver won a gold medal in the 1964 Olympics?

18. Who holds the world record in the 1,000 meter run, Steve Ovett or Sebastian Coe?

19. In what track and field event did Al Oerter compete and how did he do?

20. True or false: Jim Ryun was the first miler ever to break the four minute barrier in high school?

21. True or false: there is a foot race held every year in Scotland that awards a pair of red stockings to the winner?

22. Can you name the first woman ever to run a 10.0 second 100 yard dash? Here's a hint: she's from Taiwan.

23. True or false: a man with only one leg high jumped over 6½ feet?

24. True or false: a blind man once ran the 100 meter dash in 11.5 seconds?

25. True or false: a track runner from Scotland has had a competitive career, which has lasted longer than 70 years?

Answers

1. Unbelievable but true. On August 19 Sebastian Coe of Britain set the mile record in a time of 3:48.53. One week later countryman Steve Ovett broke that mark with a 3:48.40. Two days later Coe ran a 3:47.33 mile cutting 1.07 seconds from the previous record. All this took place within 10 days in 1981.

2. Renaldo Nehemiah broke his own record and became the first runner ever to break the 13 second barrier in the 110 meter hurdles with a time of 12.93, .07 second off the world record he established in 1979. Nehemiah set the record in Zurich, Switzerland on August 19, 1981.

3. Yes. Nehemiah, one of the best track performers of all time, set the world indoor high hurdle record over 50 yards with a time of 5.98 seconds at the Toronto Maple Leaf games in February, 1981.

4. Edwin Moses of the U.S., who has many of the world's fastest times in this event, holds the record with a time of 47.13 seconds. He also won the Olympic gold medal in 1976 and set a record for the games while doing so with a time of 47.64.

5. Bill Rodgers of the U.S. has won three consecutive Boston Marathons and four out of the last six years. He has also won four consecutive New York City Marathons, 1976, 1977, 1978 and 1979.

6. Alberto Salazar won the NYC Marathon and set the record for the race with a time of 2:09.41. Bill Rodgers who had won the last four NYC races fell down during the race and finished fifth.

7. False. The hurdles used in the 110 meter races are 42 inches high, while the hurdles in the 400 meter races are 36 inches high.

8. Ivory Crockett and Houston McTear both share the record with a time of 9 seconds flat. Crockett set the record on May 11, 1974 and McTear tied it almost a year later on May 9, 1975.

9. Bob Beamon set the world record with a jump of 29 feet, 2½ inches at the Olympic games in Mexico City. He broke the record by more than a foot in an event where the record is usually broken in inches.

10. True. Running for U.S.C., Mc-Culloch, Kuller, Simpson and Miller set the world record in the 440 yard relay with a time of 38.6 seconds.

11. Roger Bannister ran a 3:59.4 mile on May 6, 1954 on the Iffly Road track at Oxford. He became the first person ever to break the four minute barrier.

12. It can't be done, right? Wrong! Jesse Owens set records in the 100 yard dash, long jump, 220 yards straight away, 220 yards over low hurdles. The two 220 yard runs were ratified as 200 meter world records for a total of six world records.

13. Steve Ovett holds the world record in the 1,500 meter run with a time of 3:30.77 in 1983.

14. False. Billy Olson set the world record in 1983 with a vault of 19 feet, 44 inches.

15. The four member women's team from East Germany set the record in the 400 meter relay race with a time of 41.53 seconds in a meet in Berlin.

16. Calvin Smith of the U.S. broke the record in 1983 with a time of 9.93 seconds.

17. True. Bob Hayes, formerly a wide receiver with the Cowboys, won two gold medals at the 1964 Olympic games. Hayes set the record in the 100 meter dash with a time of 10.0. He also ran a wind assisted time of 9.9 in a preliminary heat.

18. Sebatian Coe set the world record in the 1,000 meter run with a time of 2:12.18 in 1981.

19. Al Oerter, a discus thrower, is the only modern day track and field participant to win four successive gold medals in the Olympics in 1956, 1960, 1964, 1968. At the 1980 Olympic trials Oerter, attempting a comeback at age 43, bested all his gold medal winning tosses but finished fourth.

20. True. As a teenager in high school in Kansas, Ryun ran the first sub four minute mile (3:59.0) in high school history. He went on to break the world record in the mile with a time of 3:51.3 and again broke his own record in 1967 with a time of 3:51.1.

21. True. The "Red Hose Race" has been held at Carnevath, Scotland every year since 1507. It is the oldest continuously held foot race in the world. First prize is a pair of hand knitted knee length red stockings.

22. In 1970 Chi Cheng became the first woman ever to run the 100 yard dash in 10.0 seconds flat. During 1970 she won all 63 races she entered and set five world records in the process.

23. True. In 1977 Arnie Boldt, a man from Saskatchewan, Canada, high jumped 6 feet, 6¾ inches indoors. This was a tremendous achievement considering that Arnie has only one leg.

24. True. A Polish runner named Kozuck recorded a time of 11.5 seconds in the 100 meter dash in spite of the fact that he was blind. This took place in 1976.

25. True. Duncan McLean, born in Scotland in 1884, won the 100 yard dash title in 1904 with a time of 9.9 seconds. In 1977 at the age of 91 years, he set the world age group record for the 100 meters with a time of 21.7 seconds, more than 72 years after his 1904 performance.

AYE, THANKS FOR THE STOCKINGS, BUT THE RED CLASHES WITH MY KILT. DO YOU HAVE THEM IN BLUE?

1. True or false: the first auto race was a 150 mile race in upstate New York in 1906?

2. True or false: the oldest auto race that is still run regularly is the Indianapolis 500?

3. What is a pit stop in auto racing?

4. What is known as a big banger to auto racers?

5. True or false: Tommy Milton was the first driver ever to win at the Indianapolis 500 twice?

6. The highest speed ever attained on a closed circuit is over 221 miles per hour. Can you name the person who accomplished this?

7. Can you name the big eleven NASCAR race tracks?

8. What does NASCAR stand for?

9. Who holds the record for the highest average race lap speed for a closed circuit?

10. Has anybody ever won the 24 hours of Lemans race more than three times?

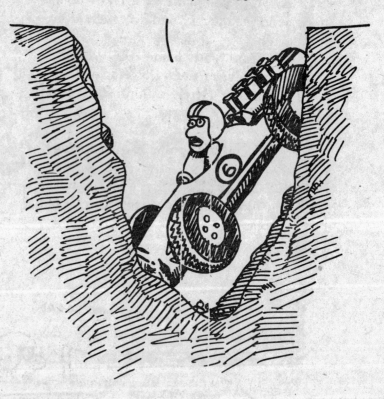

11. What does N.H.R.A. stand for?

12. What does it mean when an official waves the yellow flag during a race?

13. Can you name the only driver ever to win the Indianapolis 500 four times in a career?

14. True or false: the fastest pit stop ever took only four seconds?

15. True or false: a man once drove over 240,000 miles in one year?

16. Who has won the World Championship of Drivers the most times, Jackie Stewart of Juan Manuel Fangio?

17. Can you name the driver who has won the most Grand Prix races?

18. Can you name the youngest driver ever to win the World Championship? Here's a hint: he's from Brazil.

19. What is a spoiler in auto racing?

20. True or false: Bruce McLaren was the oldest driver ever to win a Grand Prix race?

21. What is drafting in auto racing?

22. True or false: Louis Meyer was the first driver to win the Indianapolis 500 three times?

23. Who is known as "Big Daddy" in auto racing?

24. True or false: dragsters reach speeds of up to 250 mph?

25. What is terminal velocity?

26. Is there such a thing as rocket or jet engine dragsters?

27. Has anybody ever won a million dollars for car racing?

28. What is a stroker in auto racing?

29. Can you name the driver who has won the Pike's Peak Auto Hill Climb the greatest number of times?

30. Are any of the original NASCAR race tracks still being used today?

31. True or false: In the first Indianapolis 500 run in 1911 the winning car held the record time for twelve years?

32. True or false: Cale Yarborough has won more NASCAR Grand National championships than any other driver?

33. True or false: the Indianapolis 500 has been cancelled twice because of weather conditions?

34. True or false: the first time the record speed of an automobile exceeded 200 mph was in 1941?

35. Can you name the auto racing driver who declined an offer to try out for the Washington Redskins?

36. True or false: Henry Ford once set the one mile record in an automobile?

37. Can you name the last person ever to win the Indianapolis 500 two consecutive times?

38. What does U.S.A.C. stand for in auto racing?

39. What does A.H.R.A. stand for in auto racing?

40. What does it mean when a race official takes out the black flag and waves it at a driver?

41. Who was the first U.S. driver to win the World Grand Prix championship and in what year?

42. A big race down south is the Rebel 500. Where is it held?

43. Who is known as "the snake" in auto racing?

44. True or false: funny cars reach their top speed at about 180 mph?

45. Can you name the driver who holds the record for the fastest time ever in the Indianapolis 500?

46. What is the name of the 400 mile race held every year in Brooklyn?

47. True or false: a drag strip is usually 3/4 of a mile long?

48. True or false: the Indianapolis 500 is held on Labor Day every year?

49. True or false: the Los Angeles Times 500 is held in a different city in California every year?

50. Why is the stock racer able to average the same speeds as the much more sophisticated Indy race car in the Daytona 500?

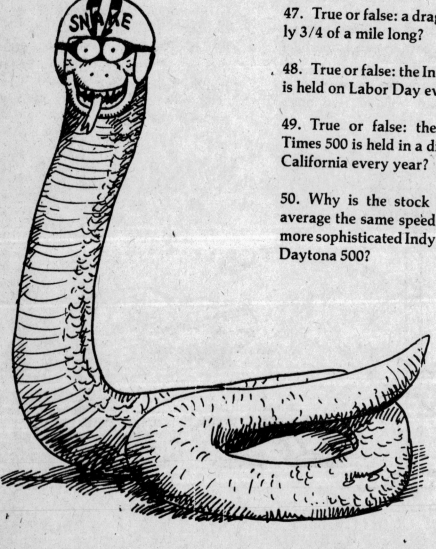

51. True or false: stock car racing is America's fifth largest spectator sport?

52. What is the pole position in auto racing?

53. What kind of racing did Curtis Turner do?

54. Who won the Western 500 held in California in 1980?

55. Who won the 24 hour endurance race at Daytona Beach, Florida in 1980: a team from West Germany, the United States or France?

56. Who won the Daytona 500 in 1983: Benny Parsons, Cale Yarborough or Buddy Baker?

57. Who won the Richmond 400 Grand National in 1983, Darrell Waltrip or Bobby Allison?

58. Who won the South African Grand Prix in 1980?

59. Who won the Atlanta 500 Grand National in 1980: Richard Petty, Dale Earnhardt, or Rusty Wallace?

60. Who won the 1980 Twin 200 in Ontario, California, Johnny Rutherford or Tom Sneva?

JONES GOT THE POLE POSITION AGAIN

61. Who won the Rebel 500 in 1980: David Pearson or Benny Parsons?

62. Who won the Virginia 500 NASCAR race in 1980: Benny Parsons or Darrell Waltrip?

63. Who won the NASCAR $315,000 500 mile race at Talladega, Alabama in 1980: Dale Earnhardt or Buddy Baker?

64. True or false: Richard Petty won the 1980 Music City 420 held in Nashville?

65. True or false: Jacques Laffite won the 38th Grand Prix of Monaco in 1980?

66. Who won the 1983 Indianapolis 500: Tom Sneva, Johnny Rutherford or Mario Andretti?

67. Where is the World 600 race held?

68. True or false: Cale Yarborough won the 1980 NASCAR 400 race in Collige Station, Texas?

69. Who won the 1980 NASCAR Gabriel 400 in Brooklyn, Michigan, Cale Yarborough or Benny Parsons?

70. Who won the 1980 Pocono 500: Johnny Rutherford or Bobby Unser?

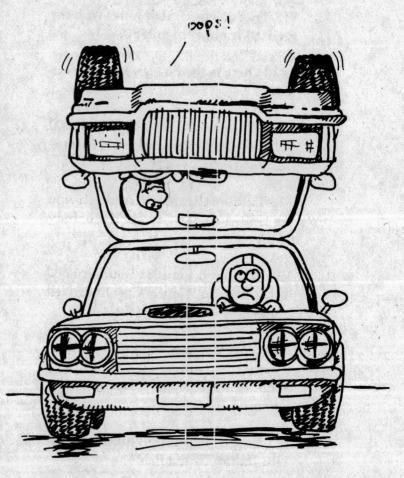

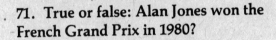

79. Can you name the dragster driver who won his ninth title at the National Hot Rod Association Spring nationals in Kukersville, Ohio?

71. True or false: Alan Jones won the French Grand Prix in 1980?

80. Can you name the driver who won the 24 hours of Lemans race for a record fifth time in 1981?

72. Where is the Firecracker 400 race held?

81. Who won the 1981 Indianapolis 500 event: Bobby Unser or Mario Andretti?

73. Who won the 1980 NASCAR 500 mile race in Cover, Delaware: Harry Gant or Darrell Waltrip?

82. Who won the World 600 NASCAR Grand National: Bobby Allison or Harry Gant?

74. True or false: Mario Andretti won the 1980 Michigan Grand Prix for Indy cars?

83. Who won the Mason-Dixon 500 in Dover, Delaware in 1981: Jody Ridley or Bobby Allison?

75. Who won the 1981 Southern 500 in Darlington, South Carolina: Neil Bonnett or Darrell Waltrip?

84. Who won the 1981 Rebel 500 Grand National race: Harry Gant or Darrell Waltrip?

76. Who won the 400 lap NASCAR Grand National in Richmond, Virginia in 1981: Harry Gant or Benny Parsons?

85. Who won the Carolina 500 in 1981: Darrell Waltrip or Cale Yarborough?

77. True or false: Alan Jones won the 1981 Italian Grand Prix?

86. Who won the 1981 Daytona 500: Richard Petty or Bobby Allison?

78. Who won the 1981 Firecracker 400 NASCAR race?

87. What is slalom in auto racing?

Answers

1. False. The first auto race was the 201 mile Green Bay to Madison, Wisconsin, run in 1878. It was won by an Oshkosh steamer.

2. False. The oldest auto race still regularly run is the R.A.C. Touris Trophy, first run in 1905 on the Isle of Man. The Indianapolis 500 was first run in 1911.

3. A pit stop in an auto race takes place when a car goes into the pit off the race track to fuel up or to change tires during the course of a race.

4. A big banger is a large engine, usually over 305 cubic inches displacement. It is also known as a big bore.

5. True. Driving a Frontenac, Tommy Milton first won the Indianapolis 500 in 1921 averaging 89.62 mph. He won again in 1923 becoming the first ever to do so. This times he drove a Miller race car with an average speed of 90.95 mph.

6. Mark Donohue, Jr. of the United States attained the speed of 221.16 mph at the Alabama International Motor Speedway, Talladega, Alabama in a 5,374 cc. turbocharged Porsche 917/30 Can-Am car on August 9, 1975.

7. 1. Daytona International Speedway, Florida
2. Martinsville Speedway, Virginia
3. Alabama International Speedway, Alabama
4. Charlotte Motor Speedway, North Carolina
5. Michigan International Speedway, Michigan
6. Pocono International Speedway, Pennsylvania
7. Darlington Raceway, South Carolina
8. Dover Downs International Speedway, Delaware.
9. North Carolina Motor Speedway, North Carolina
10. Atlanta International Raceway, Georgia
11. Ontario Motor Speedway, California.

8. National Association for Stock Car Auto Racing.

9. Richard Brickhouse of the United States averaged more than 195 mph in a 1969 Dodge Daytona Charger powered by a 6,981 cc., 600 bhp V8 engine, during a 500 mile race on the tri-oval at Alabama International Motor Speedway, Talladega, Alabama on September 14, 1969.

10. Yes, two people. Olivier Gendebien of Belgium won four times at Lemans in 1958, 1960, 1961, and 1962. Jacky Ickx of Belgium is the other with victories in 1969, 1975, 1976, and 1977.

11. National Hot Rod Association.

12. When an official waves the yellow flag he is warning the drivers of dangerous conditions on the track. During this period drivers are not allowed to improve their positions.

13. The most successful driver at the Indianapolis 500 has been A.J. Foyt, Jr., who has won the race a record four times during his career. He won in 1961, 1964, 1967 and 1977.

14. True. Driving in the Indianapolis 500, Bobby Unser of the United States took four seconds to fuel up on the tenth lap in the 1976 race.

15. True. Francis Lecot, an innkeeper from France, traveled 248,548.5 miles in 1,900 cc., 66 bhp Citroen 11 sedan mainly between Paris and Monte Carlo from July 22, 1935 to July 26, 1936. He drove 363 of the 370 days allowed.

16. Juan Manuel Fangio of Argentina won the World Championship of Drivers a record five times in 1951, 1954, 1955, 1956, and 1957. When he retired in 1958 Fangio had recorded 24 Grand Prix Victories.

17. The driver with the most Grand Prix victories in a career is Jackie Stewart of Scotland. He had 27 victories from 1965 until 1973. The winner of the most Grand Prix victories in one year is Jim Clark, also of Scotland, who won 7 in 1963.

18. The youngest driver ever to win the World Championship is Emerson Fittipaldi of Brazil who won his first world championship on September 10, 1972 at the age of 25 years, 273 days.

19. A spoiler is an air deflector which can be mounted either at the front end or the rear deck to keep a car from being lifted off the ground at high speeds. It also improves the grip of the tires on the road.

20. False. Bruce McLaren was the youngest driver ever to win a Grand Prix race. He won the U.S. Grand Prix at Sebring, Florida on December 12, 1959 at age 22 years, 104 days. The oldest driver ever to win was Tazio Giorgio Nunolari of Italy, who won the Albi Grand Prix at Albi, France on July 14, 1946 at the age of 53 years, 240 days.

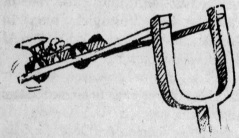

24. True. Shirley Muldowney of the United States recorded the highest terminal velocity in 1977 with a speed of 252.10 mph.

25. Terminal velocity is the speed attained at the end of a 440 yard run made from a standing start; elapsed time is the time taken for the entire run.

26. Yes. Norman Craig Breedlove of the United States drove his English Leather Special rocket dragster at speeds of up 377.754 mph (4.65 seconds for the quarter mile) in Utah in 1973.

27. The first stock car driver to win $1,000,000 racing is Richard Petty of North Carolina. He reached that mark in 1971. Others have since attained that distinction. Petty, who is still racing, holds the NASCAR records for most races won and most victories in a season with 27 in 1967.

28. A stroker tries for the middle place prize money between the top drivers who have dropped because of mechanical breakdown.

29. The Pike's Peak Auto Hill Climb was first run in 1916 in Colorado. Bobby Unser has won the event a record 13 times between 1956 and 1974—10 championships, 2 stock and 1 sports car titles.

30. Only two original NASCAR race tracks are still being used today. They are Martinsville and North Wilkesboro, original NASCAR tracks dating back to 1949.

21. Drafting or slingshotting is a technique used for passing a car. A driver follows closely behind another driver to take advantage of his slipstream. This preserves his power. At the tactical moment the drafting driver slips out of the slipstream and with the reserve power slings past the car he has been following.

22. True. Louis Meyer of the United States raced a dozen years at Indy and captured the classic three times, in 1928, 1933 and 1936. He was the first to do so. He finished second in 1929 and fourth two times, in 1930 and 1937. He retired in 1939 after an accident.

23. Don "Big Daddy" Garlits of the United States. He has the record for lowest elapsed time by a piston engine dragster over a quarter mile (5.637 seconds).

31. False. Ray Harroun driving in his Marmon automobile finished the race in 6:42:08 for an all time slow record at Indianapolis. He averaged 74.59 mph over the 500 mile course in 1911.

32. False. Between 1964 and 1975 Richard Petty has won six NASCAR Grand National titles for the record.

33. False. The Indy 500 has been postponed and sometimes shortened but never cancelled because of the weather. The race was cancelled during WWI and WWII, though.

34. False. Major H.O.D. Segrave drove a Sunbeam at a record speed of 203.791 mph in Daytona Beach, Florida on March 29, 1927.

35. Cale Yarborough was asked to attend spring camp for the Redskins but declined in order to continue racing. He did play semi-pro football in South Carolina for four years. He was also an all-state football player in high school.

36. True. In 1904 Henry Ford set the one mile record with a top speed of 91.370 mph in his own car called the Ford 999.

37. Four men have won the Indy 500 two consecutive times: Wilbur Shaw won in 1939-40, Mauri Rose won in 1947-48, Bill Vukovich won in 1953-54, and the last to do it was Al Unser, who won it in 1970-71.

38. U.S.A.C. stands for United States Auto Club.

39. American Hot Rod Association.

40. A black flag waved by an official at a driver signals the driver to come into the pits his next time around. The purpose may be to inspect the car, to discipline the driver or to remove the driver from the race because his car is too slow or dangerous to the other drivers.

WILBUR, WHEN YOU SAID YOU WERE GOING TO BORROW YOUR DAD'S CAR TO TAKE ME TO THE MOVIES, I THOUGHT YOU MEANT HIS CHEVROLET!

45. The fastest time ever for the complete 500 miles was 3:04:05.24 in the 1972 race. It was won by Mark Donohue driving a 2,595 cc, 900 bhp turbocharged Sunoco McLaren M16B-Offenhauser.

46. If you are thinking of New York, you are wrong. Brooklyn, Michigan is the home of the Gabriel 400 held annually.

47. False. A drag strip is ¼ mile long.

48. False. The Indy 500 is held annually over the Memorial Day weekend.

49. False. The Los Angeles Times 500 is held for charity at the Ontario Motor Speedway in Ontario, California.

41. In 1972 Phil Hill of the U.S. was the first American to win.

42. The Rebel 500 is held in Darlington, South Carolina.

43. Dragster Don Prudhomme is known by his fans as "the snake."

44. False. Funny cars travel over 200 mph regularly on the drag circuit.

50. The banked Daytona Track turns help a car to stay on the track, thus helping it around the curves. Indy's turns are flat, so the driver must slow down while turning.

51. False. Stock car racing is the second largest spectator sport behind horse racing.

52. The number one pole position is first in line and closest to the inside turn in the starting line-up and is earned by the driver with the fastest qualifying time. The poles are set up according to qualifying times and are arranged in two's.

53. Turner won a total of 357 stock car races in his career. He won his races in a variety of cars, on all kinds of tracks and surfaces and at every distance. He was known as "Pops" because of the way he banged into the side of another car or "dirt-popped" it.

54. Darrell Waltrip, driving a Chevrolet Monte Carlo at an average speed of 94.974 mph, won the Western 500 in Riverside, California.

55. West German drivers Rolf Stommelen, Reinhold Joest and Volkert Merl combined to drive a Porsche Turbo to victory in the 24 hour race in Daytona Beach.

56. Cale Yarborough won the Daytona 500 in 1983 and a first prize of $119,600.

57. Bobby Allison won the Richmond 400 in 1983 driving a Chevrolet.

58. Rene Arnoux, driving a 1.5 liter turbocharged Renault at an average speed of 123.265 mph, won the race by more than 30 seconds. It was his second formula I victory of the year.

59. Dale Earnhardt, driving a Chevrolet at an average speed of 134.808 mph, won the Atlanta 500 held at the Atlanta International Raceway. He finished 9 seconds ahead of second Rusty Wallace, who also drove a Chevrolet.

60. Johnny Rutherford, driving a Chaparral at an average speed of 162.053 mph won the race on the 2.5 mile Motor Speedway oval. He finished one lap ahead of Tom Sneva who was driving a McLaren.

64. True. Averaging 89.471 mph in a Chevrolet, Petty won the Music City 420. He finished one length ahead of Benny Parsons, who was also driving a Chevy.

65. False. Carlos Reutemann, averaging 81.20 mph in a Williams won. He finished 1:13.63 ahead of Jacques Laffite who was driving a Ligier.

66. Tom Sneva driving his Cosworth at an average speed of 162.117 mph won the race finishing ahead of Al Unser.

67. The World 600 is held in Charlotte, North Carolina. Benny Parsons won the 1980 event with an average speed of 119.265 mph in his Chevrolet. He finished .1 of a second ahead of Darrell Waltrip, who was also driving a Chevy.

68. True. Averaging 159.046 mph in his Chevrolet Monte Carlo, Cale Yarborough won the 1980 event by a lap over Richard Petty who also drove a Chevy Monte Carlo.

69. Benny Parsons defeated Cale Yarborough by only the length of his car to win the 1980 Gabriel 400. They were both driving Chevy Monte Carlos.

70. Bobby Unser, averaging 151.454 mph in a Penske-Cosworth won the $400,000 Pocono 500 on the 2.5 mile course at Long Pond, Pennsylvania. He finished over 20 seconds ahead of Rutherford who was driving a Chaparral-Cosworth.

61. Averaging 112.399 mph David Pearson won the 1980 Rebel 500 at the 1.366 mile Darlington, South Carolina International Raceway by 3.3. seconds over Benny Parsons. They were both driving Chevrolets. The race was shortened 258 miles because of rain.

62. Darrell Waltrip, averaging 69.049 mph in his Chevrolet, overcame a two lap penalty for a tire infraction to win the Virginia 500 held in Martinsville, Virginia by nine seconds over Benny Parsons also in a Chevrolet.

63. Averaging 170.48 mph in an Oldsmobile, Buddy Baker won first place by only three feet over Dale Earnhardt, also in an Oldsmobile.

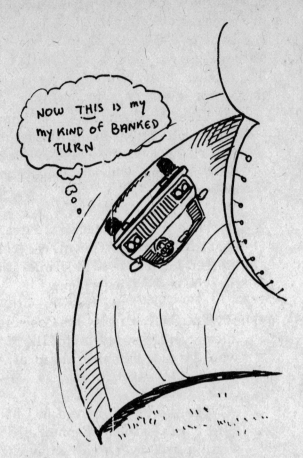

76. In a Ford, Benny Parsons averaged 69.998 mph around the .542 mile Fairgrounds Raceway track in Richmond. He finished the race in a time of 3:05.50 and beat Harry Gant by a car length.

71. True. Jones of Australia averaged 126.073 mph in a Williams-Ford to capture the sixty-sixth French Grand Prix by 4.5 seconds over French driver, Didier Pironi.

72. The Firecracker 400 race is held in Daytona Beach, Florida.

73. Darrell Waltrip averaged 116.124 mph in a Monte Carlo and won the 500 mile race by .47 seconds over Harry Gant who also drove a Monte Carlo.

74. True. Averaging 167.494 mph in a Penske, Andretti won the 150 mile race by .8 seconds ahead of Bobby Unser, who was also driving a Penske.

75. Bonnett, driving a Ford at an average of 126.410 mph, won the Southern 500 by only a car length over Darrell Waltrip who was driving a Buick.

77. False. Alain Prost won this event. He averaged 130.653 mph on the 3.59 mile circuit in a Renault. Alan Jones was second, 22.17 seconds off the pace.

78. Cale Yarborough won the event in 1981 for the fourth time in his career. He averaged 142.588 mph in his Buick Regal to win the Firecracker 400 in Daytona Beach, Florida.

79. Gary Beck won his ninth unlimited top fuel dragster title at the 1981 event in Ohio. He did the ¼ mile in 6.05 seconds, attained a speed of 224.99 mph. He beat Butch Osmon by 1.51 seconds.

80. Jacky Ickx won in 1981 for a record fifth time. He raced with Derek Bell and covered 2,997.5 miles in a Works Porsche 936, averaging 125.30 mph.

85. Darrell Waltrip, driving a Buick at an average speed of 114.594, won the Carolina 500 by 5.5 seconds over Yarborough, who also drove a Buick. The race was held at the North Carolina Motor Speedway in Rockingham.

86. Richard Petty, averaging 169.651 mph in his Buick, won the Daytona 500. Bobby Allison came in second in a Pontiac.

87. A competition in which drivers manuever their cars through a twisting course defined by rubber pylons. The drivers run against the clock. This event is also called a gymkhana and autocross.

81. Bobby Unser seemingly won his third Indy 500 but Andretti was ruled the winner because Unser passed some cars during a yellow flag, an action not permitted; therefore the stewards awarded second place Andretti the victory. Then five months later the decision was reversed and Unser was again the winner.

82. Bobby Allison averaging 129.326 mph won the World 600 in a Buick on the 1½ mile oval of the Charlotte, North Carolina Motor Speedway. He finished 8 seconds ahead of Harry Gant, who drove a Chevy.

83. Jody Ridley in a Ford averaged 116.595 mph and defeated Bobby Allison by 22 seconds at the one-mile Dover Downs International Speedway oval.

84. Darrell Waltrip averaged 126.703 mph in his Buick and won the 1981 Rebel 500 event on the 1,366 mile oval of the Darlington, South Carolina International Raceway. Harry Gant finished second, ½ second behind Waltrip.

Boating

1. True or false: the first gasoline powered boat was introduced in 1906?

2. When was the first Harmsworth Cup powerboat race held and where?

3. Which one of these countries has won the Harmsworth Cup the most often: Canada, United States or England?

4. Can you name the only boat ever to win the Harmsworth Cup three times?

5. Since 1961 the Harmsworth Cup race has not been held. What happened to the trophy?

6. Can you name the person who has won the Gold Cup the greatest number of times?

7. Can you name the longest recorded powerboat race in history?

8. True or false: the longest powerboat jump was made for a movie?

9. Is there a powerboat called a dragster?

10. True or false: a man drove a powerboat over 10,000 miles in one journey?

11. What is the origin of the word "yacht" and what does it mean?

12. Can you name the most successful racing yacht in history?

13. Has a racing yacht ever reached a speed of over 35 mph over 500 meter course?

14. True or false: the greatest number of sailing boats ever to start a race is 247?

15. Which country has won the most America's Cups in boating: the United States, Great Britain or Australia?

16. Can you name the winner of the America's Cup in 1974 and 1977?

17. What kind of boats race in the Little America's Cup?

18. Where is the Admiral's Cup competition held and how often?

19. How many races are there in the Admiral's Cup: two, four or six?

20. Where is the largest marina in the world?

21. Who won the 1980 America's Cup?

22. Can you name the boat that recorded the fastest in the America's Cup?

23. Can you name the man from Denmark who has won the most individual Olympic medals in boating?

24. The biggest sail ever made had an area of 11,000 square feet. True or false?

Answers

1. False. The first gasoline powered boat was invented by Jean Joseph Etienne Lenoir and first driven on the River Seine in Paris in 1865.

2. The sport of powerboating was introduced in 1903 with the presentation of a championship cup by Sir Alfred Harmsworth of England. The first race took place in 1903 and was run between Calais and Dover.

3. Of the 25 contests which have taken place since 1903 the United States has won 16.

4. The only boat to win three times is Miss Supertest III, owned by James C. Thompson of Canada. It was driven by Bob Hayward, also from Canada. They won in 1959, 60, 61. Miss Supertest III also achieved the record speed of 119.27 in Canada in 1961.

5. The trophy is now given to the British Commonwealth driver with the highest number of points in the World Offshore Championships.

6. Since the Gold Cup was introduced in 1903, it has been won by Bill Muncey a record eight times (1956, 57, 61, 62, 72, 77, 78, 79). He also holds the record for the highest speed for the 2½ mile lap by the unlimited hydroplane, Atlas Van Lines, with a speed of 128.338 mph achieved on the Columbia River, Washington in July, 1977 and again in July, 1978.

7. The Port Richborough (London) to Monte Carlo Marathon Offshore International event. The race was won by H.T.S. of Great Britain, driven by Mike Bellamy, Eddie Chater and Jim Brooks. They finished the 2,947 miles in 14 stages on June 10-25, 1972, in 71 hours, 35 minutes and 56 seconds. Their average speed was 41.15 miles per hour.

8. True. In the James Bond film, *Live and Let Die*, Jerry Comeaux jumped a Glastron GT-150 with a 135 hp Evinrude in Louisiana in 1972 for the record.

9. Yes. Dragsters are the fastest power boats having attained speeds of up to 200 miles per hour. A boat named Climax is reported to have gone at speeds up to 205.19 mph.

10. True. Twenty five year old Hans Tholstrup, a Dane, circumnavigated Australia (11,500 miles) from May 11 to July 25, 1971. He drove a 17 foot Caribbean Cougar fiberglass runabout with a single 80 hp Mercury outboard motor.

11. The word, yacht, is from the Dutch and it means hunt or chase.

12. The most successful racing yacht was the British royal yacht, Britannia, (1893-1935) which was originally owned by King Edward VII while Prince of Wales and subsequently by King George V. In all the Britannia won 231 races out of 625.

13. In 1977 the yacht, Crossbow II set the official world speed record of 33.4 knots or 38.46 mph over a 500 meter course in England. In an unsuccessful attempt to break its own record, Crossbow II reached a speed of 45 knots or 51 mph momentarily.

14. False. The greatest number of boats ever to start a sailing race is 1,261 at the 233 mile Round Zealand (Denmark) race in June, 1976.

15. 1984 was the first time since 1851 that the U.S. has not won this event. *Australia II* defeated the United States' *Liberty* in 1984, 4-3.

16. The boat Courageous skippered by Ted Turner, owner of baseball's Atlanta Braves, won in 1974 and 1977.

17. C-class catamarans race in the Little America's Cup, which was first introduced in 1961. Great Britain has the most wins with eight.

18. The Admiral's Cup is held by the Royal Ocean Racing Club in the English Channel in alternate years. Britain has the most wins with seven while the United States and Australia have won twice.

19 The contest is made up of four races: a 200 mile Channel race, two inshore races held during Cowes Week and a 605 mile Fastnet race from Cowes to Fastnet Rock, off Southern Ireland and back to Plymouth.

20. The largest marina in the world is Marina Del Ray in Los Angeles, California. It has 7,500 berths.

HALLO AGAIN!

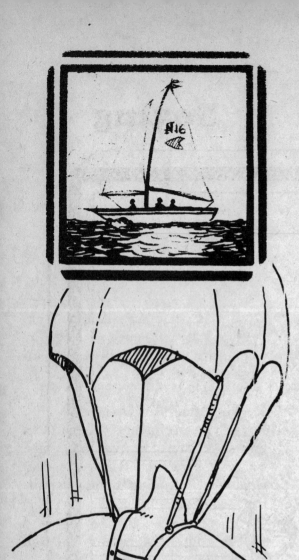

21. *Freedom*, of the United States, skippered by Dennis Conner beat Australia four races to one in the best of seven series to win the America's Cup. *Freedom* was selected to defend the cup over *Courageous*, the 1974 and 1977 winner.

22. The fastest time ever was achieved by *Gretel*, the 1962 loser. The 12 meter boat covered the triangular course of 24 miles in a time of 2 hours, 46 minutes, 58 seconds. *Weatherly* of the United States won the competition beating out her Australian challenger.

23. Paul B. Elustrom was the first sportsman to win individual gold medals in boating in the Olympic games. He won the Finn Class in 1952, 56, 60 and also the Firefly Class in the 1948 games.

24. False. The 1937 winner of the America's Cup, *Ranger*, had the largest sail ever made. The sail had an area of 18,000 square feet or more than two fifths of an acre.

5. Who is the only heavyweight to win the title three different times?

6. Who is the only heavyweight champion to have gone undefeated in his entire professional career?

7. Who fought in the first heavyweight championship fight with gloves and 3 minute rounds?

8. True or false: Wilfredo Benitez was the youngest fighter ever to win a world boxing title?

9. Can you name the oldest fighter ever to hold a boxing title? Here's a hint: he was known as Archibald Lee Wright before changing his name.

10. Can you name the only fighter to win the title five times in one weight class?

1. True or false: a professional boxing match with gloves once lasted 110 rounds?

2. Before he changed his name this fighter was known as Joseph Barrow. Can you name him and his accomplishments?

3. Can you name the heavyweight who held the title the shortest period of time?

4. Before this heavyweight fighter changed his name he was known as Arnold Raymond Cream. Can you name him?

I GOING HOME NOW.

PLEASE LOCK-UP WHEN YOU'RE FINISHED WITH THE ARENA.

ROUND 110

196

11. Who held the Heavyweight title from 1928-1930?

12. At what title fight in 1926 was the greatest paid attendance recorded?

13. True or false: the smallest attendance at a heavyweight title fight occured when Cassius Clay fought Sonny Liston?

14. What professional prize fighter made the most money in a fighting career?

15. After Leon Spinks defeated Muhammed Ali in their first fight the W.B.C. took their version of the title away from him for not fulfilling a contract agreement. To whom did they award the title?

16. Who is the only fighter to defeat Sugar Ray Leonard?

17. Sugar Ray Leonard won the W.B.A. Junior Middleweight title in 1981. Whom did he fight?

18. True or false: the Tommy Hearns-Ray Leonard contest on September 16, 1981 was the richest fight in history?

19. In Ken Norton's last professional prize fight he was knocked out by whom?

20. When President Reagan was shot in 1981 he made the comment, "I forgot to duck" to his wife. What heavyweight used that line?

29. True or false: Floyd Patterson was the first man ever to regain the heavyweight title?

30. True or false: Tommy Hearns beat Sugar Ray Leonard as an amateur?

21. Hilmer Kenty lost the lightweight title in 1981 to whom?

22. Whom did Tommy Hearns beat to win the WBA version of the welterweight championship?

23. What happened at the second Roberto Duran-Sugar Ray Leonard title fight in New Orleans?

24. Whom did Marvin Hagler beat to win the undisputed middleweight championship of the world?

25. Laszlo Papp of Hungary won the Olympic gold medal in the middleweight division in 1948 and won the 1952 and 1956 titles in the light middleweight division. Who is the only other fighter ever to win three gold medals in the Olympics?

26. To whom did Joe Frazier lose the heavyweight title in 1973?

27. True or false: Muhammed Ali was the youngest fighter ever to win the heavyweight title?

28. True or false: to compete as a featherweight a fighter can weigh up to 135 pounds?

31. Where and when was the Carnival of Champions event held and who fought?

32. True or false: Muhammed Ali holds the heavyweight record for defending his title the greatest number of times?

33. True or false: as a lightweight boxer your weight may not exceed 142 pounds?

34. True or false: Muhammed Ali never won the fighter of the year award given by Ring Magazine?

35. True or false: Joe Frazier won the gold medal in the Olympic heavyweight division?

36. True or false: Muhammed Ali won the heavyweight gold medal in the 1960 Olympic games?

37. What is the weight limit for flyweight boxers?

38. Whom did Larry Holmes fight on October 2, 1980 and what was the outcome of the bout?

39. Who was the first black heavyweight champion of the world?

40. Did Gene Fullmer ever win a world boxing title in his career?

41. Can you name the only heavyweight champions who retired as undefeated champions?

42. In weight division did Kid Chocolate hold a world title?

43. In what division did Bob Foster fight and was he ever a champion?

44. In what division did Jake La Motta become champion and who beat him to win the title?

45. Who was the biggest heavyweight champion of all time?

46. Describe an uppercut in boxing.

47. True or false: Marvin Hart was middleweight champion of the world for a record 13 years?

48. Of the three classic Rocky Graziano-Tony Zale fights who won two out of three?

49. What is a TKO in boxing?

50. Who handed Muhammed Ali his first defeat in the professional ranks?

51. What is a jab in boxing?

Answers

1. True. Andy Bowen and Jack Burke fought for 7 hours, 19 minutes from 9:15 P.M. until 4:34 A.M. on April 6-7, 1893 in New Orleans. The fight was halted after the 110th round and was called a draw when both men were unable to continue.

2. Joseph Louis Barrow was his full name. He was known simply as Joe Louis and is regarded by many as the best heavyweight ever. On June 22, 1937 Louis knocked out James Braddock in the eighth round to win the heavyweight title. He went on to defend his title 25 times (a record) over a span of almost 12 years until his retirement in 1949.

3. The shortest reign as a titleholder was that of Leon Spinks, who was champion for 212 days. Spinks defeated Muhammed Ali on February 15, 1978 only to lose to the same Ali on September 15, 1978 in New Orleans.

4. Jersey Joe Walcott, who won the heavyweight championship on July 18, 1951 when he knocked out Ezzard Charles in the seventh round. Jersey Joe was unique because at the age of 37 years, 5 months and 18 days he became the oldest man ever to win the heavyweight championship. He lost it in 1952 when Rocky Marciano came from behind and knocked out Walcott in the thirteenth round.

5. Muhammed Ali is the only heavyweight ever to win the title three times. Fighting as Cassius Clay, Ali first won the title in 1964 when opponent Sonny Liston was unable to answer the bell for the seventh round. He defeated George Foreman in 1974, after having been stripped of his title by the World

Boxing Authority on April 28, 1967. He lost the title to Leon Spinks on February 15, 1978 but regained it on September 15, 1978 by defeating Spinks in a unanimous 15 round decision in New Orleans.

6. Rocco Francis Marchegiano, known by the boxing world as Rocky Marciano. He fought 49 professional fights from 1947 until 1956 and never lost a fight. He knocked 43 of his opponents. Marciano defended his title six times and all but one of those contests ended in knockouts.

7. The first world title in the heavyweight division with gloves and 3 minute rounds took place in New Orleans, on September 7, 1892. John L. Sullivan then champion, fought "Gentleman" James J. Corbett. Corbett beat a fat, out of shape Sullivan and won in 21 rounds.

8. True. At the age of 17 years, 180 days Wilfredo Benitez of Puerto Rico won the W.B.A. light welterweight title in San Juan on March 6, 1976. He is probably best known for losing his welterweight title to Sugar Ray Leonard in 1979.

9. The oldest world champion was Archie Moore, who was recognized as the light heavyweight champion up until February 10, 1962, when it was revoked. He was between 45 and 48 years old.

10. The only boxer to do so is Sugar Ray Robinson, regarded by many to be the best fighter of all time. He beat Jake Lamotta on February 14, 1951; Randy Turpin on September 12, 1951; Bobo Olson on December 9, 1955; Gene Fullmer on May 1, 1957, and he won the title for the fifth time in the middleweight division on March 25, 1958 over Carmen Basilio.

11. Nobody. The Heavyweight Division had no champion from 1928-1930.

12. 120,757 people showed up to see Gene Tunney upset the great Jack Dempsey to win the heavyweight championship at the Sesquicentennial Stadium in Philadelphia on September 23, 1926. Ringside seats went for $27.50.

13. True. The lightest attendance was only 2,434 people at the May 25, 1965 title fight with Cassius Clay and Sonny Liston. The fight took place in Lewiston, Maine and Clay knocked out Liston in the first round with what cynics called a "phantom punch."

14. The largest amount of money ever made by a fighter or any other sports figure is over 60 million dollars amassed by Muhammed Ali in his career. This record might be in trouble if Sugar Ray Leonard continues his present pattern.

15. Ken Norton was given the W.B.C. version of the heavyweight title without even stepping into the ring. Norton lost to Larry Holmes who beat him in a very close match and as of this writing Holmes still holds the title.

16. Roberto Duran is the only fighter ever to beat Leonard. Duran won a close decision in Montreal in 1980 to win the welterweight title. The contrast in their styles produced one of the best fights ever seen in the welterweight division.

17. Leonard defeated a very tough Ayub Kalule to win the title by a ninth round knockout. He gave up the title to continue in the welterweight division.

18. True. Through the live gate and closed circuit T.V. the fight grossed close to 40 million dollars. Leonard made around 10 million by knocking out Hearns in the fourteenth round. All of the judges had Hearns ahead when the fight was stopped midway through the fourteenth round when Hearns was unable to defend himself.

19. The number one heavyweight contender Gerry Cooney knocked out Ken Norton in 54 seconds of the first round.

20. After losing to Gene Tunney in 1926 Jack Dempsey made that remark to his wife when she asked what happened.

21. Sean O'Grady won a unanimous 15 round decision over Kenty to win the WBA version of the lightweight title.

22. Tommy "The Motor City Cobra" Hearns knocked out Pipino Cuevas in the second round to win the WBA welterweight title. Until Hearns lost to Leonard he had a 32-0 record with 30 knockouts.

23. Sugar Ray regained the World Boxing Council welterweight title with an eighth round TKO of Duran, who conceded the match 2:44 minutes into the round because of stomach cramps.

24. Harvin Hagler knocked out Alan Minter in the third round of their scheduled 15 round match in 1980. When the referee stopped the fight the crowd threw bottles into the ring. Minter's home town crowd did not like the outcome of the fight.

25. Teofilo Stevenson of Cuba is the only other three-time gold medalist with 1972, 76, 80 victories in the heavyweight division.

26. On January 22, 1973 George Foreman stunned the boxing world by knocking out Joe Frazier in the second round to win the heavyweight crown in Kingston, Jamaica.

27. False. Floyd Patterson won the title vacated by retired Rocky Marciano when he knocked out Archie Moore in the fifth round at the age of 21 years, 331 days, to become the youngest champion ever in the heavyweight division.

28. False. To compete as a featherweight a boxer may not weigh over 126 pounds.

29. True. Ingemar Johansson of Sweden knocked out defending champion Floyd Patterson in the third round on June 26, 1959 to win the title. They met one year later only this time Patterson knocked out Johansson in the fifth round to become the first heavyweight ever to regain his title.

30. False. They never fought as amateurs. Their first encounter was in the ring at Las Vegas in 1981.

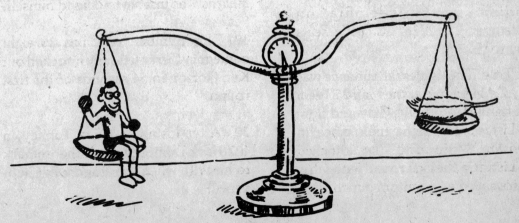

31. The Carnival of champions was held on September 23, 1937 at the old Polo Grounds. Harry Jeffra decisioned Sixto Escobar and won the bantamweight title; Lou Ambers retained his lightweight title with a decision over Pedro Montanez; Barney Ross retained his welterweight title by decisioning Ceferino Garcia, and Fred Apostoli knocked out Marcel Thil in the tenth round for the middleweight title. The New York State Athletic Commission refused to recognize Apostoli's title.

32. False. Muhammed Ali defended his title 19 times in his career but the "Brown Bomber", Joe Louis, defended his title a record 25 times during his 12 year reign as heavyweight champ.

33. False. A lightweight may not exceed the 135 pound limit.

34. False. Muhammed Ali has won the award five times. He won the first time in 1963 as Cassius Clay and won again in 1972, 1974, 1975 and 1978 as Muhammed Ali.

35. True. Frazier won the 1964 heavyweight division gold medal in Tokyo. He went on to win the world championship. He is best known for beating Muhammed Ali in 1971 in the "fight of the century."

36. False. Ali, fighting as Cassius Clay, won the gold medal in the light heavyweight division in Rome that year.

37. Flyweights may not exceed 112 pounds.

38. Larry Holmes successfully defended his title by stopping Muhammed Ali when he couldn't answer the bell for the eleventh round. Holmes won every round on all three judges' scorecards when the fight ended.

39. Jack Johnson was the first black heavyweight champion. He knocked out Tommy Burns December 26, 1908 in Australia to win the crown. Johnson held the title for seven years. He lost it to Jess Willard by a questionable KO in the twenty-sixth round.

40. Gene Fullmer won the middleweight title in 1957 and again won it in 1959. He held it until 1962.

41. James J. Jeffries (1905), Gene Tunney (1928), Joe Louis (1949) and Rocky Marciano (1956).

42. Eligio "Kid Chocolate" Sardinias from Cuba won the junior lightweight title in 1931 and in 1932 won the featherweight title by decisioning Fidel La Barba. He held both titles until 1933. In his 161 bouts he won 145 and scored 64 knockouts. He was counted out only twice in his 10 years in the prize ring.

43. Bob Foster was one of the most successful light-heavyweight boxers of all time. The only losses in his career were to heavyweights Muhammed Ali, Joe Frazier, Zora Folley, Ernie Terrell, Doug Jones and Mauro Mina. Foster won the light-heavyweight championship in 1968 when he knocked out Dick Tiger and went on to hold the title until his retirement in 1974. He won 51 of 58 pro matches with a light-heavyweight mark of 42 KO's.

44. LaMotta knocked out defending middleweight champion Marcel Cerdan in the tenth round for the title on June 10, 1949. On St. Valentine's Day in 1951 he lost the title to Sugar Ray Robinson when the referee stopped the fight in the thirteenth round because LaMotta could no longer defend himself.

45. Six foot six Primo Carnera was the heaviest heavyweight champion ever. He weighed 267 pounds and had the longest reach, 85½ inches. His other measurements were: neck, 20 inches; forearm, 16 inches; chest, 48 inches. He held the title for 350 days, beating Jack Sharkey in 1933 to win the title. He lost it in 1934 to Max Baer who decked him twelve times before he was counted out in the eleventh round.

46. A short punch thrown with either hand in an upward motion.

47. False. Marvin Hart won the heavyweight title in 1905 when he fought Jack Root for the crown after Jim Jeffries retired. He lost it a year later to Tommy Burns.

48. In their three fights not one went past the sixth round as each man went for all or nothing. Zale won the first fight with a sixth round knockout in Yankee Stadium in 1946. Graziano evened the score with a sixth round KO over Zale in Chicago. This set up the rubber match in which Zale caught Rocky and knocked him out in the third round in Newark, New Jersey on June 10, 1948.

49. TKO stands for technical knockout. This happens when the referee stops the fight because a fighter is badly hurt or unable to defend himself.

50. On March 8, 1971 Muhammed Ali lost a unanimous decision to defending heavyweight champion Joe Frazier, who knocked Ali down in the fifteenth round. The match was billed as the "fight of the century" and it lived up to that billing. Ali and Frazier had two more meetings with Ali winning both of them.

51. For a right hander a jab is usually thrown with the left as a straight punch. It is usually thrown to set up the right hand delivery.

Swimming

9. True or false: a swimming race in the Olympics was once won by the length of a fingernail?

10. Can you name the only person ever to win the diving event at three successive Olympic games?

1. The earliest reference to swimming in competition comes from what country?

2. True or false: the largest swimming pool in the world is located in Las Vegas?

3. True or false: the largest competition pool is located in Japan?

4. Has the fastest speed ever attained in the water been reached by a man or a woman?

5. Which one of these swimmers has held the most world records during his career: Mark Spitz, Arne Borg or John Naber?

6. Which one of these women holds the most world records: Ragnhild Hveger, Shirley Babashoff or Shane Gould?

7. Can you name the American swimmer who holds the Olympic record for total medals and gold medals won?

8. The Olympic record for most medals won in swimming is eight. It is held by three women. Can you name any one of them?

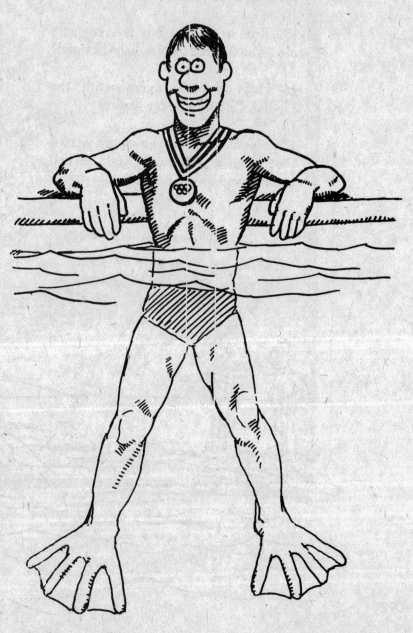

11. A perfect score for diving is a 10. Has a diver ever been awarded a 10 by all seven judges?

12. Has anybody ever swum down the length of the Mississippi River?

13. True or false: the greatest distance covered in a continuous swim is 198 miles?

14. True or false: the first person ever to swim across the English Channel without a life jacket did so in 1875?

15. True or false: a boy twelve years old swam across the English Channel?

16. Has anybody ever swum the English Channel under water?

17. Has anybody ever swum across the English Channel and turned around and swum back?

18. True or false: a man once trod water for over 60 consecutive hours?

19. Can you name the American swimmer who won both the 100 and 200 meter backstroke events at the 1976 Olympics?

20. From 1963 until 1977 two N.C.A.A. schools completely dominated swimming. Can you name them?

21. Has anybody ever swum across the English Channel three times without stopping?

HE MADE IT ACROSS THE CHANNEL — BUT HE HAS TO GO BACK BECAUSE HE DIDN'T BRING HIS PASSPORT

NICE FORM, KID.

1. The earliest reference to a swimming competition in schools was ordered by imperial edict of Emperor GoYoozei of Japan as early as 1603, but competition was known as early 36 B.C.

2. False. The largest swimming pool in the world is in Casablanca, Morocco. It is a salt water Orthlieb Pool, 480 meters long, 75 meters wide and has an area of 8.9 acres.

3. True. The world's largest competition pool is located in Osaka, Japan. The arena can hold 13,614 spectators.

4. The fastest male swimmer ever recorded is Joe Bottom of the United States. He was clocked at 5.19 mph at Cleveland, Ohio on March 24, 1977. The fastest time for a woman is 4.42 mph accomplished by Sue Hinderaker of the United States in Pittsburgh, Pennsylvania on March 16, 1979.

5. If you said Arne Borg you are right! He held 32 world records in swimming from 1921 until 1929. Borg is from Sweden.

Answers

6. Ragnhild Hveger of Denmark by far. She held an amazing total of 42 world records from 1936 until 1942.

7. Mark Spitz won an incredible 11 medals including 9 gold medals in the 1968 and 1972 Olympics. He also holds the record for most gold medals won in a single Olympics with seven. Here is a list of his gold medal performances:

100 meter freestyle	1972
200 meter freestyle	1972
100 meter butterfly	1972
200 meter butterfly	1972
4x100 meter freestyle relay	1968 and 1972
4x200 meter freestyle relay	1968 and 1972
4x100 medley relay	1972

8. Dawn Fraxer of Australia won four gold medals and four silvers at the 1956, 1960 and 1964 Olympics. Shirley Babashoff of the United States won two golds and six silvers at the 1972 and 1976 Olympic Games. Kornelia Ender of East Germany won four golds and four silvers at the 1972 and 1976 Olympics.

9. True. In the 1972 games in Munich the 400 meter individual medley final was won by Gunnar Larsson of Sweden by .002 second over Tim McKee of the United States. Length of less than 1/8 inch or the length of a fingernail grown in three weeks.

10. Italy's Klaus Dibiasi, who won a total of five medals in four games from 1964 to 1976. He is the only diver in the history of the Olympics to win the highboard event at three successive Games—1968, 1972, 1976.

11. Yes. Only once. Michael Finneran was awarded a perfect 10 by all seven judges for a backward 1½ somersault, 2½ twist free dive from the 10 meter board at the 1972 U.S. Olympic trials, held in Chicago.

12. It is the greatest recorded distance ever swum: 1,826 miles. The feat was accomplished by Fred P. Newton, an Oklahoman, at the age of 27. He started at Ford Dam, near Minneapolis and swam to Carrollton Avenue, New Orleans July 6 to December 29, 1930. Newton was in the water a total for 742 hours.

13. False. Joe Maciag swam 292 miles from Billings to Glendive, Montana in the Yellowstone River in 64 hours, 50 minutes, July 1-4, 1976.

14. True. Merchant Navy Captain Matthew Webb of Great Britain swam breaststroke from Dover, England to Calais Sands, France in 21 hours, 45 minutes on August 24-25, 1875. There is good evidence that an escaped prisoner, Jean-Marie Saletti swam after his escape from a British prison hulk, from Dover to Boulogne in July or August, 1815.

15. True. Markus Hooper of Eltham, England, swam from Dover to Sangatte, France in 14 hours, 37 minutes. He was only 12, years 53 days old at the time. The youngest girl to swim the Channel was Abla Adel Khairi of Egypt, who swam the Channel at the age of 13 years, 426 days. It took her 12 hours, 30 minutes to do it.

FWANG

16. Yes. It was first done in 1962 when Fred Baldasare of the United States, at the age of 38, swam 42 miles from France to England with scuba in 18 hours, 1 minute on July 10-11.

17. Yes. The first double crossing was accomplished by Antonio Albertondo, 42, of Argentina. He swam from England to France in 18 hours, 50 minutes and rested for about four minutes. Then he turned around and went back to England in 24 hours, 16 minutes. He did this on September 21-22, 1961.

18. True. Norman Albert trod water (vertical posture in an 8 foot square without touching the lane markers) for 64 consecutive hours at Pennsylvania State University on November 1-4, 1978.

19. John Naber, who won a total of four gold medals at the 1976 Games at Montreal. Both his individual backstroke medals were also world records.

20. From 1963 until 1966 Southern Cal. won the N.C.A.A. swimming title. In 1967 Stanford won. From 1968 until 1973 Indiana won the finals and from 1974 until 1977 Southern Cal. won again. Every year except one (1967) from 1963 until 1977 either Southern Cal. or Indiana won the N.C.A.A. swimming championship.

21. A 26 year old Phys. Ed. teacher, Jon Erikson, became the first swimmer to cross the English Channel three times nonstop. He started at Dover, England and finished 38 hours and 27 minutes later at Wisant, France in August, 1981.

Golf

1. Where did the game of golf originate: Scotland, China or Rome?

2. True or false: the highest golf course in the world is in Bolivia, South America with an elevation of 12,000 feet?

3. Are there any golf courses in the world below sea level?

4. Is there a golf hole measuring more than 800 yards anywhere in the world?

5. True or false: the largest green in the world has an area of more than 28,000 square feet?

6. True or false: there is a golf course with a bunker that covers a half acre?

7. True or false: the world's longest golf course is located in China?

8. True or false: a man once "golfed" across the entire length of the United States?

9. What is the lowest recorded score on any 18 hole golf course with a par of 70 or more: 55, 57 or 59?

10. Which one of these players holds the P.G.A. tournament record for the lowest score over 18 holes: Sam Snead, David Jagger or Al Geiberger?

11. The lowest recorded score over 18 holes (over 6,000 yards) for a woman is a 62 by whom: Nancy Lopez, Mickey Wright or Kathy Whitworth?

12. True or false: the record for a 36 hole tournament is held by Sam Snead?

13. True or false: Mike Souchak holds the record for most holes in one in a career?

14. True or false: a man once shot a 316 for 18 holes of golf.

15. True or false: the record for the highest score for one hole for a woman is 47?

16. True or false: the lowest score for throwing a golf ball around 18 holes (over 6,000 yards) is an 82?

17. Who holds the United States P.G.A. record for the longest drive, Jack Nicklaus or Valentin Barrios?

18. What was the longest putt ever recorded in a major tournament: 67, 78 or 86 feet?

19. Which one of these great golfers has the record for winning the most tournaments in a single season: Walter Hagen, Byron Nelson or Arnold Palmer?

20. Who has won the most P.G.A. tournaments in his career: Arnold Palmer, Jack Nicklaus or Sam Snead?

29. In 1979 Jack Nicklaus won his fourth U.S. Open title to become the fourth player in history to do so. Willie Anderson was the first; who were the second and third?

30. Who is the only golfer ever to win the men's U.S. Amateur title five times?

21. Who was the first golfer ever to make one million dollars in a career?

22. Which one of these golfers has made the most money in his career: Lee Trevino, Jack Nicklaus or Tom Watson?

23. Can you name the only woman as of August, 1981 to have made one million dollars in her career?

24. Who is the only golfer to win a pro golf tournament in six different decades?

25. Who is known as the "Golden Bear" to golf fans?

26. Who is the only golfer ever to win all five major titles: Jack Nicklaus, Ben Hogan or Bobby Jones?

27. What are the four major professional golf tournaments in the world?

28. Who was the first golfer ever to win four U.S. Opens?

31. Jack Nicklaus has won the British Open three times. Has anybody ever won this tournament six times?

32. True or false: a man has won the British Amateur eight times?

33. Which one of these golfers won the most U.S.P.G.A. championships: Ben Hogan, Walter Hagen or Arnold Palmer?

34. In 1980 a player tied Hagen with five victories at the P.G.A. Championship. Can you name him?

35. Can you name the only golfer in history to win a total of five Masters championships?

36. Can you name the first woman to win the U.S. Women's Open four times?

37. Can you name the only other woman to have won the U.S. Women's Open four times besides Betsy Earle-Rawls?

38. Can you name the only golfer ever to win the U.S. Women's Amateur six times?

39. Which one of these golfers holds the record for lowest score after 72 holes at the U.S. Open, Jack Nicklaus or Lee Trevino?

40. True or false: the lowest score for 18 holes at the U.S. Open is a 65?

41. What is a birdie in golf?

42. True or false: the U.S. Amateur golf tournament was first played in 1919 to commemorate the end of World War I?

43. Where was the British Open first played and in what year?

44. The record for nine holes in the British Open is a 29 held by three people. Can you name the last player to tie the record?

45. True or false: Tom Watson holds the 72 hole record for lowest score at the British Open?

46. There is a United States Amateur golf tournament every year. Is there a British Amateur?

47. What did the world cup of golf used to be called?

48. Which country has won the World Cup the greatest number of times?

49. Can you name the only two players to play on six winning World Cup teams?

50. What is the Walker Cup?

51. Who has won the Walker Cup the greatest number of times, the United States or Great Britain?

52. Who has won the Ryder Cup the greatest number of times, between the United States and Britain?

53. True or false: the Curtis Cup is played annually by the three top players from Europe and the three top players from North America?

54. Who has won the Curtis Cup the greatest number of times?

55. **Who won the most money on the 1982 tour?**

56. A first place prize of $100,000 was awarded to the winner of the World Open in 1973. Who won?

57. Who won the 1981 World Series of golf in Akron, Ohio: Tom Kite, Tom Watson, Bill Rodgers, or Jack Nicklaus?

58. Who won the twenty-eighth Walker Cup in 1981?

59. True or false: Nancy Lopez-Melton won the World Championship of Women's Golf in 1981?

60. True or false: Bing Crosby's son won the 1981 U.S. Amateur Championship?

— ONLY GOLF COURSE IN THIS COUNTRY WITH QUICKSAND TRAPS!

61. What country won the Ryder Cup in 1981?

62. Can you name the player who won the 1980 and 1981 U.S. Women's Amateur Championship?

63. Can you name the woman golfer who broke the LPGA record for 36 holes in 1981?

64. What is a rut iron used for in golf?

65. True or false: Larry Nelson won the 1981 PGA championship?

66. Which one of these women won the 1981 Women's Open: Nancy Lopez-Melton, Beth Daniel or Pat Bradley?

67. Can you name the player who won the 1981 British Open?

68. True or false: Arnold Palmer won the 1981 U.S. Senior Open in Birmingham, Michigan?

69. Can you name the Division 1 college team that won the 1981 AIAW title?

70. Who won the 1981 U.S. Open: Jack Nicklaus, David Graham or Tom Watson?

71. Can you name the woman who won the 1981 LPGA championship in Mason, Ohio?

72. Is there a New Orleans Open in Professional golf?

73. Who won the 1981 Tournament of Champions golf event in Carlsbad, California?

74. Which one of these players won the 1981 U.S. Masters Championship: Johnny Miller, Tom Watson or Jack Nicklaus?

75. Is there a Hawaiian Open for professional golfers?

76. Who won the 1980 player of the year award for golf?

77. When does the PGA season start and when does it end?

78. True or false: Jack Nicklaus won his first professional tournament in 1961?

79. True or false: the U.S. Open is held annually at Pebble Beach?

80. What is a hacker in golf?

Answers

1. They have all laid claim to the game. A stained glass window from 1350 Scotland portrays a golfer-like figure. The Romans had a game called paganica which may have been carried to Britain before 400 A.D. and even the Chinese take credit with their own ch'ui wan — the ball hitting game from the third century B.C.

2. False. The Tuctu Golf Club in Morococha, Peru has the highest elevation, which is 14,335 feet above sea level at its lowest point. Golf has been played at 16,000 feet in Tibet.

3. Yes. The Sodom and Gomorrah Golfing Society at Kallia, Qulya on the northern shores of the Dead Sea, 1,250 feet below sea level. It is no longer in existence. The lowest golf course in the world today is the Rotterdam Golf Club in the Netherlands. It is 26 feet below sea level.

4. No. In 1927 the sixth hole at the Prescott Country Club in Arkansas measured 838 yards. Today the longest golf hole is the seventeenth (par 6) at the Black Mountain Golf Club in North Carolina. It's 745 yards long.

5. True. The world's largest green is located at the International Golf Club in Bolton, Massachussetts. It has an area of more than 28,000 square feet at the fifth green.

6. True. Hell's Half Acre on the seventh hole of the Pine Valley course in New Jersey. It was built in 1912 and is one of the most difficult courses in the world.

7. False. The world's longest golf course is the 8,101 Dub's Dread Golf Club course in Piper, Kansas. It is a par 78.

8. True. Floyd Satterlee Rood used the United States as his own personal golf course. He played from the Pacific to the Atlantic from September 14, 1963 to October 3, 1964. Rood completed the course in 114,737 strokes, losing 3,511 balls on the 3,397 mile trip.

9. If you said 55, you are right! Alfred Edward Smith of England shot a 55 at Woolacombe on January 1, 1936. What a way to bring in the New Year. The course measured 4,248 yards.

10. The United States P.G.A. record is a 59 (30+29) by Al Geiberger in the second round of the Danny Thomas Golf Classic on June 10, 1977. The course measures 7,249 yards and is a par 72. Sam Snead and David Jagger both shot 59's in non-P.G.A. tournaments.

11. Mickey Wright recorded the lowest women's score over an 18 hole course at the Hogan Park Course (6,282 yards Midland, Texas in November, 1964.)

12. True. Snead shot a 122 (59 + 63) in the 1959 Greenbrier Open on May 16 and 17, 1959 for the 36 hole record.

13. False. Souchak holds the record for lowest score over a first class golf course. He shot a 257 (27 under par) for 72 holes in the Texas Open at Brackenbridge Park, San Antonio in February, 1955. Souchak averaged 64.25 per round.

14. True. Chevalier von Cittern shot a 316 at the Biarritz, France in 1888. Over the 18 holes he averaged 17.55 shots per hole.

15. False. In 1912 at the Shawneee Invitational for Ladies at Shawnee-on-Delaware, Pennsylvania an unknown woman shot a 166 for the 130 yard sixteenth hole. She hit the ball into a river and set out in a boat to finish the hole. When she finally got the ball on shore, one and one half miles downstream, she had to play the ball through a forest to finish the hole out.

16. True. Joe Flynn, age 21, recorded a score of 82 at the 6,228 yard Port Royal Course, Bermuda on March 27, 1975. He threw the ball around the entire course.

17. Jack Nicklaus holds the United States P.G.A. record with a 341 yard drive in July, 1963. Valentin Barrios of Spain once drove a golf ball 568½ yards on an airport runway at Palma, Majorca on March 7, 1977.

18. Cary Middlecoff made a putt from 86 feet on the thirteenth green at the Augusta National, Georgia in 1955. He went on to win the tournament. Bobby Jones supposedly made a putt in excess of 100 feet at the fifth green in the first round of the 1927 British Open.

19. Byron Nelson of the United States won a total of 19 tournaments in 1945 including a record 11 consecutively.

20. Sam Snead holds the U.S. P.G.A. record for most tournament wins with a total of 84 and he has been credited with 165 total tournament victories since 1934.

24. If you said Sam Snead, you are right! He has won at least one tournament in every decade from the 1930's to the 1980's. Snead has won seven major golf titles in his career, including three P.G.A.'s, three Masters and a British Open.

25. One of the greatest golfers of all time, Jack Nicklaus, who is also the leading money winner of all time.

26. Jack Nicklaus is the only golfer ever to win all five major tournaments including the U.S. Amateur.

21. Arnold Palmer is the first golfer ever to make one million dollars playing golf. He reached that mark in 1968 and up till August 1981 he has made a total of $1,860,967 in his career.

22. As of 1983, Jack Nicklaus has won the most money playing golf with over $4 million to his credit.

23. The record for career earnings by a woman is held by Jo Anne Calner, as of July 1983, with a total of $1,506,287.

27. The four top professional golf tournaments are the Masters, the P.G.A. Championship, the U.S. Open, and the British Open.

28. Willie Anderson was the first player to win four U.S. Open titles in 1901, 1903, 1904, 1905.

29. Bobby Jones and Ben Hogan. Jones won the U.S. Open in 1923, 1926, 1929, 1930 and Hogan won in 1948, 1950, 1951, 1953.

30. Bobby Jones is the only golfer ever to win the men's U.S. Amateur title five times. He won in 1924, 1925, 1927, 1928, 1930.

31. Unbelievable, but true, Harry Vardon won the British Open a record six times. He won in 1896, 98, 99, 1903, 1911, 14.

32. True. John Ball, one of the world's greatest amateurs, won the event a record eight times from 1888 to 1912.

33. Walter Hagen has the record for the most U.S.P.G.A. championships with five. He has also won three British Opens and two U.S. Opens.

34. Jack Nicklaus, of course, who has to be regarded as one of the greatest golfers of all time.

35. The Golden Bear, Jack Nicklaus, who has won a total of five Masters titles in 1963, 65, 66, 72, 75.

36. Betsy Earle-Rawls was the first woman to four U.S. Opens for women in 1951, 53, 57, 60.

37. Mickey Wright is the only other woman to have won the U.S. Women's Open four times. She won in 1958, 59, 61, 64.

38. Glenna Collett Vare is the only woman ever to win the U.S. Women's Amateur a record six times in her career, 1922, 25, 28, 29, 30, 35.

39. The lowest 72 hole score at the U.S. Open is 275 by both Jack Nicklaus in 1967, and Lee Trevino in 1968.

40. False. On June 17, 1973 Johnny Miller shot a 63 for 18 holes at the Oakmont course in Pennsylvania, a 6,921 yard, par 71 course.

HOLD IT - I THINK WE'VE BEEN SPOTTED!

41. A modern term meaning one under par for the hole. It is an American term which came into use between 1914 and 1939. Example: "He birdied the sixth hole with a nice putt."

42. False. The U.S. Amateur was inaugurated in 1893. The record for the lowest score over nine holes. is a 30, shot by Franics D. Oiumet in 1932.

43. The British Open was first played in 1860 at Prestwick, Strathclyde, Scotland.

44. Tom Haliburton and Peter W. Thomson both shot 29's in the first round of the 1963 British Open. The last person to do so was Tony Jacklin of Great Britain, who shot a 29 in the first round at St. Andrews, Scotland in 1970.

45. True. Tom Watson set the British Open record in 1977 when he shot a 72 hole total of 268 (68, 70, 65, 65) at Turnberry, Scotland on July 9.

46. Yes. The British Amateur was first introduced in 1885 and has been held annually ever since except for WWI and WWII. The lowest score for 18 holes is a 61 shot by Michael Francis Bonallack in 1968 at Ganton, Yorkshire.

47. The World Cup was formerly known as the Canada Cup and was founded in 1953 by John Jay Hopkins of Canada with the idea that the cup would help international goodwill. Each country is represented by a team of two, the winners being the best four round aggregate. Argentina won the first World Cup. Their players were Antonio Cerda and Roberto De Vincenzo.

48. The World Cup has been won the most often by the United States with 15 victories between 1955 and 1979.

49. Two of golf's greatest, Arnold Palmer and Jack Nicklaus. Palmer played with Nicklaus on four of those teams in 1963, 64, 66, 67. Palmer also won in 1960 and 1962. Nicklaus also won in 1971 and 1973.

50. The Walker Cup, instituted in 1921, is a United States versus Great Britain-Ireland series played every other year. Named after George H. Walker, president of the U.S.G.A., it was originally intended to be an annual event but became a biennial event after being played in 1922, 1923, and 1924.

51. The Walker Cup has been won by the United States 25½ times (½ means a draw) compared to Great Britain's 2½. Joe Carr of Great Britain has played in the greatest number of matches with 10 from 1947 until 1967.

52. The biennial Ryder Cup, instituted in 1927, has been won 18½ times by the United States compared to Great Britain's 3½. In 1979 the United States played a team from Europe for the first time and won for the nineteenth time.

53. False. First introduced in 1932, the Curtis Cup is played every two years by teams of women golfers from the United States and Great Britain.

54. Since the introduction of the Curtis Cup in 1932 the United States has won 17 times including 1980 with Great Britain winning twice. They have had two draws.

55. Jo Anne Calner led the ladies with a total of $310,399 on the 1982 tour.

56. Out of a total purse of $500,000 the winner, Miller Barber of Texas, received $100,000. Barber won the award, the greatest first place in golf history, in 1973 at Pinehurst, North Carolina on November 8-17. The World Series of Golf also carries a first place prize of $100,00.

57. Bill Rodgers defeated Tom Kite by one stroke to win the $400,000 World Series of Golf in 1981, with a 5 under par 275.

58. The United States defeated Great Britain-Ireland 15-9 in Pebble Beach, California to increase their lead in the series to 16½ to 2½.

59. False. Beth Daniel shot a four under 284 to win the $150,000 World championship of Women's Golf in 1981 beating Jan Stephenson by one stroke in Shaker Heights, Ohio.

60. True. Nathaniel Crosby sank a 15 foot birdie putt on the thirty seventh hole (the first overtime hole in this tournament since 1950) to win the eighty first U.S. Amateur Championship over Brian Lindley.

227

61. The United States defeated Europe 18½-9½ to win the twenty fourth Ryder Cup at Walton Heath, England. It was the twentieth Ryder Cup victory for the United States and its second straight win over Europe.

62. Juli Inkster of California won her second consecutive U.S. women's amateur title in 1981 by defeating Australia's Linda Goggin one-up in Portland, Oregon.

63. Jan Stehhenson shot an 18 under par 198 to defeat Sandra Haynie by 11 strokes for the LPGA record in a $150,000 tournament in Dallas, Texas.

64. It is a club with a small round head used for getting out of ruts, cartracks or similarly difficult places. It is also called a track iron.

65. True. Nelson shot a seven under par 273 to win the $400,000 PGA championship in Duluth, Georgia. Zoeller was second four shots behind.

ARE YOU SURE YOU
DON'T WANT TO STOP
AND WAIT FOR THE
WIND TO DIE DOWN?

66. Pat Bradley shot a nine under par 279 to defeat Beth Daniel by one stroke in the $150,000 U.S. Women's Open in La Grange, Illinois.

67. Bill Rodgers shot a four under par 276 beating Bernhard Langer by four strokes to win the 1981 British Open in Sandwich.

68. True. Palmer's playoff round of 70 beat Bob Stone by four strokes and Billy Casper by seven to win it.

69. Florida State, with a team total of 1,220 beat Georgia by three strokes to win the title in Athens, Georgia. Terry Moody of the Lady Bulldogs was the Individual champ.

70. David Graham fired a seven under par 273 to win the eighty first U.S. Open in Ardmore, Pennsylvania. It was the second lowest U.S. Open score in history. Nicklaus shot a 272 for the record.

71. Donna Caponi shot an eight under 280 to beat out Jerilyn Britz and Pat Meyers by one stroke to win the 1981 LPGA championship. Caponi has also won the 1969 and 1970 U.S. Opens and the 1979 LPGA titles.

72. Yes. In 1981 Tom Watson shot an 18 under par 270 to win the $350,000 event beating Bruce Fleisher by two strokes.

73. Lee Trevino shot a 15 under par 273 to defeat Ray Floyd by 2 strokes to win the $300,000 Tournament of Champions.

74. Tom Watson shot an eight under 280 to win the forty-fifth Masters by two strokes over Miller and Nicklaus. Watson also won in 1977 at Augusta with a 276.

75. Yes. In 1981 Hale Irwin won it with a 23 under par 265 to beat out second place Don January by six strokes in the $325,000 event.

76. Tom Watson won the player of the year award winning $530,808 in tournaments, a record. It was the fourth consecutive year that he was the leading money winner.

77. The PGA season starts in January and ends in December. It's the longest season in a start and finish sport.

78. False. Nicklaus won his first professional tournament in 1957 when he won the Ohio Open.

79. False. the U.S. Open changes its sites every year.

80. A hacker is an unskilled golfer usually in the learning process.

Harness Racing

1. True or false: a maiden horse in harness racing is a female horse?

2. True or false: a green horse is a very old gelding competing in its last race?

3. What is a sulky in harness racing?

4. A blowout in harness racing occurs when a horse breaks out of the jockey's control during a race?

5. True or false: a pacer moves with high stepping, straight ahead gait with left front and right hind legs moving in unison?

6. Why does a trotter wear toe weights?

7. Why do pacers wear hobbles?

8. What is the Little Brown Jug?

9. What are the races that makes up the Triple Crown for harness racing?

10. Can you name the horse that won the **1983 Little Brown Jug?**

11. Can you name the horse that won the 1981 Kentucky Pacing Derby?

12. Who won the Cane Pace in 1981?

13. True or false: the record for the one mile run by pacers is under 1:50?

14. Where is the Acorn run and for what kind of racing, pacing or trottering?

15. Where is the Fox Stake held and for what kind of racing, pacing or trotting?

16. True or false: Temujin, who also won the Kentucky Pacing Derby, won the Fox Stake in 1981?

17. True or false: a dash in harness racing is a quick ¼ mile race on a straight away?

18. True or false: Nevele Pride held the pacing record for the mile before 1900?

19. Can you name the horse which holds the world record for pacers in the mile as of 1981?

20. True or false: Niatross won the 1980 Little Brown Jug classic?

24. Can you name the horse that won the 1983 **Hambletonian Stakes?**

25. Can you name the horse that won the Messinger Stakes in 1981?

26. There was a $100,000 Challenge Cup trot run at Roosevelt Raceway in 1981 which was won by a French horse. Can you name the horse?

27. Is Defiant Yankee a pacer or a trotter?

28. True or false: because of new equipment now used in constructing sulkys, drivers are permitted to choose whether to wear a helmet or not?

29. How big are the tracks used in harness racing?

30. How are harness races timed?

31. How many officials are needed in harness racing?

32. What is the difference between a futurity and a stake race in harness racing?

21. The Hambletonian Stakes has been held on the state fairgrounds at Du Quoin, Illinois for the last twenty four years until 1981 when it was moved. Where is it held now?

22. Can you name the last horse to win the Triple Crown for pacers?

23. Where is the Woodrow Wilson Pace held?

Answers

1. False. A maiden horse, either mare or gelding, is a horse which has never won a heat or a race.

2. False. A green horse is one that has never trotted or paced in a public race or against time.

3. A very light racing seat with bicycle type wheels and weight between 29 and 37 pounds.

4. False. A blowout is a workout prior to the race, usually the day before.

5. False. What was described is the movement of a trotter. A pacer moves with a swaying motion, swinging the right front and right hind legs forward at the same time.

6. The toe weights, usually brass or lead, are clipped to the horse's front hoofs to extend a horse's stride.

7. Hobbles are leather straps encircling the front and hind legs to keep the legs moving in unison and to help the horse maintain its gait.

8. The Little Brown Jug is the final leg or the Triple Crown for three year old pacers. It is held in Delaware, Ohio.

9. The Little Brown Jug in Delaware, Ohio; the William H. Cane Futurity held in Yonkers, New York and the Messenger Stake held at Roosevelt Raceway, Westbury, New York make up the Triple Crown for harness racing.

10. Ralph Hanover with Ron Waples in the sulky took first place.

I REALLY DON'T THINK THESE HOBBLES ARE ON RIGHT.

11. Temujin won the Clarence Martin, Sr. in the sulky at the $209,200 Kentucky Pacing Derby at Louisville Downs by a half length over Icarus Lobell. Temujin covered the mile in 1:56 1/5.

12. Wildwood Jeb, driven by James Marohn, won the Cane Pace (second leg of pacing's triple crown). The three year old colt finished the mile in 1:58 1/5, 1¼ lengths ahead of Brand New Fella and Eastern Skipper.

13. True. Niatross set the record with an 1:49.1 on October 1, 1980.

14. The Acorn has been run annually since 1945 for two year old filly trotters at Historic Track, Goshen, New York. Deanna with Gibson White in the sulky won the first Acorn in 1945 in record time, 2:04.

15. The Fox Stake is for two year old pacers and has been annually since 1927 at the Indiana State Fair, Indianapolis, Indiana.

16. True. Temujin with Clarence Martin in the sulky won the $161,000 Fox Stake with 1-4 finishes in two heats, beating Icarus Lobell, who set the track record with a time of 1:54.2 in the second heat but finished eleventh in the first heat and was second overall.

17. False. A dash is a race that is decided in a single trial rather than in heats.

18. False. Nevele Pride set the mile record for trotters with 1:54 4/5 in 1969 at Indianapolis, Indiana with Stanley Dancer driving.

19. Niatross set the world record in 1980 in winning the second leg of the American Pacing Classic with a time of 1:52 1/5.

20. True. Niatross won in straight heats and set the world record for the one mile on a half-mile track with a time of 1:54 4/5 and also set the mark combined time in two heats, 3:49 4/5.

21. The Hambletonian Stakes was moved to the Meadowlands Race Track in New Jersey in 1981.

22. Niatross, one of the greatest pacers of all time, won the Can Futurity, Messenger Stakes, and the Little Brown Jug to win the pacers' triple crown in 1980.

23. The Woodrow Wilson Pace is held at the Meadowlands. McKenzie Almahurst won the 1:81 contest driven by Billy Haughton. He finished a nose ahead of Lon Todd Hanover in a time of 1:56 1/5 for the mile. This race is for two year olds.

24. The 1983 edition of the Hambletonian Stakes was won by Duenna driven by Stanley Dancer.

25. Seahawk Hanover with Ben Webster in the sulky, won the $224,955 Messenger Stakes at Roosevelt Raceway by a half length over Eastern Skipper. Seahawk Hanover covered the mile in a time of 1:58 2/5.

26. Jorky and Ideal Du Gazeau, both French horses, finished in a dead heat, a very rare event in horse racing. They both covered the 1½ mile course in 3:05 2/5.

27. Defiant Yankee won the 1981 $233,955 Dexter Cup at Roosevelt Raceway. The three year old trotter, driven by Howard Beissinger, covered the mile in 2:01.

28. False. Protective helmets with a hard shell and adequate padding must be worn by all drivers. The chin straps must be used also.

29. The tracks are oval in shape and the lengths vary but are usually ½ mile to 1 mile long.

30. Using either an approved electric device or three official timers, times are taken when the first horse leaves the gate until the winner's nose reaches the wire. Times are always recorded in minutes, seconds and fifths of a second.

31. There are timers, a program director, presiding judge, finish wire judge and clerk of the course.

32. A futurity is a race in which competing horses are nominated before being foaled. A stake is a race for which entries chosen the year before the race and to which all nominating and starting fees are added to the purse.

I THINK I NEED A LONGER CHIN STRAP

Thoroughbred Racing

5. True or false: horse racing was a part of the ancient Olympic games?

6. True or false: there is a race course in England for horses that is over four miles in length?

7. True or false: there was once a horse race over 1,000 miles long?

8. True or false: the horse, Champion Crabbet, was the first triple crown winner in history?

1. Can you name the races that make up the triple crown for thoroughbreds?

2. Where is the Kentucky Derby held?

3. Where is the Preakness held?

4. Where is the Belmont Stakes held?

9. What is the record for the most horses entered in a single race: 42, 58, or 66?

10. Has a horse ever attained a speed of over 40 miles per hour on the race track?

11. Has any horse ever gone unbeaten in over fifty races?

12. Which one of these horses holds the record for most money won in one year: Affirmed, Spectacular Bid, or Seattle Slew?

13. Can you name the first horse to win the triple crown and in what year?

14. True or false: Spectacular Bid was the last horse to win the triple crown?

15. Can you name the last triple crown winner?

16. Has a triple crown winner ever sired another triple crown winner?

17. True or false: Spectacular Bid is the most valuable horse in History?

18. Since the introduction of the photo-finish, has there ever been a dead heat in a horse race?

19. Which one of these jockeys has ridden the most winners in his career: Laffit Pincay, Willie Shoemaker or Johnny Longden?

20. Who was the jockey who won the Kentucky Derby in 1982 and 1983?

I DON'T THINK THIS PICTURE CAPTURES THE 'REAL' ME. DO YOU MIND TAKING ANOTHER ONE?

21. Which one of these horses never won the triple crown: Whirlawind, Count Fleet or Assault?

22. What are the Ecliple Awards?

23. Can you name the first horse to win the Horse of the Year two times?

24. From 1974 to 1977 one horse won the older, horse or gelding award. Can you name the horse?

25. Can you name the first woman jockey to win a major stakes race?

26. Can you name the horse that won the Kentucky Derby in 1981?

27. Can you name the horse who holds the record for career earnings?

28. Can you name the horse who in 1973 became the first triple crown winner in 25 years?

29. Who has won more outstanding jockey awards: Steve Cauthen, Laffit Pincay, Jr. or Braulia Baeza?

30. Can you name the owner who won outstanding owner award in 1974, 75, and 76?

31. Can you name the horse who won the Outstanding Two Year Old and Three Year Old Filly awards in 1974 and 1975?

32. Can you name the horse that was voted the number one horse in the half-century by the Associated Press in 1950?

33. True or false: Willie Shoemaker holds the record for riding the most Kentucky Derby winners?

34. True or false: the Rose Bowl is the only spectator event that outdraws the Kentucky Derby?

35. Can you remember how Forward Pass was awarded first place at the 1968 Kentucky Derby?

36. True or false: Man O'War won the triple crown in 1920 with three different jockeys?

37. True or false: Count Fleet is the only triple crown winner who also won an Olympic medal in the Equestrian event?

38. Which one of the triple races is the oldest?

39. Can you name the horse who won the Jockey Club Gold Cup held at Aqueduct five consecutive times?

40. Do jockeys wear any head gear when racing?

41. What is the difference between a filly and a mare?

42. What is the difference between a colt and a horse?

43. True or false: younger horses dominate the longer races?

44. What was greatest sum won on a $2 ticket?

Answers

1. The triple crown consists of the Kentucky Derby, the Preakness and the Belmont Stakes.

2. The Kentucky Derby has been run annullay since 1875 at Churchill Downs. It is a 1¼ mile course for three year olds. In 1875 Aristides was the first winner and the purse was $2,850.

3. The Preakness Stakes has been held annually since 1873, except for 1890-93. It is held at the Pimlico Race course in Maryland. The track is 1 3/16 miles in length and this race is for three year olds. Survivor was the first winner and the purse was $1,800.

4. The Belmont Stakes is held at Belmont Park in Elmont, New York. The Belmont Stakes has been run every year since 1867, except for 1911 and 1912. Ruthless won the first race for a purse of $1,850. The track is 1½ miles long.

5. Horse racing has been dated back as far as 1400 B.C. as an important part of the Hittite culture of Anatolia, Turkey. The thirty third Olympic games of 648 B.C. featured horse racing.

6. True. The world's longest racecourse is the Newmarket course in England, on which the Beacon Course, the longest of 19 courses, is four miles and 397 yards long. It was founded in 1636.

7. True. There was a horse race of 1,200 miles in Portugal, won by Emir, a horse bred from Egyptian-bred Blunt Arab stock. It is the longest recorded horse race in history.

8. False. Champion Crabbet holds the world record for long distance racing and speed. The horse covered 300 miles in 52 hours, 33 minutes, carrying 245 pounds in 1920.

9. The record for flat racing is 58 at the Lincolnshire Handicap in England, on March 13, 1948, but the record is 66, in the Grand National Steeplechase on March 22, 1929, held at Aintree, England.

10. Several horses have surpassed the 40 miles per hour mark. The fastest was Big Racket of Mexico, who ran the ½ mile in 20.8 seconds for a speed of 43.26 mph on a course in Mexico City, Mexico on February 5, 1945.

11. Camarero has a winning streak of 56 races, 1953-55 and won a total of 73 out of 77 starts altogether. The horse with the best overall won-lost record was Kincsem, a Hungarian mare foaled in 1874, who never lost a race in 54 starts (1876-79) including the English Goodwood Cup of 1878.

12. Spectacular Bid holds the record of most money won in a single year with $1,279,334 in 1979.

13. Sir Barton was the first winner of the triple crown in 1919.

14. False. Spectacular Bid never won the triple crown. The horse lost the Belmont Stakes to Coastal in 1979 to end the Bid's bid.

15. Affirmed was the last horse to win the triple crown in 1978. To date, Affirmed is also the greatest money making horse of all time.

16. The only triple winner to sire another was Gallant Fox, the 1930 winner, who sired Omaha, the 1935 winner.

17. True. Spectacular Bid was syndicated for $22,000,000 in 40 shares of $550,000 each in March, 1980 making him the most valuable horse in history.

18. Yes. The highest number of horses in a dead heat has been three on several occasions.

19. Johnny Longden's record of 6,032 was broken by Willie Shoemaker in 1970. Shoemaker is still adding to his own record. His winnings have amounted to over 75 million dollars in his career, also a record.

20. E. Delahoussaye captured both races with Gato del Sol in 1982 and Sunny's Halo in 1983.

21. This is another tricky question. They have all won the triple crown. Whirlawind won in 1941, Count won in 1943 and Assault won in 1946.

22. The Eclipse Awards are the Horse of the year; Older Colt, horse or gelding; three year old Colt: two year old Colt; Outstanding Apprentice Jockey; Outstanding Jockey; Outstanding Owner; Steeplechase or Hurdle Horse; Champion Female Turf Horse; Champion Turf Horse; Older Filly or Mare; Three year old Filly; Two year old Filly; Sprinter; Outstanding Trainer. They are awarded by vote of the Thoroughbred Racing Association, the National Turf Writers Association and the Daily Racing Form. They have been given since 1971.

23. The 1973 triple crown winner, Secretariat, won the Horse of the Year award in 1972 and 1973. The horse also won the two year old Colt award in 1972 and the three year old Colt award in 1973.

24. If you said Forego, you are right. Forego also won the Horse of the Year award three consecutive times, 1974, 1975 and 1976.

25. Robyn Smith was the first woman to win a major stakes race when she won the $27,450 Paumanauk Handicap aboard North Sea at Aqueduct Race Track, New York on March 1, 1973. She broke the ice for women, who only recently were allowed to become licensed jockeys.

26. Pleasant Colony, who won six out of 24 races in his career, won both the Kentucky Derby and the Preakness before his third place finish in the Belmont Stakes. A leg injury to the horse caused his retirement at the end of 1981 after earning $965,383.

27. John Henry has accumulated $3,706,197 in total purses and ranks #1.

28. In 1948 Citation won the triple crown. Not until 1973 did another horse win it. That was Secretariat, one of the greatest thoroughbreds of all time. On the final leg of the triple crown, the Belmont Stakes, Secretariat won by an incredible 31 lengths to capture the thoroughbred's highest honor.

29. Laffit Pincay, Jr. is the correct answer. He won the Outstanding Jockey award in 1971, 73, 74, 79 for a total of four while Cauthen won once (1977) and Baeza won the award twice in 1972 and 1975.

30. Dan Lasater who also holds the record for most winners in one year with 494 and most prize money won in one year with $3,022,960, all in 1974.

31. Ruffian, who was one of the greatest fillies ever to race. Ruffian was leading in a match race with Foolish Pleasure when she fell and broke a leg. The leg could not be repaired and she had to be put down. She was buried in the Belmont Park infield.

32. Man O'War, who won a total of 20 of 21 races in 1919-1920. During that span he established five American track records.

33. False. Eddie Arcaro holds that record with a total of five Derby winning performances in his career.

34. False. The Rose Bowl draws up to 105,000 fans every year whereas the Kentucky Derby hardly ever draws fewer than 120,000 fans.

35. Dancer's Image won the 1968 Derby but was later disqualified because of traces of a drug found in his system. The second place horse, Forward Pass, was given first place.

36. Fasle. Man O'War never won the triple crown. He won the Preakness and the Belmont Stakes that year, though.

37. False. None of the triple crown winners ever competed in the Olympics.

38. The Kentucky Derby was first run in 1875; the Preakness Stakes was first run in 1873; but the oldest is the Belmont Stakes, which was first run in 1867.

39. Kelso, who first won in 1960 as a three year old and won it for the fifth straight time in 1974 as a seven year old.

40. In a race a jockey must wear a crash helmet or skull cap.

WHAT MAKES YOU THINK THAT HE'S ON DRUGS?

41. A filly is a female horse until the age of five, then she is known as a mare.

42. Male horses are known as colts until the age of five and are known as horses thereafter.

43. False. In most cases, long races favor the older horses and the younger horses dominate the sprints.

44. At Hialeah Track on January 25, 1982 a $2 bettor won a total of $382,344 for the "Pix Six" selection of six winners.

Soccer

9. True or false: the largest live crowd ever to see a soccer match was 93,000 at the Meadowlands in New Jersey, when the Cosmos played an exhibition match against Brazil in 1977?

10. When was the first World Cup played an how often is it held?

1. Where are the earliest references to the game of soccer found: China, England or North America?

2. True or false: the highest score in a first class soccer match was 21-0?

3. True or false: the highest one-sided score in an international soccer match was recorded in 1951 and the score was 17-0?

4. True or false: the record for goals scored by one player in a first class soccer match is 9?

5. By what name is Edson Arantes de Nascimento known to the soccer world?

6. What does NASL stand for?

7. The most successful coach in soccer history comes from West Germany. Can you name him?

8. True or false: the longest first class soccer match in history lasted for 3½ hours?

11. True or False? Brazil is the only country to win the World Cup three times.

12. True or false: Pele holds the World Cup record for goals scored in one competition?

13. Only one player has scored three goals in the final game of the World Cup. Can you name him and his country?

14. What country did Gerd Muller play for and what World Cup record does he hold?

15. True or false: the biggest goalie on record weighed more than 300 pounds during his playing career?

16. Which one of these countries is the only one to win three Olympic gold medals in the soccer competition: East Germany, Hungary, England or Brazil?

17. Is there a women's international soccer competition anywhere in the world?

18. True or false: a man once headed a ball for 79 consecutive minutes without missing?

19. What does dribbling mean in soccer?

20. Is a hat trick in soccer the same thing as a hat trick in hockey?

21. Where are the linesmen stationed and what are their responsibilities during a soccer game?

22. True or false: a man once maneuvered a soccer ball from his feet, legs and head without letting it touch the ground for over four hours?

23. True or false: two teams played a marathon soccer game that lasted longer than two days?

24. What is obstruction in a soccer game?

25. True or false: pitch means a strong overhead kick that scores a goal?

26. Can you name the country that won the 1978 World Cup?

27. What does ASL stand for in soccer?

28. Only one team has ever won the NASL Championship two consecutive years, which one?

29. How many teams are there in the North American Soccer League?

30. Can you name the teams in the Eastern Division of the NASL?

252

31. Can you name the teams in the Southern Division of the NASL?

32. What New York Cosmos player led its league in scoring in 1972?

33. Can you name the teams in the Western Division of the NASL?

34. What ex-Giant football player's son led the NASL in scoring in 1973?

35. Which one of these teams won the NASL in 1980: Strikers, Cosmos or the Rowdies?

36. Can you name the two teams that played for the 1980 ASL championship?

37. True or false: The New York Cosmos won the 1981 Soccer Bowl for the second consecutive year?

38. What is a shootout in soccer?

39. True or false: there is an indoor soccer league in the United States?

40. Can you name the team which won the Major Indoor Soccer championship in 1979, '80, '81, '82?

41. What is the World Club Cup?

42. What are the dimensions of an outdoor soccer field?

43. True or false: in 1980 the New York Cosmos won their first Soccer Bowl?

44. True or false: a sweeper is another name for a goalkeeper?

45. What does it mean when a player tackles his opponent in soccer?

46. There are eleven positions in outdoor soccer. How many can you name?

47. Can you name the three time winner of the television superstar competition who played NASL soccer?

48. What player holds the world record for scoring the most goals in one soccer season?

49. True or false: soccer was not played in the United States until 1962?

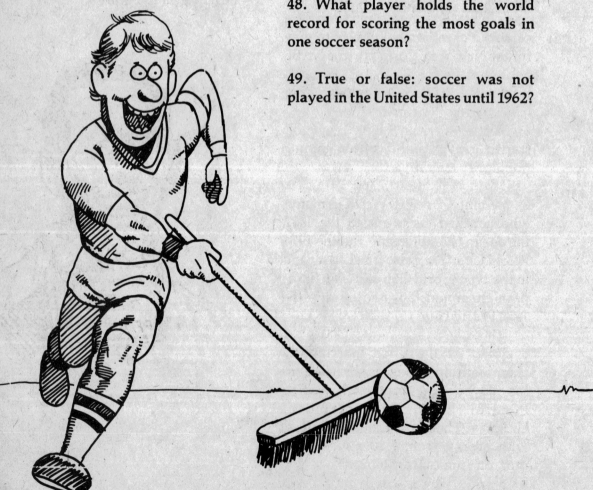

Answers

1. The earliest reference to a game similar to soccer occurs in the third and fourth centuries B.C. in China. The game was called tsu-chu.

2. False. The highest score occured in the Scottish Cup match between Arbroath and Bon Accord. Playing on their home turf Arbroath destroyed Bon Accord 36-0 on September 5, 1885.

3. True. England took apart Australia in Sydney on June 30, 1951 by the score of 17-0.

4. False. Stephan Stanis of the Racing Club de Lens scored a record 16 goals against Aubry-Asturies in Lens, France on December 13, 1942.

5. Pele of Brazil. He scored 1,216 goals in his 18 year career in Brazil. He came out of retirement in 1975 to play for the New York Cosmos in the NASL and when he retired in 1977 his goal total was 1,281 in 1,363 games.

6. North American Soccer League. It started in 1968 and has been gaining popularity ever since.

7. Helmut Schoen of West Germany, who coached his teams to the 1972 European championship and the 1974 World Cup. They also finished second in the 1966 World Cup and 1976 European championships and third in the 1970 World Cup.

8. True. At the Copa Libertadores championship in Santos, Brazil, Santos played to a draw with visiting Penarol F.C. of Montevideo, Uruguay. The games lasted 3½ hours, with breaks, from 9:30 p.m. until 1 a.m. on August 2-3, 1962.

9. False. The largest crowd ever to see a soccer match was 205,000 at the 1950 World Cup final when Brazil played Uruguay in Rio de Janeiro.

10. The first World Cup competition was held in 1930 in Uruguay and is held every four years.

DO YOU KNOW ME?

NATIONAL EXPRESS
7361 5409X
PELE

16. The only country to win three official Olympic soccer titles is Hungary in 1952, 1964 and 1968. The United Kingdom won in 1908 and 1912 and also won the unofficial title in 1900.

17. Yes. The first world competition for women was held in Taipei, Taiwan during October, 1978. The competition was delayed by typhoons and France and Finland were declared co-champions.

18. True. Istvan Halaszi of Hungary headed a soccer ball 12,374 times in a span of 79 minutes, 24 seconds at the Jewish Community Center, Milwaukee, Wisconsin on April 29, 1979.

19. Dribbling means that a player maneuvers the ball past his opponents with his feet.

20. Yes. As in hockey, when a soccer player scores three goals in one game his feat is called a hat trick.

11. False. Italy has also won the cup three times, the last in 1982.

12. False. Just Fontaine of France scored six goals in six games in the final stages of the 1958 competition for the record.

13. Geoffrey Hurst of England against West Germany on July 30, 1966, scored a record three goals. He is the only person ever to do so.

14. Muller scored 14 goals for West Germany in two World Cup competitions, 1970 and 1974. His country won the 1974 competition with his tremendous play throughout the competition.

15. True. Willie "Fatty" Foulke of England (1874-1916) stood six feet, three inches and weighed 311 pounds. Fatty once stopped a game because he snapped the crossbar.

21. The two linesmen are stationed on the touchlines and assist the referee. Their main job is to decide which team receives the throw-in and to help the referee spot offsides.

22. True. Adrian Walsh, 34 years old, juggled a soccer ball for four hours, three minutes and 43 seconds non-stop on June 24, 1979. He hit the ball 23,547 times without dropping it at the Town Park, Mallow, County Cork, Ireland.

23. True. The longest recorded marathon game lasted 51 hours, 30 minutes. It was played by two teams of 11 members a side from Security Squadron, RAF Laarburch, Germany, August 29-31, 1979. Two teams of five on a side played for 62 hours, 51 minutes with no substitutes in England, June 22-24, 1979.

28. The New York Cosmos were victorious in 1977 and 1978.

29. There are 12 teams in the NASL, each division has three teams.

30. The New York Cosmos, Chicago Sting, Toronto Metros and Montreal Fury.

24. Any attempt to impede or prevent an opponent's progress whether he has the ball or not.

25. False. Pitch is a British term meaning field.

26. Argentina defeated Holland 3-1 to win the World Cup in 1978. This game attracted the largest TV history, except for the Olympics, with 400 million viewers.

27. The American Soccer League. At the start of the 1981 season the ASL had eight teams.

31. The Tulsa Roughnecks, Ft. Lauderdale Strikers, Tampa Bay Rowdies and Team America.

32. Randy Horton captured the league lead with 22 points.

33. The Vancouver Whitecaps, Golden Bay Seals, Seattle Sounders and San Diego Sockers.

34. Kyle Rote's son, Kyle Jr., led the league in 1973 with 30 points.

35. The New York Cosmos defeated the Fort Lauderdale Strikers 3-0 in the 1980 Soccer Bowl.

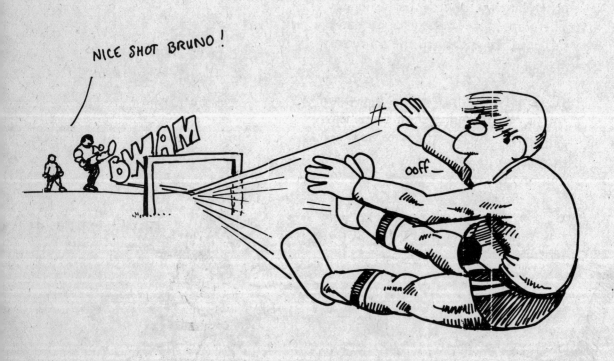

36. The Pennsylvania Stoners defeated the Sacramento Spirit 2-1 to win the 1980 ASL title.

37. False. The Chicago Sting defeated a very tough New York Cosmos team 1-0 in a shootout.

38. If, after 90 minutes of regulation play (45 minutes per half) and 15 minutes of overtime, two teams are tied, the NASL employs the shootout rule, which sends one team home a winner. The shootout works this way: each team is awarded five penalty shots to be taken on an alternate basis. If after five shots the teams are still deadlocked, then alternate shots are taken until one team connects and one misses.

39. True. The Major Indoor Soccer League. There are players on each team, including the goalkeeper. The ball is always in play because it bounces off the walls. Players can check each other into the boards, as in hockey. There are more shots on goal than in the outdoor game and the scores are higher.

40. The New York Arrows have won the first four league championships.

I DON'T THINK THIS IS THE RIGHT PLACE FOR INDOOR SOCCER!

47. Kyle Rote, Jr., son of football great, Kyle Rote, Sr., played for the Dallas Tornado and won the rookie of the year award and league scoring title in 1973. In 1979 the Houston Hurricane bought his contract and the price was said to be the most ever spent for an American born player. He won the Superstars' Competition in 1974, 1976 and 1977.

48. The greatest player of all time, Pele, who scored 127 goals for the Brazil National team in 1959, an incredible record, one that will be hard to beat.

49. False. Italian citizens in St. Louis formed their own teams and leagues as early as the 1880's in America.

41. A competition held annually since 1960 between the winners of the European Cup and the winners of Copa Libertadores de America, the South American Club Cup.

42. They vary but on the average they are 120 yards long by 50 yards wide.

43. False. The Cosmos have won four Soccer Bowls (1972, 77, 78, 80) with such great players as Pele, Randy Horton, Franz Beckenbauer and Giorgio Chinaglia.

44. False. A sweeper is a center fullback who plays behind his other two fullbacks. His job is to cover for a beaten fullback, much like the job of a free safety in football.

45. An attempt to kick the ball away from an opponent or to make him lose control of the ball, to cause him to hurry a pass or just to distract him from setting up a play.

46. The eleven positions are: goalie, left, center and right fullbacks, left and right wings, left and right half; and a left, center, and right inside.

Sport Shorts

I COULDN'T FIND THE PLASTIC BIRDIE!

SQUAK

BOP

Answers

1. The game of badminton or a very similar game was played in China in the second millennium B.C. The modern game was devised in England in 1863.

2. The Uber Cup is the international women's team championship which is held every three years since its institution in 1956-57.

3. The United States team won the first three Uber Cup titles in 1956-57, 1959-60, and 1962-63. Since then the Japanese have won every year except 1974-75 when Indonesia won. Japan has won a record four times.

1. In what country did badminton originate: England, United States or China?

2. What is the Uber Cup in badminton?

3. Has the United States ever won the Uber Cup and which country has won it the most often?

4. Who holds the record for most singles titles at the All-England Championships in badminton, a man or a woman?

4. Judy Hashman of the United States holds the record for most badminton singles titles with 10, a record for either sex.

1. Who was the first American squash champion: Mitch Wechter, J.A. Miskey or Abe Speller?

2. True or false: as in golf there is a British Open championship for squash?

3. Can you name the only person ever to win the British Open six consecutive times?

4. Are there women's championships in squash?

Answers

1. J.A. Miskey of Philadelphia won the first American Amateur Singles Championship in 1906. He became the first recognized champion of any country in the world in squash.

2. True. Since 1930, the British Open Championship, an annual event, has been played with both amateurs and professionals competing. Until recently it was regarded as the unofficial world championship.

3. Hashim Khan of Pakistan is the only person ever to win the British Open six consecutive times, 1950 to 1955. He and Geoffrey Hunt of Australia are co-holders of the record for total wins with seven.

4. Yes. As with most other sports women are now becoming more involved in squash! Heather McKay is a perfect example. She has sixteen British Women's Open Championships in a row from 1962 until 1977. McKay also won the first World Open title in 1978. As of this writing she has not lost a match since 1961.

1. Which country won the First World Team Championships in 1978: United States, Great Britain or Canada?

2. True or false: the first hang gliding ride by man took place in 1893?

3. What is the greatest distance ever covered by a hang glider in free flight: 61.8, 52.98 or 95 miles.?

4. True or false: The World Individual Championships have been won most often by Australians?

5. Has a hang glider ever descended from a distance of more than 30,000 feet?

Answers

1. Great Britain won the first World Team Championship in 1978. The contest was held at Chattanooga, Tennessee in October.

2. False. The monk Elmer is reported to have flown from the sixty foot tall tower of Malmesbury Abbey, Wiltshire, England in the eleventh century. Otto Lilienthal of Germany made numerous flights between 1893 and 1896.

3. The official F.A.I. record for distance covered is 95 miles by George Worthington of the United States in an ASG-21 (Rogalle) over California on July 21, 1977.

4. False. The World Individual Championships, instituted in 1948, have been won a record five times by West Germans.

5. Yes. Bob McCaffrey, who was 18 years old at the time, was released from a balloon over the Mojave Desert, California on November 21, 1976 at an altitude of 31,600 feet, a record.

1. The first five trampolining individual championships in the women's class were won by whom?

2. Can you name the last American man to win the world individual championship in trampolining?

3. True or false: a team of six recorded the longest trampoline bouncing marathon of 52 days?

4. Has anybody ever bounced on a trampoline for over 150 hours straight with only a five minute break per hour?

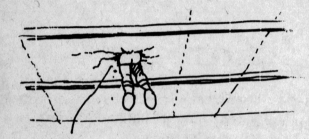

I'M AFRAID IT'S STILL A LITTLE TOO BOUNCY

Answers

1. Judy Wills of the United States won the title from 1964 (the first year of the competition) until 1968. Since 1968 the event has been held every two years.

2. In 1970 Wayne Miller won his second individual title (he also won in 1966) in trampolining. Dave Jacobs won the title in 1967 and 1968 to become the first male to win successive titles. These were the last American men to win.

3. Incredible but true. From June 24 to August 15, 1974 a team of six bounced on a trampoline for 1,248 hours, taking turns, of course, in Phoenix, Arizona.

4. Yes. Geoffrey Morton of Broken Hill, N.S.W., Australia bounced for 179 hours with a five minute break every hour. He did it from March 7 until March 14, 1977.

BOING

1. When was parachuting instituted as a sport for world championships?

2. Which country has won the most world titles in parachuting: USSR, United States, or Germany?

3. Can you name the woman who won the individual title in 1978?

4. True or false: a man once made over 200 jumps in a 24 hour time period?

UH-OH, LOOKS LIKE I PUT ON MY BACKPACK INSTEAD OF MY PARACHUTE!

Answers

1. The first world championships for parachuting were held in 1951. Team championships were introduced in 1954 and women's events were included in 1956.

2. The USSR has the record for both men's and women's competitions. They won the men's title in 1954, 58, 60, 66, 72, 76 and the women's title in 1956, 58, 66, 68, 72, and 76.

3. Jacqueline Smith of Great Britain scored an amazing ten consecutive dead centers on a 4 inch target in the 1978 world championships in Yugoslavia to win the accuracy title.

4. True. David Parchment made 233 jumps in 24 hours at Shobdon Airfield, Hereford, England on June 19, 1979.

4. True or false: the largest rodeo in the world is held annually in Baja, California?

5. In 1979 Tom Ferguson tied this man for the record for Professional Rodeo Cowboys Association All-Round Championships with six in 1979. Can you name him?

6. True or false: the youngest rodeo champion in history was only 11 years old?

1. True or false: Honky Tonk was the top bucking bull of all time according to most experts?

7. True or false: a standard ride in bronco riding lasts a full 30 seconds before the rider can dismount?

2. True or false: the origins of rodeos date back to the early 1400's in Spain?

8. True or false: even though Jim Shoulders was regarded as one of the best cowboys of all time he never won a world title?

3. Can you name some of the events at a rodeo?

YAHOOOO!!

Answers

1. True. The 11 year old Brahma of the International Rodeo Association, Honky Tonk, was retired in September, 1978 after compiling a mark of unseating 187 riders in 187 tries without a single defeat.

2. False. Rodeos came into being in the eighteenth century in the early days of the North American cattle industry. The earliest reference to the sport is at Santa Fe, New Mexico in 1847.

3. Steer wrestling first entered rodeo history in 1900 with Bill Pickett from Texas. Other events in a rodeo are calf roping, bull riding, saddle bronc riding and bareback bronco riding.

4. False. The largest rodeo in the world is the Calgary Exhibition and Stampede at Calgary, Alberta, Canada. This rodeo holds the records for attendance with over 1,000,000 spectators in 1977 and over 140,000 in one day in 1974.

5. Tom Ferguson tied Larry Mahan, who won his first title in 1966 and his last in 1973. Ferguson holds the record for most earnings in one season with $131,233 in 1978.

6. True. Metha Brorsen of Oklahoma won the International Rodeo Association Cowgirls barrel racing event in 1975 at the age of 11 years; thus she became the youngest winner ever.

7. False. A standard ride lasts for eight seconds. Riders used to compete in the now discontinued ride-to-a-finish event and have been recorded to stay on as long as 90 minutes until there was not a buck left in the animal.

8. False. Shoulders holds the record for most world titles won with 16 championships between 1949 and 1959.

GIVE UP, KID.

1. True or false: the origins of table tennis date back to 716 B.C. in China?

2. What is the Swaythling Cup in table tennis?

3. What is the Corbillon Cup in table tennis?

4. Has the United States ever won either the Corbillon Cup or the Swaythling Cup?

5. True or false: the fastest recorded speed of a smacked ping pong ball has been clocked at 81.12 miles per hour?

Answers

1. False. The earliest reference to a game resembling table tennis was found in the catalogues of London sports goods manufacturers in the 1880's. The first Ping Pong Association was formed in America in 1902.

2. The Swaythling Cup is the men's team world championship which has been held annually since 1927 until 1957 with the exception of the war years and from 1957 it has been held biennially.

3. This is the Women's team World Championship, which was first held in the 1933-34 season until 1957 and biennially since then. Germany won the first Marcel Corbillon Cup in 1934.

4. The United States won the Swaythling Cup only once in 1937 and the Corbillon Cup twice in 1937 and 1949. Hungary has won the Swaythling cup the most times with 12 titles and Japan has won the Corbillon Cup the most times with 8.

5. False. No real conclusive measurements have been published as of this writing but in a lecture by M. Sklorz of West Germany, he stated that a smacked ball has been measured at speeds of up to 105.6 miles per hour.

Answers

1. Bullfighting was first reported to have been seen by the Romans when they entered Spain in the third century B.C.

2. The record for most kills in a career was set by Logantijo (1841-1900), born Rafael Molina, who killed a total of 4,867 bulls in the ring.

3. The law set requires compulsory retirement at age 55. The longest active career of any Matador was by Bienvenida (1922-75) from 1942 until 1974.

4. Romano set the record with 18 bulls in one day in 1884. The record for one year is 114, a spanish record, by El Litii in 1949.

1. Where was Bullfighting originated: South America, Spain or Australia?

2. Can you name the man who holds the record for most kills in a career?

3. When is a Matador required to retire by modern Spanish law: 45 years, 50 years, or 55 years old?

4. What is the record for most bulls killed in one day by a single matador, 8, 12, or 18?

1. Is the longest jump on water skis over 100 feet, under 100 feet, or over 200 feet?

2. True or false: a man once water skied for over 1,000 miles non-stop in 1977?

3. True or false: a man from China water skis at speeds of 200 miles per hour as a daily routine?

4. When were the first water skiing championships held and what are the events?

5. Can you name the woman who has won three world championships (overall) and eight individual titles in water skiing?

Answers

1. The longest recorded jump on water skis is 197 feet by Michael Hazelwood of Great Britain at Moomba, Australia, on March 9, 1980. The record for women is 129 feet held by Deena Brush of the United States at Tyler, Texas, on July 9, 1979.

2. True, Will Coughey of New Zealand traveled 1,124 miles non-stop on water skiis on Lake Karapiro, New Zealand, in 30 hours 34 minutes, February 26-27, 1977.

3. False. The record speed for water skiing is 125.69 miles per hour by Danny Churchill of the United States at the Oakland Marine Stadium, California, in 1971. Craig Wendt, also of the United States, claims 128.16 m.p.h. at Long Beach on August 19, 1979. His record is still waiting notification.

4. The first world championships were held in 1949 at Juan Les Pins, France. The events are the slalom, tricks and jumping, and a separate contest for best overall.

5. Elizabeth Allan-Shetter of the United States was the over titles in 1965, 1969 and 1975 to go along with her eight individual titles.

1. True or false: the first world championships in horseshoe pitching was held in Sydney, Australia in 1972?

2. True or false: Ted Allen of the United States holds the record for the most men's world titles in horseshoe pitching?

3. Is the record percentage of ringers in one game held by a man or a woman?

4. Has there ever been a marathon horseshoe pitching session of more than 75 hours continuously?

Answers

1. False. The first world championship was held in Bronson, Kansas, in 1909. The sport was originated by military Farriers and is of great antiquity.

2. True. Ted Allen of Boulder, Colorado holds the men's record with ten titles in 1933, 34, 35, 40, 46, 53, 55, 56, 57 and 59. Vickie Chapelle Winston of Missouri holds the Womens' record with 9 titles from 1956 until 1975.

3. Ruth Hangen of Getzville, New York holds the percentage record with 95% in 1973. She also holds the record for consecutive ringers with 42 in 1974. Ted Allen holds the men's record with 72% in 1951.

4. Yes. A four man contest, two teams pitching continuously and without substitution was played by Gary Alexander, Ralph Lewis, Steven Padgett and Stephan Moss, in Lakewood, Colorado, on July 1-4, 1979, and it lasted 76½ hours.

Answers

1. True. Donal Heathey of New Zealand tangled with a black Marlin for 32 hours 5 minutes off Mayor Island off Taucanga, New Zealand on January 21-22, 1968.

2. True. Walter Kummerow holds the record for the longest fresh water cast with a 574 feet 2 inch cast for the Bait Distance Double-Handed 30-gram event held at Lenerheide, Switzerland, in the 1968 championships.

3. The largest fish ever taken under water was an 804 pound giant black grouper by Don Pinder of the Miami Triton Club, Florida, in 1955.

4. True. Archer Davidson harpooned a 97 foot blue whale in Twofold Bay, New South Water, Australia, in 1910. Its tail flukes measured 20 feet across and its jaw bone 23 feet 4 inches.

1. True or false: the longest recorded fight with a fish lasted over 30 hours?

2. True or false: a man from West Germany holds the record for the longest fresh water cast?

3. In Spear-fishing can you name the longest fish ever taken under water?

4. True or false: a man once hand harpooned a whale 97 feet in length and killed it?

IT'S BEEN A GOOD FIGHT BUT I'M BETTING THE FISH KNOCKS HIM OUT NEXT ROUND

1. What are the dimensions of a standard four-wall handball court?

2. True or false: official handballs are always purple and weigh 1½ ounces?

3. True or false: in championship handball players never wear white shirts or gloves?

4. True or false: games are decided by the first side to reach 15 points and must win 3 out of 5 games to win the match?

5. Where were the first world championships in handball held and in what year?

6. The most successful player in U.S.N.A. National Four-Wall Championships has been an American, can you name him?

Answers

1. The standard four-wall court is 40 feet long, 20 feet high, 20 feet wide, with back wall minimum height of 12 feet.

2. False. A standard handball is made of black rubber, and weighs 2.3 ounces. When dropped from a height of 5 feet 10 inches it should bounce 3 feet 6 inches to 4 feet at a temperature of 20°.

3. False. Players must wear white shirts, shorts, socks, and shoes. And gloves must be worn.

4. False. A player or team must have 21 points to win a game and 2 out of 3 games to win the match.

5. They were first held in New York in October, 1964, with players from Australia, Canada, Ireland, Mexico, and the United States. The United States is the only country to win twice in 1964 and 1967.

6. Jim Jacobs has been the most successful player with 6 singles titles (1955-57, 1960, 64, 65) and 6 doubles titles (1960, 62, 63, 65, 67, 68).

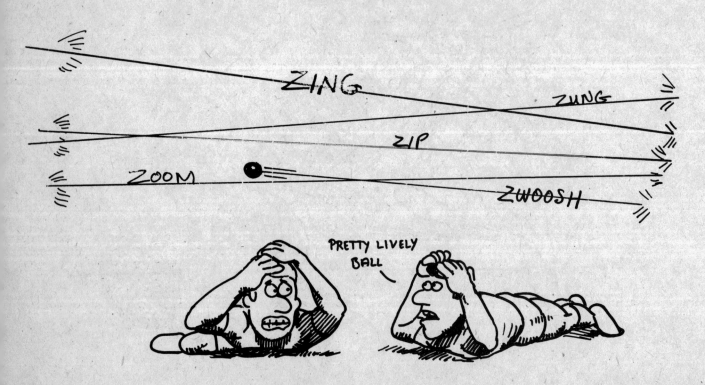

PRETTY LIVELY BALL

1. What does NRL and IRA stand for in Racquetball?

2. Who has won the Masters Championships singles title the most times, Randy Dimayo or Bud Bueleisen?

3. What is Cutthroat in Racquetball?

4. What is a "Z" save in Racquetball?

Answers

1. The IRA or International Racquetball Club was founded in 1969. The NRC or National Racquetball Club is responsible for governing the professional racquetball tour.

2. Bud Bueleisen of San Diego, California, who has won a record three times in 1972, 73, and 1977.

3. A game involving three players with the server playing against the other two.

4. A legal serve that hits the front wall, then a side wall, travels crosscourt bouncing on the floor behind the short line before hitting the opposite wall. After hitting the side wall, the ball rebounds parallel to the back wall.

1. Can you name the only two men who have won four world titles in Judo?

2. What is the color of the belt to be worn by the highest degree of Judo excellence?

3. True or false: the first Judo championships were held in Tokyo in 1817?

4. True or false: the world Kendo championships have been won by the United States the last two competitions?

5. What is a waza-ari in karate?

6. During a karate match the referee signals "soremade": what does this mean?

Answers

1. Wilhelm Ruska of the Netherlands won the 1967 and 1971 heavyweight titles and he also won the 1972 Olympic heavyweight and open titles. Shozo Fujii of Japan also won four world titles in the middleweight division in 1971, 73, 75, and 1979.

2. The highest awarded is the very rare Red Belt Judan (10th class), given only to seven men. The Judo protocol calls for Juichidan (11th class), who would also wear a Red Belt, and even a Junidan (12th class) who would wear a white belt twice as wide as an ordinary belt, and even a Shihan (highest of all), but these have never been achieved by anyone.

3. Judo World Championships were first held in 1956 and are now held biennially. They were cancelled in 1977 but were resumed in 1979.

4. False. Held since 1970 and every three years thereafter, the competition has been won by the country of Japan every time.

5. Waza-ari is worth a half-point and is awarded for a blow that is less correct but still effective, for example: the opponent is moving away from the blow, the blow is slightly off target or the blow is delivered from an unstable position.

6. The referee halts the match if he sees an ippon (a good strong blow) scored. He signals "soremade" and the contestants return to the starting lines. The match is given to the person who struck the ippon.

Wrestling

5. The 1964 Olympic free-style champion was unbeaten and unscored upon in over 100 straight matches. Can you name him or his country?

6. What is the greatest number of world championships ever won by a wrestler: 6,8 or 10?

7. Only one wrestler has won six successive world titles. Can you name him?

1. True or false: before the rules were changed amateur wrestling was the slowest moving sport?

8. True or false: the heaviest wrestler ever in Olympic competition weighed over 400 pounds?

2. True or false: the earliest reference to wrestling dates back to 2350 B.C.?

9. True or false: sumo wrestling which is mainly a Japanese sport originated in China?

3. True or false: wrestling was a major part of the ancient Olympic games?

4. The Graeco-Roman style of wrestling is of Italian origin and dates back to the ancient Olympic games?

10. Which one of these schools won the NCAA Division I wrestling championship in 1978, '79, '80, '81, '82, '83: Oklahoma State, Iowa, or Iowa State?

Answers

1. True. Before the rules were changed wrestlers could be locked in holds for so long that a single bout once lasted 11 hours, 40 minutes.

2. True. Depictions of wrestling holds and falls on the walls of the tomb of Ptahhotep (Fifth Dynasty Egypt) prove that wrestling (organized) dates back to before 2350 B.C.

3. True. Wrestling was first introduced to the ancient games in the eighteenth Olympiad in 708 B.C.

4. False. The Graeco-Roman style is of French origin and dates back to about 1860. It is a modern Olympic event.

5. Osamu Watanabe of Japan was unbeaten and unscored upon in an amazing 187 consecutive matches.

6. Aleksandr Medved of the USSR won the light-heavyweight title in 1962, 1963, 1964 (Olympic) and 1966. He then moved up in class to the heavyweights and won the 1967 and 1968 Olympic titles. That wasn't enough. Medved won the super-heavyweight titles in 1969, 1970, 1971 and 1972 (Olympic) for a record total of ten titles.

7. Abdollah Movahed of Iran is the only man ever to win six straight world titles. He did it in the light-weight division in 1965-70. Roman Rurcia of the USSR holds the Graeco-Roman record of five successive titles in the featherweight division in 1966, 1967, 1968 (Olympic), 1969 and 1970.

8. True. Chris Taylor of the United States won the bronze medal in the Super-heavyweight class in 1972. He stood 6 feet, 5 inches tall and weighed over 420 pounds, an Olympic record.

9. False. The sport of Sumo wrestling dates back to 23 B.C. in Japan.

10. Oklahoma State.

Surfing

5. True or false: The first World Championships of Surfing were held in California in 1937?

6. Was the first surfer to win a World title in surfing two consecutive times a man or a woman?

7. What is a surf-off?

8. How is a surfing competition run and judged?

9. What is a wipe-out in surfing?

1. True or false: Surfing's origins are credited to the Hawaiians?

2. Where are the highest waves in the world for surfing, Australia, United States, or Mexico?

3. Has anybody ever ridden a wave of over 50 feet while surfing?

4. A few times a year surfers can ride waves for more than 5,000 feet in this area, where is it?

HEY, WHEN ARE WE GOING TO GET SOME DECENT SIZE WAVES OUT HERE!

Answers

1. True. Amo amo iluna ka lau oka nalu which means surfing on a board was first seen by James King of the Royal Navy in March, 1779, at Kealakekua Bay, Hawaii Island.

2. Makaha Beach, Hawaii, has the highest and best consistent waves as high as 30-35 feet.

3. The highest wave ever ridden was "perhaps 50 feet" when Tsunami struck Minole, Hawaii, on April 3, 1868. It was ridden by a Hawaiian named Holua to save his life.

4. In Matanchen Bay near San Blas, Nayauit, Mexico, waves can be ridden distances of up to 5,700 feet about 4 to 6 times a year.

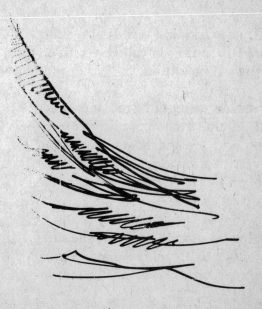

5. False. The first World Championship of Surfing was held at Sydney Australia in 1964.

6. Joyce Hoffman of the United States, a woman, became the first surfer ever to win two titles with victories in 1965 and 1966.

7. The final round or a tie-breaking round in surfing is called a surf-off during a competition.

8. Surfers are required to ride 6 waves in 45 minutes in championship competition and are judged on how soon they catch the wave, the length of the ride, and ability in maneuvering the board on the wave.

9. A wipe-out is the loss of the surfboard due to breaking wave action or the surfer looses his or her balance.

Polo

1. True or false: Polo has the largest playing field of any sport in the World?

2. Where are Polo's origins from, China, Tibet, or Persia?

3. What is the greatest number of goals scored in an international Polo match, 20, 30 or 40?

4. True or false: The United States won the Olympic gold medal in the Polo event at the 1972 and 1976 games?

5. Thomas Hitchcock holds the record for most internationals in Polo, which country did he play for: United States, England, or India?

6. True or false: Besides having the world's largest playing field Polo also claims the world's largest sporting trophy?

7. True or false: There are six players from each team on the field at one time in Polo?

8. How long is a Polo match?

I SAY Smyth, OLD-BOY, WE'VE BEEN RIDING IN THIS DIRECTION FOR HOURS — ANY SIGHT OF THE GOAL YET?

Answers

1. True. The largest field in any sport is for Polo with a maximum length of 300 yards and a width of 200 yards without sidebounds. An area of 12.4 acres.

2. Polo, played as Pulu, is of Persian origin as early as 525 B.C. Tibet and China claim the game as their own from 250 A.D.

3. The most goals scored in an international match is 30, when Argentina beat the United States 21-9 at Meadowbrook, Long Island, New York in September, 1936.

4. False. Polo has been an Olympic sport five times, 1900, 1908, 1920, 1924, and 1936 and has not been used in Olympic competition since then.

ALL RIGHT!! WHO SHORTENED MY MALLET!

5. Thomas Hitchcock Jr. played for the United States five times against England (1921, 24, 27, 30, 39) and twice against Argentina (1928 and 1936) for the record.

6. True. The Bangalore Limited Handicap Polo Tournament Trophy. It stands 6 feet tall on its plinth and was presented in 1936 by the Indian Raja of Kolanka.

7. False. Each team consists of four players. There are substitutes only if a player is ill or injured.

8. A match is divided into eight seven minute periods or "chukkos" amounting to 56 minutes of playing time. There is a three minute interval between periods and five minute break at half-time.

Weight Lifting

5. Of the 90 Olympic medals won up until 1976 which country has won the most, United States, Russia, or France?

6. Do weightlifters exceed 500 pounds in the clean and jerk regulary?

7. Can you name the weightlifter who won the gold medal in the super heavyweight class in the 1972 and 1976 Olympic games?

8. Has one man ever lifted over 6,000 pounds?

9. True or false: a woman once lifted 286 pounds over her head?

10. Lifters are grouped into nine categories; can you name them?

1. True or false: amateur weightlifting dates back to the old Olympic games in Greece?

2. Can you name the first person ever to raise 400 pounds over his head?

3. What is the difference between a barbell and a dumbbell in weightlifting?

4. True or false: Vasili Alenyer of Russia holds the record for most Olympic medals in weightlifting?

I WILL NOW SHOW THE DIFFERENCE BETWEEN A BARBELL AND A DUMBBELL.

Answers

1. False. Weightlifting as a sport is of modern origin with the first world Championship at the Cafe Monico, Piccadilly, London on March 28, 1891. Prior to that professional exhibitions were held with the advertised weights open to doubt.

2. Karl Swoboda of Austria lifted 401½ pounds in Vienna in 1910, using the continental clean and jerk style.

3. A barbell is a long bar, about 5 feet or more, and is held with two hand. A dumbbell is made to be lifted with one hand.

4. False. Norbert Schemasky of the United States won a record four Olympic medals and became the oldest man to break a world record when he set the heavyweight snatch mark at the age of 37 years and 10 months.

5. The United States has won 15, France has won 9, but the USSR holds the record with 26 as of the 1976 Games.

6. Yes, the super heavyweights are now exceeding 560 pounds from the ground in the clean and jerk.

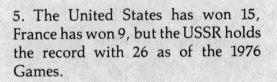

I'VE ALMOST GOT IT !

7. Vasili Alexer of the USSR won the gold medal at the 1972 and 1976 Olympics. He has also broken 80 official and world super heavyweight records during his career.

8. Yes, Paul Anderson of the United States, the 1956 Olympic heavyweight gold medalist, raised 6,270 pounds in a back lift off of trestles on June 12, 1957, at Torcoa, Georgia. Anderson weighed 364 pounds at the time.

9. True, Katie Sandivina of Germany raised 286 pounds in a continental jerk in 1911. She stood 5 feet 11 inches tall and weighed 210 pounds. She is reputed to have shouldered a 1,200 pound cannon taken from the tailboard of a Barnum Bailey circus wagon.

10. Flyweight, bantamweight, featherweight, lightweight, middleweight, light heavyweight, middle heavyweight, heavyweight, and super heavyweight.

Pool & Billiards

11. True or false: 3-cushion billiards dates back to 1878?

12. How much does a pool ball weigh, 4, 5 or 7 ounces?

13. How big are pool tables?

1. True or false: when Columbus came to North America he not only discovered America but the game of billiards as well, an invention of the Indians?

2. Who is the only person ever to win over 50 world titles in billiards?

3. How many pockets are there on a billiards table?

4. Can you name the woman who won eight consecutive amateur world titles?

5. What is the color of the eight ball?

6. Can you name the pool player who won the world professional title 19 times in his career?

7. Can you name the pool player who completely dominated the professionals from 1941 to 1957?

8. Has anybody ever pocketed over 600 balls in a row in pool?

9. True or false: a man once sank over 11,000 balls in a 24 hour period?

10. True or false: Steve Mizerack never won the world professional pool championship?

Answers

1. False. The earliest mention of the game was in France in 1429. Rubber cushions were introduced in 1835 and slate beds a year later.

2. Willie Hoppe of the United States won an amazing total of 51 titles between 1906 and 1952.

3. If you said six you are wrong. There aren't any pockets on a billiards table, but a pool table has six.

4. Vera Selby holds that record having won those titles from 1970 to 1978.

5. The eight ball is always colored black.

6. Ralph Greenleaf of the United States won the title 19 times from 1919 until 1937.

7. Willie Mosconi for the United States won the world professional pool title 13 times in that span and he once sank 525 balls in a row.

8. Yes. Michael Eufemia holds the record for most consecutive balls sunk with a total of 625. He accomplished this feat on February 2, 1960 at Logan's Billiard Academy, Brooklyn, New York.

9. True. Gary Mounsey pocketed 11,700 balls in a 24 hour period in Hamilton, New Zealand, June 30-July 1, 1979. He did it at a rate of one ball per 7.5 seconds.

10. True. Mizerack never won the world title but did win the U.S. Open title from 1970 to 1973.

11. True. The world governing body of 3-cushion billiards, Union Mondiale de Billiard, was formed in 1928, 50 years after the invention of the game.

12. All 15 balls must be of the same weight, between 5½ and 6 ounces.

13. Tables range in size from 3½ feet by 7 feet to 5 feet by 10 feet. The length is always twice the width.

WOW! HAVE I GOT A HEADACHE!!

More Sport Shorts

10. What is a strike in bowling?

11. What is a spare in bowling?

12. What is a turkey in bowling?

1. True or false: bowling can be traced back to the tomb of an Egyptian child of 5,200 B. C.?

2. There was a bowling alley that had had 252 lanes. Was it in the United States, Tokyo or Australia?

3. What does the ABC stand for in bowling?

4. What does the WIBC stand for in bowling?

5. True or false: the PBA was formed in 1928 as an amateur bowling league?

6. What is the record for most consecutive strikes in a sanctioned match: 22, 33 or 44?

7. Which one of these bowlers holds the record for most PBA titles won in one season: Mark Roth, Earl Anthony, Dick Weber, or Johnny Petraglia?

8. Only three bowlers have ever won three consecutive professional tournaments. Which one of these bowlers did not do it: Johnny Petraglia, Dick Weber, Earl Anthony, or Mark Roth?

9. True or false: a man once bowled for over 150 hours in a six day period in 1978?

Answers

1. True. There were nine pieces of stone to be set up as pins at which a stone ball was rolled. The ball had to roll through an archway made up of three pieces of marble.

2. The world's largest bowling arena was the Tokyo World Lanes Center in Japan. It had a total of 252 lanes but was recently closed.

3. The American Bowling Congress. It comprises almost 5 million men who bowl in leagues and tournaments.

5. False. The Professional Bowlers Association (PBA) was formed in 1958. The PBA consists of over 2,000 of the world's best bowlers.

6. The record for consecutive strikes in a sanctioned match is 33 by John Pezzin of the United States at Toledo, Ohio on March 4, 1976.

7. The record number of titles won in one PBA season is 8. The record was set by Mark Roth of North Arlington, New Jersey, in 1978.

8. Earl Anthony is the only one of these four players not to win three consecutive professional tournaments. Dick Weber did it in 1961, Johnny Petraglia in 1971, and Mark Roth in 1977.

9. True. Tom Oestowet bowled 709 games with a 16 pound ball from April 2–8, 1978. He bowled for 150 hours, 15 minutes in Dublin, California.

10. A strike is scored when a player knocks down all ten pins with his first ball of a frame.

11. A spare is scored when a player knocks down all ten pins with both balls in a frame. This includes knocking down all ten pins with the second ball of a frame.

12. A turkey in bowling is three consecutive strikes by one player at any point during a game.

THE CRYSTAL BALL BROKE.

1. True or false: the game of volleyball dates back to the Ming dynasty in China as a betting event for the heads of state?

2. How fast does a volleyball travel when being smashed over the net: 50, 60, or 70 miles per hour and how high is the net?

3. True or false: a girls' volleyball team in Connecticut had a winning streak that spanned 11 seasons?

4. The world championship of volleyball was instituted in 1949. Which one of these countries has won the most titles: USSR, China, South Korea, or North Korea?

5. True or false: the longest recorded volleyball marathon by two teams of six is held by a fraternity at a college in West Virginia?

6. Is volleyball an Olympic sport?

7. Has any volleyball player won five medals in Olympic competition?

8. In international competitions are the matches the best 2 out of three or the best 3 out of 5?

9. True or false: in international competition the ball is two different colors and has to weigh at least 300 grams?

NICE TRY, GEORGE

EL DIPPO BEACH VOLLEYBALL CLASSIC

Answers

1. False. Volleyball was invented as "minnonette" in 1895 by William G. Morgan at the Y.M.C.A. gymnasium at Holyoke, Massachusetts and now has grown to be a world wide sport.

2. A volleyball when smashed travels up to 70 miles per hour over the net. The net is 7 feet, 11½ inches high in the men's sport and 7 feet, 4½ inches high in the women's sport.

3. True. Maloney High School in Meriden, Connecticut, had a winning streak of 159 games over an 11 season period. The streak was snapped in the semi-finals of the state tournament in 1980.

4. The USSR has won a total of nine titles: five men's titles and four women's titles. The record crowd for this event is 60,000 for the 1952 match in Moscow.

5. True. The Beta Theta Pi fraternity at Bethany College in West Virginia set the marathon record by two teams of six on October 3-6, 1979. They played for 75 hours.

6. Yes. Volleyball was first held in the Olympics in 1964 for both men and women. Japan and the USSR have dominated both the men's and women's volleyball events in the Olympics.

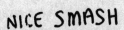

NICE SMASH

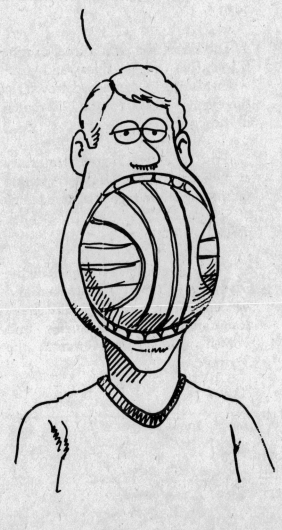

7. No. The record is four by Inna Ryskel of the USSR. She won silver at the 1964 and 1976 games and gold medals in the 1968 and 1972 Olympic games.

8. In international competition matches are the best 3 out of five sets. A set is won when a team reaches 15 points with a two point lead. If a game is tied it continues until one team has a two point lead.

9. False. The ball is made of a leather casing with a bladder of rubber or a similar synthetic product. The ball must be one color and weigh between 260 and 280 grams. The circumference must be 65–67 centimeters.

1. In which one of these countries was the roller skate developed: Belgium, United States, Australia or Japan?

2. True or false: since 1905 there has been an international competition called Roller Hockey, which is very similar to ice hockey?

3. What is the fastest speed ever attained on roller skates: 20, 25 or 30 miles per hour?

4. True or false: the record for roller skating by one person is more than 300 continuous hours?

5. True or false: a man once roller skated over 5,000 miles across the United States?

VROOMSH

Answers

1. Josiph Merlin of Huy, Belgium, invented the roller skate in 1760 and the invention first worn in public in London. The modern day four-wheel roller skate was produced by James L. Plimpton of New York City in 1863. Currently there is a roller skate boom all over the United States.

2. True. In 1905 the Amateur Rink Hockey Association was formed and in 1913 it became the National Rink Hockey Association (now Roller Hockey). The first world championship was played in 1936 and Great Britain won. Portugal holds the lead for most victories with 11 from 1947 until 1973.

3. The fastest speed ever attained on roller skates is 25.78 miles per hour by Guiseppe Cantarella of Italy. He completed 440 yards on a road at Catania, Italy in 34.9 seconds on September 28, 1963.

4. True. From June 12 until June 26, 1977 Randy Reed of Springfield, Oregon recorded a time of 322 hours, 20 minutes of continuous roller skating.

5. True. Theodore J. Coombs of Hermosa Beach, California skated 5,193 miles from Los Angeles, California to New York and back to Yates Center, Kansas from May 30 to September 14, 1979.

1. True or false: a man once attained a speed of over 140 miles per hour on a bicycle in 1973?

2. True or false: a man once stayed stationary while balancing on a bicycle without support for 19½ hours?

3. Is bicycling an Olympic sport?

4. Has anybody ever won three gold medals in cycling in one Olympiad?

5. True or false: the Tour de France has been held since 1814 and is now held every three years with the race taking place in a different European country every time?

6. Louison Bobet of France won the Tour de France three times from 1953 to 1955. Has anybody ever won the race five times?

7. True or false: the Tour de France is a three day event that covers over 300 miles?

8. In cycling is there a strict dress code?

9. What is a Lanterne Rouge and a Maillot Jaune in cycling?

Answers

1. True. Dr. Allan V. Abbott of San Bernardino, California attained the highest speed ever achieved on a bicycle in 1973. He reached a speed of 140.5 miles per hour behind a windshield mounted on a in 1955 Chevy. This would have been impossible but for the slipstreaming effect of the Chevy that enabled him to do this.

2. False. The record for balancing on a stationary bicycle without support is 9 hours, 15 minutes, achieved by David Steed of Tucson, Arizona on November 25, 1977.

3. Yes. Cycling has been a part of the Olympic games since its revival in 1896.

4. Yes, three people: Paul Masson of France won three in 1896, Francisco Verri of Italy in 1906, and Robert Charpentier of France in 1936. Marcus Hurley of the United States won four gold medals at the unofficial cycling competition in the 1904 Olympics.

5. False. The Tour de France has been held annually since 1903, except for the war years in France and in some cases in surrounding countries. Maurice Garin of France was the first winner in 1903.

6. Yes. Jacques Anquetil of France and Eddy Merckx of Belgium are the only two people ever to win the Tour de France five times. Anquetil won it in 1957, 1961-64 and Merkx won it in 1969-72 and 1974.

7. False. The Tour de France takes place over 23 days and the course is usually about 3,000 miles long but varies from year to year. The longest race was 3,569 miles in 1926.

8. Yes. All competitors must wear a jersey or undershirt with sleeves and dark colored racing shorts. A padded crash helmet must be worn for track events. Shoes should fit perfectly. Socks, gloves or mitts are optional, but are usually worn.

9. The Lanterne Rouge is a booby prize for the last man in a stage race. A Maillot Jaune is worn by the current leader in the Tour de France and some other major cycling events.

ACCORDING TO THIS
TOUR DE FRANCE MAP
I BOUGHT - THIS
SHOULD BE THE CENTER
OF PARIS.

1. True or false: the game of field hockey dates back to ancient Egypt?

2. Is field hockey an Olympic sport?

3. Which one of these countries has won the field hockey gold medal the greatest number of times in the Olympic games: the United States, India or Pakistan?

4. True or false: the ball used in field hockey is made of cork and twine and is colored white?

5. How many players are there on each field hockey team and what is the object of the game?

Answers

1. True. In Tomb Number 17 at Beni Hasan, Egypt, a representation of two players with curved snagging sticks in an orthodox "bully" position was found. It dated back to 2050 B.C.

2. Yes. Field hockey was first included in the 1908 Olympic games held in London. England was the first winner of the field hockey event. The event was not held again until 1920 and has been included in every Olympiad since 1928.

3. India has won the Olympic field hockey event the greatest number of times with seven victories overall including six straight titles from 1928 until 1956.

4. True. The ball is white and is made of cork and twine covered in stitched or seamless leather. The ball weighs between 5½ and 5¾ ounces.

5. Field hockey is a game with 11 players to a side. They use a curved stick to hit the ball along the ground. The object of the game is to hit the ball into the opponent's goal, and the team with the most goals wins!

1. True or false: Bobby Fisher of the United States at the age of 15 became the youngest International Grandmaster of all time?

2. Dr. Emanuel Lasker held the world title of chess from 1894 to 1921. What country is he from?

3. True or false: the two greatest women champions of chess are both from the USSR?

4. True or false: Bobby Fisher holds the Grandmaster chess record for the longest winning streak of all time?

5. True or false: the longest chess game on record is one of over 150 hours?

6. True or false: a man played chess against 56 opponents and did not lose a single game, the catch being that he was blindfolded?

7. Since 1950 has anybody ever lost the world championship of chess and then regained it?

8. Is there a World Team Championship for chess?

9. Which one of these countries has won the chess olympiad the greatest number of times: the United States, the USSR, or Hungary?

Answers

1. True. Bobby Fisher is also regarded on the officially adopted ELO system to be the greatest Grandmaster of all time. He also has an I.Q. of 187.

2. Dr. Emanuel Lasker holds the record for the longest undisputed holder of the world championship of chess. Lasker held the title for 27 years. He was from Germany.

3. True. Vera Menchik Stevenson held the women's title from 1927 until her death in 1944 and defended it a record seven times. Nona Gaprindasvili, also from the USSR, defended the title four times was champion from 1962 until 1978.

4. True. Bobby Fisher won a Grandmaster chess record 20 consecutive games from December 2, 1970 until September 30, 1971.

5. True. Philip Thomas and Andrew Harris of Nottingham University, England, played for 165 hours, 9 minutes from October 6 until October 13, 1979.

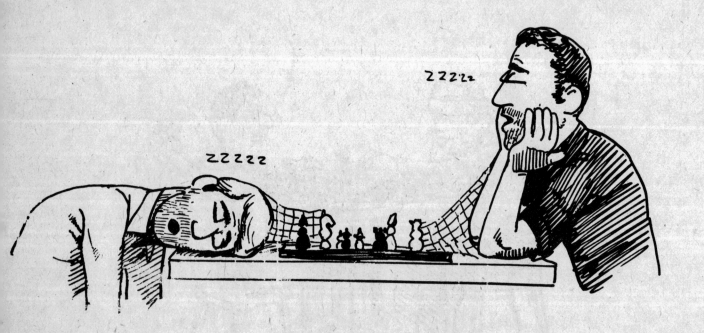

6. True. George Koltanowski of Belgium and later the United States, played 56 people blindfolded and won 50, drew 6, and did not lose in 9 hours, 45 minutes at the Fairmont Hotel, San Francisco on December 13, 1960.

7. Mikhail Botvinnik of the USSR first won the world championship in 1948 before losing it in 1957. He regained it the next year and held on to it until 1961. Mikhail Tal, also of the USSR, won the title in 1961 and held it until 1962 when Botvinnik again won the championship and held it until 1964.

8. Yes. The World Team Championship for chess, also called the Chess Olympiad, was first held in 1927 and Hungary took the title. Since 1931 the event is now held every two years.

9. The USSR has won the most Team titles with 20 victories including the 1980 event. The United States has won five times and Hungary three times.

NO WONDER I'm LOSING, HE KEEPS MOVING MY MEN.

1. True or false: the first shooting club on record was formed in 868 in a small town in China called Pup-Kun (popgun)?

2. Which one of these men has won the most Olympic gold medals: Michael Di Marzo, Carl Osburn or Charley Oslund?

3. True or false: Carl Osburn is the only marksman to win a total of 11 medals in Olympic shooting competition?

4. True or false: Carl Osburn of the United States is the only person in Olympic shooting competition to win three individual gold medals?

5. True or false: the greatest recorded number of birds killed is 556,000 by one person?

6. This woman was best known for the ability to split a playing card end-on, hit a dime in mid-air or shoot a cigarette out of her husband's mouth, all from 30 paces. Can you name her?

7. Did the United States have any gold medalists in the shooting events in the 1976 Olympic games?

Answers

1. False. The first shooting club was formed in 1466 in Switzerland and was called The Lucerne Shooting Guild. The first shooting matches were held in Zurich in 1472.

2. Carl Osburn holds the Olympic record in shooting along with six other marksmen of five gold medals. Osburn is from the United States.

3. True. Along with the five gold medals that Carl Osburn won, he has also won four silver medals and two bronze medals for a record total of 11.

4. False. The only marksman ever to win three individual gold medals in the shooting competition is Gulbrandsen Skattebac of Norway, who won individual medals in the 1906, 1908, and 1912 Olympics.

5. True. The second Marquess of Ripon of England bagged 556,000 birds including 241,000 pheasants. He himself dropped dead on a grouse moor after shooting his fifty second bird on September 22, 1923.

6. Annie Oakley was the greatest trick shot artist of all time. From the age of 27 until 62 she demonstrated her ability to shoot 100 out of 100 in trap shooting.

7. Yes. Lanny Bassham shot a 1,162 out of a possible 1200 in the Small Bore Rifle 3 Positions from 50 meters and Donald Haldeman shot a 190 out of 200 in the trap shooting event to win the gold medal at the 1976 Olympic games.

1. What is the difference between men's and women's fencing?

2. Describe the foil used in fencing.

3. Alador Gerevich won the gold medal in the men's saber competition in the 1948 Olympics. Describe the saber.

4. True or false: in fencing, touche is said by both competitors to acknowledge the beginning of the match?

5. Which one of these great fencers has won more Olympic medals: Christian d'Oriola, Edoardo Mangiarotti or Ramon Fonst?

Answers

1. In men's fencing the winner is the first competitor to score five hits. In women's fencing the winner is the first to score four hits. The time limit for men is six minutes and for women four minutes.

2. The foil must weigh less than 500 grams. The flexibility of the blade should measure 5.5-9.5 centimeters if a 200 gram weight is hung from the button and the blade held firm 70 centimeters from the end. The blade is three feet long and the handle is eight inches long.

3. The saber must weigh less than 500 grams. The blade must not be too rigid nor too flexible. Any curve must be continuous, of less than 4 centimeters and not in the direction of the cutting edge.

4. False. Touche is the word used to acknowledge a hit in fencing.

5. Edoardo Mangiarotti of Italy holds the Olympic record of 13 medals won. He won six gold, five silver and two bronze medals in the foil and epee competitions from 1936 to 1960.

1. What is the ball in jai alai called?

2. What is the cesta in jai alai?

3. True or false: in jai alai there is a certain dress code which has to be followed?

4. True or false: in jai alai a fronton is the time when the first two teams are eliminated after the first round?

5. The world's fastest throw of a jai alai ball (pelota) was electronically measured at a speed of: 155 mph, 174 mph, or 188 mph?

6. How many walls are there in a jai alai court?

Answers

1. The ball is called a pelota. It has a hard rubber core covered with a layer of linen thread and two layers of goatskin. It is 2 inches in diameter and weighs 4½ ounces.

2. The cesta is a wicker basket made to a players's liking and is used to catch the pelota. Players in the front court usually have smaller cestas than the players in the rear court.

3. True. Players wear helmets with white rubber soled shoes, a white or colored shirt with a number, a colored sash belt and white trousers.

4. False. The playing court in jai alai is called a fronton.

5. Jose Ramon Arcitio holds the record with a throw of 188 miles per hour at the Rhode Island fronton on August 3, 1979.

6. The court has three walls. The front wall is called the frontis; the back wall the rebote; and the side wall is called the lateral. The frontis is made of granite blocks; the rebote and lateral are made of granite which is a pressurized cement.

NOW I SEE WHY THIS APARTMENT'S RENT IS SO LOW.

ZZZIPPPP

1. Which one of these people has won more archery world titles: Hans Deutgen of Sweden or Mrs. Janina Spychajowa-Kurkowska of Poland?

2. True or false: archery has been an Olympic sport since the Olympic revival of 1896?

3. True or false: Gary Sentman holds the record for the greatest pull in archery?

4. Can you name the man and woman who won Olympic gold medals in archery in 1976?

Answers

1. Mrs. Janin Spychajowa-Kirkowska of Poland has won the greatest number of world archery titles, seven, in 1931-34, 36, 39, and 1947. The men's record is four won by Hans Deutgen of Sweden in 1947-50.

2. True. Archery has been a part of the Olympics since 1896. Hubert Van Innis of Belgium has been the most successful performer in the Olympics with six gold medals and three silver medals at the 1900 and 1920 Olympic Games.

3. True. Gary Sentman of the United States drew a longbow weighing a record 176 pounds to the maximum draw of the arrow (28¼ inches) at Forksville, Pennsylvania on September 20, 1975.

4. Darrell Pace and Luann Ryun, both Americans. Pace also holds the record for the best single FITA round of 1,316 points out of a possible 1,440. Ryun scored 1,282 points out of a possible 1,440 for the women's record and a gold medal.

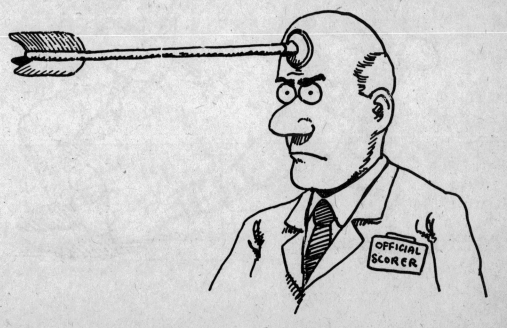

1. True or false: lacrosse was derived from a game played by the Iroquois Indians in upper New York State and lower Canada?

2. Was lacrosse played at the 1976 Olympic Games in Montreal?

3. Which one of these countries won the first Men's World Championship in 1967: Canada, United States or Great Britain?

4. Which one of these colleges won the NCAA Division 1 championship in lacrosse in 1978, 79, 80: Cornell, John Hopkins, or Maryland?

5. Which one of these colleges has won the most national championships in lacrosse: John Hopkins, Navy, or Harvard?

6. How many players on a lacrosse team and what are the positions?

7. Is the color of a lacrosse ball white or orange?

8. Can an attacking player enter the opposing team's goal crease at any time in lacrosse?

Answers

1. True. The Indians of lower Ontario, Canada and upper New York State played a game called baggataway. There is no real record of how long they had been playing the game before the arrival of European settlers.

2. No. Lacrosse was included in the 1908 Games and after that it was dropped. It was featured as an exhibition in the 1928 and 1948 Games.

3. The United States won the first world championship of lacrosse in 1967. They also won the second in 1974. Canada won the third in 1978, beating the United States in overtime 17-16.

4. John Hopkins University won the lacrosse title in 1978-80 in Division 1. Lacrosse is so popular that these games have often drawn more spectators than the Baltimore Orioles.

5. John Hopkins University, Baltimore, Maryland has won or shared the nationals championship 36 times, Navy 16 times, and Harvard 13 times.

6. There are 10 players to a side in lacrosse: a goalkeeper, three defenders, three midfielders and three attackmen. Each team must at all times keep four players in its own half and three in the opposing side's half.

7. The ball is made of India rubber, colored either white or orange and weighs 4½-5 ounces. It must bounce 47-50 inches when dropped from a height of 100 inches onto concrete. Its circumference is 7 3/4-8 inches.

8. No attacking player may enter the goal crease at any time. If such a player enters the crease with any part of his body his side automatically loses the ball. He may reach into the crease with his stick to catch a ball.

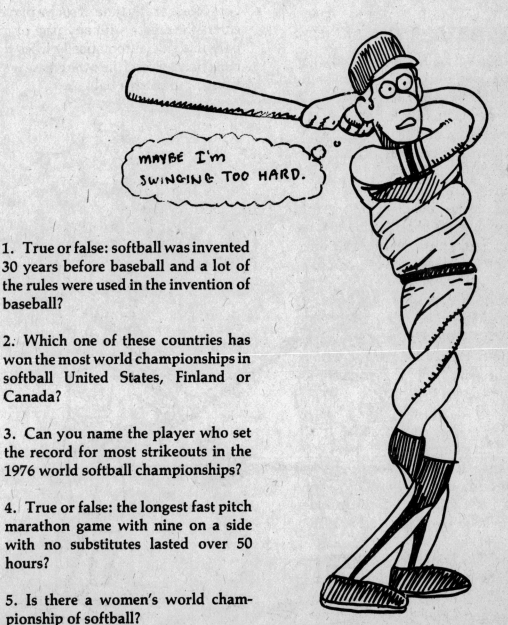

MAYBE I'M SWINGING TOO HARD.

1. True or false: softball was invented 30 years before baseball and a lot of the rules were used in the invention of baseball?

2. Which one of these countries has won the most world championships in softball United States, Finland or Canada?

3. Can you name the player who set the record for most strikeouts in the 1976 world softball championships?

4. True or false: the longest fast pitch marathon game with nine on a side with no substitutes lasted over 50 hours?

5. Is there a women's world championship of softball?

Answers

1. False. Softball was invented as an indoor derivative of baseball by George Hancock in Chicago in 1887. It was called Kitten Ball. International rules were established in 1933 when the name Softball was officially introduced.

2. Since the introduction of the World Championship of Softball in 1966, the United States has won the most often with three victories in 1966, 68 and 76.

3. Ty Stofflect of the United States set the record for most strikouts with 98 at the 1976 World Championships. He also holds the pitching record with 14 straight wins with the York, Pennsylvania team, 1977-79.

4. True. The longest fast pitch marathon game lasted 55 hours, 50 minutes. The competitors were two teams of nine from the Y.C.W. Softball Association, Melbourne, Australia on December 16-18, 1978.

5. Yes. The Women's World Championship of Softball was instituted in 1965. The United States has won twice in 1974 and 1978.

Baseball

WELL KID, YOU'RE JUST ONE OUT AWAY FROM THROWING A PERFECT GAME IN THE WORLD SERIES. ARE YOU NERVOUS?

1. Who is the only pitcher ever to throw a perfect game in World Series history and for what team did he play?

2. Did Don Larsen have over a .500 winning percentage in the major leagues?

3. In 1977 Bob Watson became the first player in major league history to hit for the cycle in both leagues. Has anybody ever hit for the cycle four times in his career?

4. Which one of these players hit the most homeruns at the age of 40 in the major leagues: Willie Mays, Carl Yastrzemski, or Hank Aaron?

5. Who holds the major league record for the longest hitting streak in history?

6. Since Joe DiMaggio set the record for the longest hitting streak in history, who has come the closest to his record?

7. Which one of these players holds the major league record for most total bases in a double header, Nate Colbert or Al Oliver?

8. Can you name the only pitcher ever to pitch a no-hitter on opening day?

9. Can you name the Yankee hurler who pitched a no-hitter on the final day of the 1951 season?

10. True or false: Joe Torre of the Mets was the last player-manager in the major leagues?

11. Only two active switch-hitters in the major leagues have had 100 or more hits from each side of the plate in one season. Can you name them?

12. True or false: when the Baltimore Orioles won the World Championship in 1966 Earl Weaver did not manage them?

13. True or false: Dave Winfield, who signed the biggest contract in major league history up to 1981, never hit over 30 homeruns in a season?

14. Which on of these pitchers is not a left hander: Tommy John, Steve Carlton, Rollie Fingers or Tug McGraw?

15. Which one of these players is not a switch-hitter: Pete Rose, Jerry Mumphrey, Ricky Henderson or Willie Wilson?

16. Can you name the only relief pitcher in major league history to pitch in 90 games in each of three different seasons?

17. True or false: Nolan Ryan holds the major league record for best ratio of strikeouts per nine innings for one season?

18. Who was the last American League player to hit 40 or more home runs in one season?

I WANTED TO LEARN TO BE A SWITCH-HITTER WHEN I WAS YOUNG BUT COULDN'T FIND A STORE IN TOWN THAT SOLD LEFT-HANDED BATS.

26. True or false: Tom Seaver never struck out more than 300 batters in a single season?

27. Can you name the former Detroit Tiger pitcher who won 19 games in his rookie season in 1976?

19. Who were the first five players elected to the Hall of Fame in 1936?

20. Which on of the five players elected to the Hall of Fame in 1936 received the most votes?

21. Of the 15 players in major league history to collect 3,000 or more hits only two have never won a league batting title. Can you name either of them?

22. In the 1980 World Series rookie Bob Walk of the Phillies started the first game and won. Only one other rookie pitcher has started the first game of a series before Walk. Can you name him?

23. True or false: Ty Cobb holds the record for most major league games played in during a career?

24. Can you name the only three currently active players who have had 230 hits or more in a season?

25. True or false: Nolan Ryan holds the major league record for most walks in a season?

28. In 1978 the Yankees won the World Series beating the L.A. Dodgers. Who were the two 20 game winners on the Yankees staff that year?

29. Can you name the current Houston Astro pitcher who lost 13 straight games to the Chicago Cubs while pitching for the Los Angeles Dodgers?

30. Can you name the only four active pitchers in the major leagues who played in the 1969 World Series for the New York Mets?

31. True or false: the Yankees are the only team in history to have had three players who hit 40 or more homeruns in the same season?

32. The best homerun trio for one season in the major leagues played for the New York Yankees in 1961. Can you name them?

33. Has a team ever had four players collect 200 or more hits in the same season?

34. Which one of these great players holds the record for most homeruns in his final major league season: Ted Williams, Babe Ruth or Hank Aaron?

35. Can you name the great outfielder who hit 36 homeruns and stole 40 bases in the 1956 season?

36. True or false: Mike Schmidt was the last player to hit four homeruns in a single game?

37. Who holds the record for most homeruns hit by a catcher in a single season?

38. Can you name the pitcher who won 21 games in the major leagues at the age of 40 in 1979?

39. Can you name the Pittsburgh Pirates shortstop and second baseman who established a major league record for double plays in 1966?

40. True or false: Curt Flood holds the major league record for most consecutive games without an error?

41. True or false: Ralph Kiner holds the World Series record for doubles and triples in a career?

42. Which one of these players holds the record for most pinch-hit homeruns in a row: Reggie Jackson, Jay Johnston or Del Unser?

I CALL THIS MY "TRIPLES TRIPLE"!

43. Can you name the only player ever to lead the National League in triples three consecutive seasons? Here's a hint: he plays for the St. Louis Cardinals.

44. What Philadelphia Phillie pitcher allowed four grand slam homeruns in 1979?

45. True or false: Steve Carlton holds the major league record for most balks in one season?

46. Can you name the Yankee starting pitcher who won the ERA title in 1978 and 1979?

47. Can you name the two expansion major league teams that won their division in the shortest period of time?

48. Can you name the player who holds the record for most hits in a single season in the American League?

49. True or false: George Sisler never played in a World Series?

50. George Sisler had two sons who played in the major leagues. Can you name them?

51. Can you name the player who holds the National League record for most hits in a season?

52. What currently active player holds the American League record for hitting in the most games in one season?

53. Ty Cobb hit a total of 118 home-runs in his career. True or false: he once hit three out in one game?

54. True or false: Lou Gehrig played his entire major league career at first base?

55. True or false: if a batter hits a broken bat ground ball to shortstop and a piece of the bat hits the shortstop as he is throwing causing him to throw the ball into the stands, interference is called and the batter is out?

56. True or false: Pete Rose won the rookie of the year award in the National League in 1963?

57. When Mel Stottlemyre won 21 games in 1968 for what team was he playing?

58. Can you name the four 20 game winners on the Orioles in 1971?

59. Can you name the parish house where Babe Ruth grew up and learned to play baseball?

60. Can you name the National League team which holds the record for fielding percentage for one season?

61. Can you name the pitcher who threw a perfect no hitter in 1981?

62. Can you name the pitcher who threw a perfect game in 1968 in the American League?

63. Who was the last National League pitcher to hurl a perfect game and what team did he do it against?

64. Can you name the oldest park in the major leagues?

65. Often considered the greatest team ever, the 1927 New York Yankees, were weak at only one position catcher, who were the three Yankee catchers that year?

66. Did Ted Williams win the most valuable award in 1941 when he hit .406?

67. Can you name any of the seven former Yankee catchers who became major league managers?

68. Lee MacPhail has been President of the American League since 1974, who was the League's president before him?

69. True or false: Reggie Jackson never hit over 50 homeruns in a single season?

70. Did the Los Angeles Dodgers great left handed pitcher Sandy Koufax ever pitch more than one no-hitter?

71. Did Dick Allen ever win the homerun title in the National League?

72. The New York Mets lost the 1973 World Series in seven games to what team?

73. Before the Braves were in Atlanta they were in Milwaukee. Where were they before Milwaukee?

74. True or false: Roger Maris set a major league record in 1961 for intentional walks?

75. When was the last time the American League won the All-Star game?

76. How many times did Brooks Robinson win the golden glove award in his career?

77. Who won the National League's Manager of the Year Award in 1980?

78. True or false: Babe Ruth is the only player to win the most valuable award in the 1920's in the American League?

79. True or false: Willie Mays never hit over 50 homeruns in a single season in his career?

80. In 1963 the Yankees lost the World Series to what team?

81. Can you name the only pitcher to throw a no-hitter in the 1980 season?

82. The New York Yankees traded John Ellis, Jerry Kenney, Rusty Torrez, and Charlie Spikes to the Cleveland Indians. Who did they receive in return?

83. Can you name the only team since 1946 to have hit at least 100 homeruns a year except the 1981 season?

84. True or false: the New York Yankees are the only American League team to draw over one million in attendance every year since 1964?

85. Can you name the New York Met pitcher who won the Rookie of the Year award in 1972?

86. True or false: Mel Stottlemeyer holds the Yankee record for most career losses?

87. True or false: Roger Maris was the first player to hit a homerun in the Houston Astrodome?

88. True or false: during the 1981 World series Yankee stadium set an all time attendance record for one game at this historic park?

89. Who is the only Detroit Tiger player to have his number retired and what was his number?

90. Can you name the last San Francisco Giant pitcher to throw a no-hitter?

98. If you can answer this question you should write a trivia book. Who gave up Mickey Mantle's last home-run in his career?

99. How many times did Mickey Mantle lead the league in homeruns?

100. Who was known as the Commerce comet?

91. When the New York Mets defeated the Baltimore Orioles in 1969 for the world championship, who was the winning pitcher in the final game?

92. Alan Courtney recorded a very popular song in the 1940's, do you recall the name of it?

93. Can you name the five Yankee players who are in the top 25 of home-run hitters of all time?

94. Which one of these players was the only Yankee ever to hit four home-runs in a single game, Babe Ruth, Lou Gehrig, Mickey Mantle, or Roger Maris?

95. True or false: Ron Guidry was the last Yankee to lead the American League in strikeouts?

96. True or false: during Joe Dimaggio's 56 game hitting streak in 1941 he hit only one homerun?

97. Off of what team did Babe Ruth hit his 60th homerun and who was the pitcher?

101. Did Thurman Munson hit over 100 homeruns in his career with the New York Yankees and how many major league teams did he play on?

102. Who was known as the Splendid Splinter in baseball?

103. True or false: Chief Bender led the American League in stolen bases six consecutive seasons during the 1920's?

104. True or false: the Watts Walloper bat was outlawed in the late 60's?

105. Can an infielder keep his foot on the bag even though he is not making a play?

106. Was there ever a nine inning game that took less than one hour to play in the major leagues?

107. There have been a total of 11 perfect games pitched in the major leagues, only three of the pitchers who threw one are now in the Hall of Fame. Can you name any of them?

108. In 1958 Dale Long of the Chicago Cubs caught two games. What was odd about this besides Long being a first baseman is that he was left-handed. Has there been a left-handed catcher in the major leagues since then?

109. How is a pitcher's earned run average calculated?

110. Who struck out more times in his career, Donn Clendenon or Billy Williams?

111. True or false: Mickey Mantle once hit 40 homeruns in a season but did not have over 100 RBI's?

112. What former homerun hitter was known as Dr. Strangeglove?

113. Can you name the former New York Knick star who played major league baseball?

114. What brother combination was known as Dizzy and Daffy?

115. In what year did Maury Wills steal 104 bases?

116. Who was known as the Thumper in baseball?

117. When Joe Adcock led the league in homeruns what team did he play for?

118. What is the record for putouts by a first baseman in a nine inning game: 16, 19 or 22?

119. True or false: Brooks Robinson holds the record for putouts by a third baseman in a nine inning game?

120. The former California Angel second baseman in the late 60's set the record for putouts in a nine inning game. Can you name him?

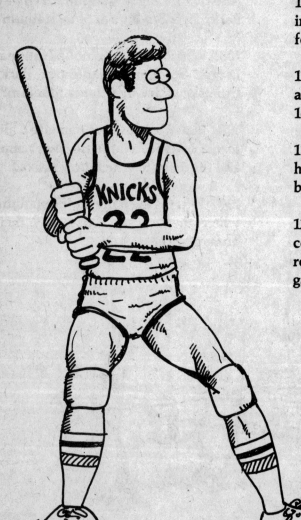

121. What is the record for putouts in a nine inning game by a shortstop: 9, 11 or 13?

122. What position did Jim Bottomley play and did he ever lead the league in homeruns?

123. What team did Lou Boudreau play for? Is he in the Hall of Fame?

124. Jerry Grote set the record for putouts by a catcher in a nine inning game with 20 in 1970. Who was pitching?

125. Cliff Melton as a rookie pitcher won 20 games in 1937. For what team did he play?

126. Which one of these stadiums has the largest seating capacity: Yankee Stadium, Cleveland Municipal Stadium or Dodger Stadium?

127. Which of these stadiums is not an American League stadium: Fenway Park, Tiger Stadium or Shea Stadium?

128. Which of these is not a National League Stadium: Candlestick Park, Comiskey Park or Atlanta Stadium?

129. New York lost two teams to California in 1958. Name the two teams and the cities to which they moved.

130. What is the name of the stadium where the Chicago Cubs play their home games?

131. There is only one stadium in all of baseball that still does not have lights. Can you name it?

132. Who had a higher career batting average, Jimmie Foxx or Joe DiMaggio?

133. Name the four players in National League history to win back to back MVP awards.

134. True or false: Ted Lyons, Hall of Fame pitcher who won 260 games in his career, never lost a World Series game?

135. What former major league pitcher was known as "the barber"?

136. True or false: Cap Anson holds the major league record for most seasons played?

137. What former RBI leader had the distinction of playing with ten different teams during his career?

138. Which one of these players holds the record for playing with the most teams in one league: Frank Thomas, Bobby Bonds or Sparky Lyle?

139. Can you name the only two players who ever played all nine positions in one game?

140. Which one of these players led the major leagues eleven times in batting, including seven straight, in his career?

SHAVE ?

141. True or false: Rogers Hornsby holds the National League record for leading the league the most consecutive times in batting?

142. Who was known as the Flying Dutchman in baseball?

143. How many times during his career did Honus Wagner hit .400 or better?

144. Did Honus Wagner have a brother who played major league baseball?

145. Which one of these players never played in the National League: Billy Williams, Babe Ruth or Ty Cobb?

146. Can you name the player who first said, "I hit 'em where they ain't"?

147. For what tead did Tony Oliva play during his major league career and did he ever win the batting crown?

148. When Hank Aaron broke Babe Ruth's career homerun record in 1974, who was pitching?

149. True or false: when Graig Nettles led the American League in homeruns in 1976 he was playing for the Cleveland Indians?

150. Did Graig Nettles have a brother who played major league baseball?

151. When Hank Aaron won the most valuable player award in which city did his Braves play, Atlanta or Milwaukee?

152. Did Hank Aaron have a brother who played major league baseball?

153. Did Hank Aaron ever lead the National League in batting during his career?

154. True or false: homerun king Hank Aaron never hit more than 50 homeruns in one season?

155. Can you name the former Philadelphia Phillie pitcher who threw a no-hitter and hit two homeruns in the same game in 1971?

156. Can you name the Detroit Tiger pitcher who won the Cy Young award twice in the late 1960's?

157. What great Hall of Fame pitcher was known as Big Six?

158. Can you name the Cincinnati Reds player who hit 52 homeruns in 1977?

159. True or false: Ty Cobb once led the American League in homeruns?

160. What former Yankee shortstop was known as "the Crow"?

161. Can you name the Philadelphia Athletic first baseman who led the American League in homeruns four consecutive seasons from 1904 to 1907?

162. Since 1900 who was the first player ever to hit 20 or more homeruns in a single season?

163. Who was known as "the Silver Fox" in baseball?

164. True or false: Duke Snider never led the league in homeruns?

165. When Ralph Garr won the batting title in 1974 what team did he play for?

166. True or false: Steve Garvey played his first two major league seasons with the Atlanta Braves?

167. Who was known as "the Reading Rifle" in baseball?

168. Did Carl Furillo ever lead the National League in batting average during his career?

169. Can you name the teams in the American League's Eastern Divison?

170. Can you name the teams in the American League's Western Division?

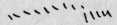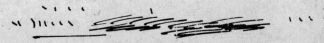

179. True or false: Ted Williams led the American League in homeruns four times during his career?

180. True or false: when Maury Wills set the stolen base record in 1962 with the Los Angeles Dodgers it was the only time in his career that he led the league in that department?

171. Can you name the teams in the National Leagues Western Division?

172. Can you name the teams in the National Leagues Eastern Division?

173. Did a player ever get traded to the team he was playing against in a doubleheader after the first game?

174. Which one of these players has the highest career batting average, Rod Carew, Ty Cobb, or Joe Jackson?

175. Which one of these players holds the record for highest career batting average in the National League, Stan Musial, Rogers Hornsby, or Dave Parker?

176. True or false: Rogers Hornsby led the National League in homeruns twice during his career?

177. Who had a higher lifetime batting average: Ted Williams or Tris Speaker?

178. True or false: Tris Speaker led the American League in homeruns three consecutive years with the Boston Red Sox?

181. True or false: Boog Powill led the American League in homeruns twice during the 1960's?

182. If you can answer this you know your baseball trivia: Who hit .435 in the 1887 season for the second highest average of all time?

183. The highest recorded batting average ever in major league baseball was .438 in 1894. Can you name the player who did it?

184. Who is the all-time winningest pitcher in major baseball history?

185. What was Cy Young's real first name?

186. True or false: Stan Musial was known for his great hitting ability but he also led the league in strikeouts 10 times?

187. Stan Musial hit 475 career homeruns for the St. Louis Cardinals in his 22 year career. How many times did he lead the National League in that department?

188. Can you name the first major league team that Babe Ruth played on?

189. True or false: Babe Ruth, as a pitcher, had two consecutive 20 or more wins seasons?

190. Did Babe Ruth win any games as a pitcher for the New York Yankees?

191. How many homeruns did Babe Ruth hit in his career?

192. In 1936 Hal Trosky led the American League in RBI's. For what team did he play and what position did he play?

193. Can you name the only four players who have hit 58 or more homeruns in a single season in major league history?

194. Can you name the American League's Cy Young award winner for the 1981 season?

195. Which one of these pitchers holds the major league record for saves in a career: Sparky Lyle, Rollie Fingers or Hoyt Wilhelm?

196. Can you name the only other relief pitcher besides Rollie Fingers to win the Cy Young award in the American League?

197. True or false: the New York Yankees won the 1981 World Series in six games?

198. Can you name the Yankee pitcher who lost three games in the 1981 World Series?

199. Can you name any of the three co-winners for the 1981 World Series Most Valuable Player award?

200. True or false: Steve Garvey, the Dodgers' first baseman, led both teams with 10 hits in the 1981 World Series?

201. When was the last time before the 1981 World Series that the Dodgers won the world championship of baseball?

202. The Detroit Tigers last won the World Series in 1968. Whom did they beat to become champions of the world?

203. True or false: Tommy John, who won one game in the 1981 World Series, pitched against the Yankees in the 1978 series?

204. Which one of these players won the National League batting title in the 1981 season: Dusty Baker, Bill Madlock or Pete Rose?

205. Can you name the New York Mets rookie third baseman who hit over .300 in the 1981 season?

206. Which one of these players led the National League in homeruns in 1981: Andre Dawson, Dave Kingman or Mike Schmidt?

207. Before 1980 did Mike Schmidt ever win the homerun title in the National League?

208. Mike Schmidt won the 1980 MVP award in the National League by a unanimous vote. Can you name the only other player in National League history to do this? Here's a hint: the player won it with the Cardinals in 1967.

209. In Orlando Cepeda's 17 year major league career did he ever win a homerun title?

210. Norm Cash was a great homerun hitter in the 60's and early 70's. What position did he play and with what team did he have all his success?

WHO VOLUNTEERED TO COUNT THE BALLOTS?

219. Two players tied for the National League lead in triples during the 1981 season. One played with the Astros, the other with the Padres. Can you name them?

220. Which one of these pitchers had the best won-lost percentage in 1981: Steve Carlton or Tom Seaver?

211. Which one of these players led the National League in runs batted in during the 1981 season: Mike Schmidt, George Foster or Andre Dawson?

212. Can you name the rookie from the Montreal Expos who led the major leagues in stolen bases in 1981?

213. **Name the 1st and only Major League player to win the MVP award in his second season.**

214. True or false: Mike Schmidt, besides leading the National League in homeruns and RBI's, also led the league in runs scored?

215. True or false: Pete Rose led the major leagues in total hits for the Phillies in 1981?

216. Who is known as "Charlie Hustle" in the major leagues?

217. Can you name the Chicago Cubs player who led the major leagues in doubles in 1981?

218. Who holds the major league record for most doubles in a career: Stan Musial, Ty Cobb or Tris Speaker?

221. Which one of these teams had the highest batting average in the National League in 1981: Cardinals, Reds or Phillies?

222. Which one of these teams had the worst batting average in the National League for the 1981 season: Mets, Braves or Cubs?

223. Which one of these players had the highest average for shortstops in the 1981 National League season: Garry Templeton, Dave Concepcion or Larry Bowa?

224. True or false: Miller Huggins, who coached the 1927 Yankees never played major league baseball?

225. For what team did Dave Kingman play during the 1981 season and did he hit over 20 homeruns?

226. What position does Steve Garvey play and has he ever led the league in batting?

227. Which one of these pitchers led the National League in earned run average for the 1981 season: Joe Sambito, Burt Hooton or Nolan Ryan?

228. For what National League team does power hitter Bob Horner play?

229. Can you name the teams in the Eastern Division of the National League?

230. Can you name the teams in the Western Division of the National League?

238. Which one of these teams won the second half of the 1981 season in the Western Division in the National League: Los Angeles Dodgers, Houston Astros or the Cincinnati Reds?

239. True or false: the Oakland Athletics won the second half of the 1981 season in the Western Division in the American League?

240. Can you name the team that won the second half of the 1981 season in the Eastern Division of the American League?

231. Can you name the teams in the Eastern Division of the American League?

232. Can you name the teams in the Western Division of the American League?

233. What team won the first half of the season in the Eastern Division of the National League in 1981?

234. Which one of these teams won the first half of the 1981 season in the Western Division of the National League: Astros, Dodgers, or Reds?

235. True or false: The Chicago White Sox won the first half of the 1981 season in the Western Division of the American League?

236. Which one of these teams won the first half of the 1981 season in the Eastern Division of the American League: Milwaukee Brewers, New York Yankees, or the Baltimore Orioles?

237. True or false: the Montreal Expos won the second half of the 1981 season in the Eastern Division of the National League?

241. True or false: The Kansas City Royals had an overall losing record but still came in first in the Western Division in 1981?

242. Which one of these teams had the best overall record in the major leagues in 1981: Oakland Athletics, Cincinnati Reds or the Los Angeles Dodgers?

243. Only three pitchers in the American League won 14 games in 1981. Can you name any of them?

244. What team did Mike Norris pitch for in the 1981 season?

245. Which one of these teams did not win 60 games during both halves of the 1981 season: Detroit Tigers, New York Yankees, or the Milwaukee Brewers?

246. True or false: the Chicago Cubs were the only team in major league baseball not to win 40 games overall in the 1981 season?

247. Who was the only pitcher in the National League to win 14 games in the 1981 season?

248. Can you name the Boston Red Sox third baseman who led the American League in batting average in the 1981 season?

249. Four players tied for the American League lead in homeruns with 22. Can you name any of the four players and their teams?

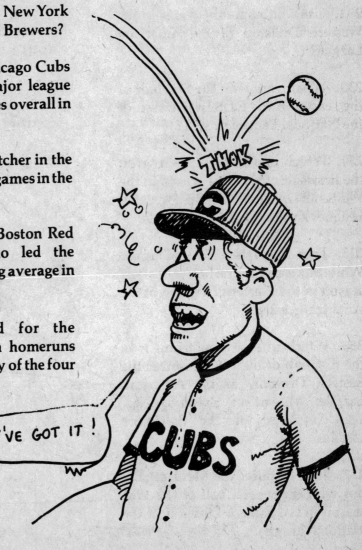

254. True or false: a player once won a batting title with a mere .301 average?

255. Did Carl Yastrzemski ever win the triple crown in his career with the Boston Red Sox?

256. Which one of these players led the American League in runs scored in the 1981 season: Ricky Henderson, Dwight Evans or Willie Wilson?

257. Who was known as the Say Hey Kid?

250. Which one of these players led the American League in runs batted in for the 1981 season: Tony Armas, Ben Oglivie, or Eddie Murray?

251. Who has hit more homeruns in his career, Reggie Jackson or Carl Yastrzemski?

252. True or false: Ron Leflore of the Chicago White Sox led the American League in stolen bases in the 1981 season?

253. True or false: Ty Cobb holds the American League record for stolen bases in a single season?

258. True or false: Willie Mays never led the National League in runs batted in during his career?

259. How many teams did Bill Mazeroski play for in his major league career?

260. True or false: Willie Wilson of the Kansas City Royals led the American League in hits in 1981?

261. Who was known as "Little Poison"?

262. Who was known as "Big Poison"?

263. Which one of these players holds the major league record for most seasons with 200 or more hits, Ty Cobb or Pete Rose?

264. Can you name the player who holds the major league record for most homeruns by a switch hitter in a career?

265. True or false: Cecil Cooper of the Milwaukee Brewers led the American League in doubles in the 1981 season?

266. Who holds the National League record for career homeruns by a switch hitter?

267. True or false: George Brett of the Kansas City Royals led the American League in triples in 1981?

268. Can you name the American League player who hit .390 in 1980?

269. Which one of these pitchers led the American League in strikeouts in 1981: Len Barker, Britt Burns, or Ron Guidry?

270. What team does Jim Palmer pitch for?

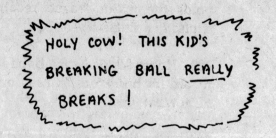

HOLY COW! THIS KID'S BREAKING BALL REALLY BREAKS !

271. What team did Gavvy Cravath play for when he led the National League in homeruns?

272. What position does Ozzie Smith play and for what team?

273. Did Rod Carew hit over .300 in the 1981 season for the California Angels?

274. True or false: Ken Singleton of the Baltimore Orioles started his major league career with the New York Mets.

275. Can you name the former Oaklands A's pitcher who won the MVP and Cy Young awards in 1971?

276. Who was the first black manager in major league history?

277. Can you name the only player in major league history to win the most valuable player award in both leagues?

278. Did Jackie Robinson ever win the batting average title in the National League?

279. True or false: Babe Ruth holds the single season record for slugging average?

280. Which one of these great players holds the major league record for most hits in a single season: Rogers Hornsby, George Sisler or Bill Terry?

281. Which one of these players holds the major league record for doubles in a single season: Earl Webb, Pete Rose, or Stan Musial?

282. True or false: Owen Wilson holds the major league record for triples in a single season?

283. Roger Maris broke Babe Ruth's record for homeruns in a season with 61 in what year?

284. Who threw the pitch that Roger Maris hit to break Babe Ruth's record for homeruns in a single season?

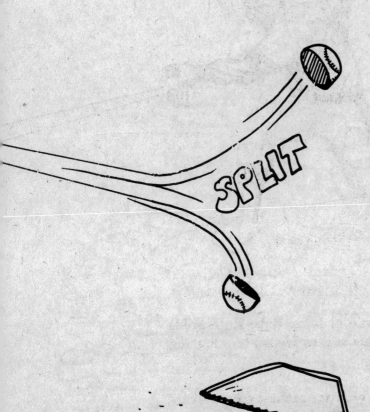

285. True or false: Babe Ruth holds the major league record for most total bases in a single season?

286. True or false: Babe Ruth holds the major league single season record for RBI's?

287. Which one of these players holds the record for most base on balls in a single season: Babe Ruth, Ted Williams, or Randy DiMarzo?

288. Maury Wills set the major league record for stolen bases in a single season with 104 in 1962. Who broke Wills' record and in what year did he do it?

289. True or false: Ed Kranepool set the major league record for pinch hit batting average with the New York Mets in 1974?

290. Which one of these power hitters holds the major league record for striking out the most in a season: Bobby Bonds, Reggie Jackson, Willie Stargell, or Mike Schmidt?

298. Which one of these players has the highest lifetime slugging average: Ted Williams, Babe Ruth, Lou Gehrig, or Willie Mays?

299. True or false: Hank Aaron holds the lifetime major league record for total bases?

300. Who had more lifetime total bases: Babe Ruth or Ty Cobb?

I'VE GOT THE MOST TOTAL BASES!

291. Has any pitcher ever won more than 40 games in a single season since 1900 in the major leagues?

292. Can you name the relief pitcher who set the record for wins in one season and winning percentage?

293. Bob Gibson had an incredible 1.12 ERA in 1968 for the St. Louis Cardinals. Is that a major league record?

294. Sandy Koufax set the record for strikeouts in a single season with 382 in 1965 with the Dodgers. Who broke that record?

295. Which one of these strikeout pitchers holds the record for most seasons of 300 or more strikeouts: Sandy Koufax, Nolan Ryan or Walter Johnson?

296. What pitcher was known as "the Big Train"?

297. Which one of these pitchers holds the record for most shutouts in a single season: Bob Gibson, Grover Alexander or Walter Johnson?

301. Which one of these pitchers has won more games in his career Tom Seaver or Steve Carlton as of 1983?

302. Who has struck out more batters in his career, Steve Carlton or Tom Seaver?

303. Can you name the Yankee top relief pitcher from 1958 until 1960 who was best known for his milk-bottle-thick tinted glasses and his unique pre-inning warmup: he threw very fast pitches into the dirt, over the catcher's head, against the back stop and into the stands?

304. Carl Erskine pitched in the major leagues from 1948 until 1959 for what team?

305. On April 22, 1970 Tom Seaver set the major league record for consecutive strikeouts with 10 against the San Diego Padres. Whose record did he break?

306. The World Series record for most shutout victories in a single series is three by a pitcher who was nicknamed "Big Six." Can you name him?

307. Lefty Grove had seven consecutive seasons of 20 or more victories from 1927 until 1933 for what team?

308. True or false: a pitcher in the major leagues had a toothpick surgically attached to his lower lip?

309. Iron Man Joe McGinnity won over 30 games two straight seasons in 1903 and 1904 for what team?

THAT'S THE WRONG WAY AGAIN.

310. Who made these six statements:

1. Avoid fried meats which angry up the blood.

2. If your stomach disputes you, lie down and pacify it with cool thoughts.

3. Keep the juices flowing by jangling around gently as you move.

4. Go very light on the vices, such as carrying on in society; the social ramble ain't restful.

5. Avoid running at all times.

6. Don't look back; something might be gaining on you.

311. Can you name the pitcher who won the Cy Young Award in the National League in the 1981 season?

312. Can you name the Houston Astro pitcher who won the 1981 earned run average title?

313. Rollie Fingers won the American League ERA title in 1981 with a 1.04 performance. Can you name the AL starting pitcher who had the best ERA?

314. Did Hall of Famer Eddie Collins get more than 3,000 hits in his major league career?

315. Can you name the Dodger catcher who won the most valuable player award three times during the 1950's?

316. Who was the last National Leaguer to hit .400 in a regular season? Here's a hint: he played for the N.Y. Giants.

317. For what team did Roberto Clemente play and did he have a lifetime average over .300?

318. Can you name the American League pitcher who has had the lowest ERA since the live ball era beginning in 1920?

319. What Dodger player was known as "the Silver Fox?"

320. Joe DiMaggio had two brothers who played major league baseball. Can you name them?

321. True or false: Kiki Cuyler was one of the outstanding pitchers in the National League for 15 years?

322. Which one of these pitchers won more games in his career, Grover Cleveland Alexander or Christy Mathewson?

323. Can you name the only pitcher in history to throw no-hitters back-to-back?

324. In 1916 the New York Giants ran off winning streaks of 17 and 26 games, the latter being a record. Did they win the pennant that year?

325. When Babe Ruth hit his sixtieth homerun in 1927 for the major league record, whose record did he break?

326. In 1927 Babe Ruth hit 60 home-runs and in 1961 Roger Maris hit 61. Both men played for the Yankees. Who hit more homeruns at home in their record breaking seasons?

327. True or false: Rube Marquard holds the major league record for most consecutive victories with 19?

328. Can you name the former Cardinal pitcher who broke Grover Cleveland Alexander's record for lowest ERA in a season in the National League?

HAVEN'T I SEEN YOU TWO GUYS AROUND SOMEWHERE?

331. Can you name the former Cleveland Indian pitcher who established a new major league record with 12 one hitters in his career?

332. What Philadelphia Phillie third baseman established a National League record (for third basemen) with 404 assists in 1974?

333. What catcher, who played from 1931 until 1947, was known as "Schnozz" and "Bocci"?

334. What great homerun hitter was known as "Double X" and "the Beast"?

329. Which one of these catchers has posted the highest single season batting average: Roy Campanella, Bill Dickey or Yogi Berra?

330. What former Yankee catcher's first names are Lawrence Peter?

335. Jimmie Foxx hit 50 homeruns in 1938 for the Boston Red Sox but did not lead the league, who did?

336. Only two players in the history of baseball have had 13 consecutive seasons of 100 or more RBI's one is Jimmie Foxx, who is the other?

337. True or false: Frank Robinson is the only player in the modern ERA to lead both leagues in homeruns?

338. Who won the Manager of the Year Award in the American League in 1981?

339. Which one of these former Minnesota Twin Players became the first rookie ever to win a batting title: Rod Carew, Tony Oliva, or Harmon Killebrew?

340. Which one of these Cincinnati Reds players led the National League in RBI's from 1976 til 1978: Pete Rose, George Foster, or Johnny Bench?

341. True or false: a pitcher won the first Most Valuable Player Award in the American League in 1931?

342. A St. Louis Cardinal player won the first Most Valuable Player Award given in the National League in 1931; who was it?

343. The highest batting average ever attained in this century by a shortstop is .388 by a White Sox player who's first name is Luke, can you name him?

344. This former Pittsburgh Pirate outfielder led the National League in homeruns his first seven seasons, can you name him?

345. Can you name the shortstop who led the American League in stolen bases from 1956 until 1964?

346. From 1927 until 1932 this St. Louis Cardinal player had seasons of .329, .336, .349, and .344, can you name him?

347. In 1912 this pitcher posted a 34-5 record with a 1.91 earned run average for the Red Sox, his nickname was "Smoky", can you name him?

348. When Willie Mays was called up from the minors in May, 1951, he went hitless in his first few games and then broke out to get his first major league hit, a homerun, off of whom?

349. Can you name the player who played from 1924 until 1944 and hit a career .334, his nickname was "Bucketfoot Al"?

350. What former New York Giant pitcher was known as "King Carl" and "the meal ticket"?

351. What team did the great pitcher Christy Mathewson play for during his major league career?

352. When the New York Mets won the World Series in 1969 one of their pitchers won 25 games that year, can you name him?

353. What position did Three Finger Brown play during his major league career?

354. George Sisler hit a career .340 in 15 major league seasons, what position did he play?

355. Who was known as "the Iron Horse"?

356. What player who played from 1930 until 1947 was known as "Hammerin' Hank"?

357. Jackie Robinson became the first black to play major league baseball in 1947, what team did he play for?

358. True or false: Willie Stargell won the Most Valuable Player Award in the National League in 1979?

359. Which one of these great pitchers holds the major league record for lowest earned run average: Whitey Ford, Bob Gibson, Ed Walsh, or Christy Mathewson?

360. Which one of these pitchers has walked more batters in his career, Nolan Ryan or Early Wynn?

361. Which one of these batters once had seven consecutive hits in a single game: Rod Carew, Cesar Gutierrez, Manny Mota, or Stan Musial?

362. Lou Gehrig holds the American and Major League record for most consecutive games played, which one of these players holds the National League record: Willie Mays, Billy Williams, or Hank Aaron?

363. Which one of these pitchers is not right handed: Rube Waddell, Sandy Koufax, Nolan Ryan, or Tom Seaver?

364. Which one of these batters holds the career record for being hit by pitches: Ron Hunt, Pete Rose, or Mel Ott?

365. True or false: Even though Cy Young has won more games in his career than any other pitcher in major league history, he never threw a no-hitter?

371. In 1968 what Washington Senator player hit 10 homeruns over a six game span?

372. True or false: the catcher is charged with an error when the pitcher walks the batter?

373. True or false: In major league baseball the designated hitter cannot be pinch hit for?

374. Four former New York Mets players are not in the Hall of Fame, can you name them?

375. Tom Tresh won the Rookie of the Year Award in the American League in 1962, what team did he play for at the time?

366. Which one of these former Pittsburgh Pirate players once hit homeruns in eight consecutive games: Ralph Kiner, Dale Long, or Arky Vaughan?

367. Lou Gehrig hit a total of 493 homeruns in his career with the Yankees, did he ever hit more than 50 in one season?

368. Which one of these great hitters walked more times during his major league career: Babe Ruth, Ted Williams, or Ralph Kiner?

369. Who struck out more times in his career Mickey Mantle or Babe Ruth?

370. Can you name the Braves' great third baseman from 1952 until 1967 who hit 509 homeruns in his career?

376. Can you name the Boston Red Sox player who won both the Rookie of the Year Award and the MVP Award in 1975?

377. Is Jim Rice of the Boston Red Sox a right handed or left handed batter?

378. True or false: Tommie Agee won the Rookie of the Year Award in 1966 with the New York Mets?

379. Can you name the pitcher who was the Rookie of the Year Award in the American League in 1955 and also led the league his first two seasons in strikeouts?

380. Jackie Robinson was the first black ball player to play in the major leagues in 1947; did he win the Rookie of the Year Award?

381. True or false: Johnny Bench won the Rookie of the Year Award in 1968 with the Cincinnati Reds?

382. Richie Allen won the Rookie of the Year Award in 1964 for what team?

383. Which one of the current and former New York Met pitchers never won the Rookie of the Year Award in the National League: Tom Seaver, Jerry Koosman, Jon Matlock, or Pat Zachry?

CENTER
FIELD FENCE
12 MILES →

Answers

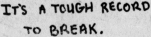

IT'S A TOUGH RECORD TO BREAK.

56 GAMES

1. In the fifth game of the 1956 World Series Don Larsen of the New York Yankees threw the only no-hitter in Series history beating the Brooklyn Dodgers 2-0.

2. Don Larsen finished his major league career (1953-1967) with an 81-91 record for a .471 percentage, but in World Series competition he posted a 4-2 record with a 2.75 ERA.

3. No. The record is three held by Bob Meusel of the Yankees and Babe Herman of the Brooklyn Dodgers. Herman did it on May 18, July 24 and September 30, 1931. Meusel did it on September 5, 1921; July 3, 1922 and July 26, 1928.

4. In 1979 at the age of 40 Yastrzemski hit 24 homeruns compared to Mays' 18 in 1971 and Aaron's 20 in 1974.

5. Joe DiMaggio of the New York Yankees hit in 56 consecutive games in 1941 to break Willie Keeler's record of 44 games. DiMaggio finished the 1941 season with a .357 batting average and 30 homeruns to go along with a league leading 125 RBI's.

6. Pete Rose hit in 44 straight games in 1978 thus tying the National League record set by Willie Keeler in 1897. During Rose's attempt to break DiMaggio's record he hit .385, going 70 for 182.

7. Nate Colbert set the major league record in 1972 while playing for the San Diego Padres. He hit 5 homeruns and drove in 13 runs in a doubleheader against the Atlanta Braves. In all he had 22 total bases. Al Oliver holds the American League record with 21 total bases in a doubleheader against Detroit in 1980.

11. Garry Templeton when with the St. Louis Cardinals had 111 hits left-handed and 100 right-handed in 1979 and Willie Wilson of the Kansas City Royals is the other with 130 hits left-handed and 100 right-handed in 1980.

12. True. Hank Bauer, former Yankee great, managed the World Series winning Orioles in 1966.

13. False. Winfield, who played for the San Diego Padres in the National League, hit 34 homeruns in 1979.

14. Rollie Fingers, currently with the Milwaukee Brewers and one of the best relief pitchers in history, is a right-handed pitcher.

15. Ricky Henderson of the Oakland Athletics is a right-handed batter.

16. Mike Marshall pitched in 106 games in 1974, 92 in 1973 and 90 in 1979 for a record. The only other relievers to have pitched in 90 or more games are Kent Tekulve, who pitched in 94 games in 1979 and 91 in 1978 and Wayne Granger, who appeared in 90 games in 1969.

8. Bob Feller of the Cleveland Indians no-hit the Chicago White Sox on April 16, 1940, opening day. He fanned eight and walked five in winning 1-0.

9. Allie Reynolds of the Yankees threw a no-hitter against the Boston Red Sox in the first game of a double-header of September 28, 1951, the last day of the season. It was Reynolds' second no-hitter of the season.

10. False. Don Kessinger, shortstop of the Chicago White Sox, was the last playing manager in the major leagues. He retired on August 3, 1979. Tony La Russa took over the White Sox after that.

17. False. Sam McDowell of the Cleveland Indians struck out 325 batters in 273 innings for a 10.71 ratio per nine innings. Nolan Ryan posted a 10.57 mark in 1973 and Sandy Koufax also had a 10.57 mark in 1962.

18. Both Reggie Jackson of the Yankees and Ben Oglivie of the Brewers —each tied for the lead in 1981 with 41 homeruns.

19. The first five players elected in 1936 were Ty Cobb, Babe Ruth, Honus Wagner, Christy Mathewson and Walter Johnson.

20. Ty Cobb led the 222 votes followed by Ruth with 215; Mathewson, 205 and Johnson with 189.

21. The only two players to collect 3,000 or more hits in their careers and not win a league batting title are Lou Brock and Eddie Collins.

22. The Brooklyn Dodgers ace rookie Joe Black started the first game of the 1952 world series beating the Yankees 4-2.

23. False. Carl Yastrzemski holds the record with a total of 3,308 games played followed by Hank Aaron with 3,298 games. Ty Cobb played 3,033 games.

24. In 1980 Willie Wilson collected 230 hits, Pete Rose had 230 hits in 1973, and Rod Carew collected 239 hits in 1977.

25. False. Bob Feller of the Cleveland Indians holds this record with a total of 208 in the 1938 season. He finished the season with a 17-11 record with 240 strikeouts.

26. True. Seaver's best strikeout performance in one season was in 1971 when he k'd 289. He also led the league with a 1.76 ERA and won 20 games for the Mets.

27. The Bird, Mark Fidrych of the Tigers won 19 games while losing only 9 and has a 2.34 ERA. He also won the rookie of the year award. Fidrych hurt his arm and hasn't pitched up to his 1976 form since.

28. Ron Guidry was 25-3 and Ed Fiqueroa was 20-9 for the Bronx Bombers in 1978.

29. Don Sutton, who is now one of the top pitchers in all of baseball, from 1966 through 1969 just could not beat the Cubs.

30. Tom Seaver, now with the Chicago Whitesox, Nolan Ryan, now with the Houston Astros, Tug McGraw, now with the Philadelphia Phillies, and Jerry Koosman, now with the Minnesota Twins.

31. False. In 1973 the Atlanta Braves set this record. Dave Johnson hit 43, Darrell Evans hit 41, and Hank Aaron hit 40.

32. Roger Maris hit 61, Mickey Mantle hit 54, and Bill Skowron hit 28 for a total of 143 homeruns, a record.

33. The 1937 Detroit Tigers had four players who collected 200 or more hits. Gee Walker with 213, Pete Fox with 208, Charlie Geringer with 209, and Hank Greenberg with 200 hits.

34. Ted Williams holds the record for most homeruns in his final season with 29. He also had a batting average of .316.

35. One of the greatest players the game has ever seen, Willie Mays, who did that with the New York Giants that year.

36. True. On July 17, 1976, in a ten inning game, Mike Schmidt hit four homeruns for the Phillies and to this date is the last to do so in the major leagues.

37. Roy Campanella set the record for homeruns by a catcher with 41 in 1953 while playing for the Brooklyn Dodgers, a record which still stands today.

38. Phil Niekro accomplished something that only a handful have done. He won 21 and lost 20 for the Braves in 1979. The only other pitchers to have won 20 games or more at the age of 40 are Cy Young (22-15 in 1907), Eddie Planks (22-11 in 1915), Grover Alexander (21-10 in 1927), Warren Spahn (21-15 in 1961), and Gaylord Perry (21-6 in 1978).

39. The shortstop was Gene Alley and the second baseman was Bill Mazeroski. Mazeroski took part in 161 double plays and Alley 128. As a combination they completed 289 double plays.

40. False. Al Kaline of the Detroit Tigers holds the record with 242 consecutive games without an error (1970-1972).

41. False. In Kiner's ten professional seasons he never played in a world series game.

42. Del Unser of the Philadelphia Phillies holds the record with three straight pinch-hit homeruns on June 30, July 5, and July 10, 1979.

43. Garey Templeton, who plays shortstop for the Cardinals, led the National League in triples in 1977, 1978, 1979 for the record.

44. Tug McGraw tied a major league record by allowing four grand slams in 1979.

45. True. Carlton, one of the best pitchers in baseball in the 70's, allowed a major league record 11 balks in 1979.

46. Ron Guidry established a major league record by winning two consecutive ERA titles despite allowing more than one run per game than in the previous season: 1.74 in 1978 and 2.78 in 1979.

47. The New York Mets, who became a major league team in 1962 and won the pennant and World Series in 1979 and the Kansas City Royals, who entered the league in 1969 and won their division in 1976, but lost the championship series to the Yankees.

NO SWEAT

HE'S SUCH A HOT
HITTER HIS NAME
SHOULD BE SPELLED
S·I·Z·Z·L·E·R

48. George Sisler holds the American and major league record with 257 hits with St. Louis in 1920.

49. True. Although one of the greatest hitters of all time, Sisler never played in a World Series game. He hit .340 in his 15 years of major league play.

50. Dick Sisler, who played for 8 seasons and had a career average of .276 and Dave Sisler, who pitched for seven seasons and compiled a 38-44 record.

51. Lefty O'Doul of the Philadelphia Phillies and Bill Terry of the New York Giants both had 254 hits in one season. O'Doul did it in 1929 and hit .398; Terry did it in 1930 and hit .401.

52. Rod Carew of the Minnesota Twins. He hit in 131 of 155 games he played in 1977. Carew had 239 hits and a .388 batting average that season.

53. True. On May 15, 1925 Cobb hit three homeruns, two singles and a double in six at bats, setting a then total base record for one game.

54. False. Gehrig played in the outfield nine games and even played shortstop one game. His career spanned 17 years and 2,163 games (2,130 played consecutively, a major league record.)

57. Stottlemyre was 21-12 with an ERA of 2.45 and six shutouts for the New York Yankees.

58. The four 20 game winners were: Mike Cuellar (20-9), Pat Dobson (20-8), Jim Palmer (20-9), and Dave McNally (21-5).

59. St. Mary's, which is located in Baltimore. Ruth was signed by the Baltimore team in the International League directly out of St. Mary's.

60. The 1977 Cincinnati Reds hold the record with a .984 percentage. They were led by second baseman Joe Morgan and shortstop Dave Concepcion. Both led the league that year to help set a new record.

55. False. The rule states, "If a bat breaks and part of it is in fair territory and is hit by a batted ball or part of it hits a runner or fielder, play shall continue and no interference called."

56. True. In Pete Rose's first full season, 1963, with the Cincinnati Reds he hit .273 wth 170 hits in 157 games, good enough to allow him to be selected as the league's rookie of the year.

61. Len Barker of the Cleveland Indians pitched a perfect game against the Toronto Blue Jays on May 15, 1981, to become the first to do so since 1968.

62. Jim "Catfish" Hunter of the Oakland A's set down 27 straight Minnesota Twins on May 8, 1968, to become the first pitcher to do that in the American League since 1922 in regular season play.

BLIP   BLOP

63. On September 9, 1965, Sandy Koufax of the Los Angeles Dodgers threw the last perfect game in the National League beating the Chicago Cubs 1-0. The losing pitcher, Bob Hendley, only allowed one hit for the Cubs.

64. The oldest parks in the major leagues are either Comiskey Park, Chicago, built in 1910, or Tiger Stadium, Detroit, known as Bennett Park when it was built in 1910.

65. The three catchers were: Pat Collins, who hit .275 with 7 homeruns and 36 RBI's, Johnny Grabowski, who hit .277 with no homeruns and 25 RBI's, and Benny Bengough, who hit .247 with no homeruns and 10 RBI's.

66. No, Yankee Joe Dimaggio won it in 1941. That was the year he hit in 56 straight games for the world champions.

67. The seven former Yankee catchers are: Ralph Houk, Yogi Berra, Darrel Johnson, Bill Dickey, Gabby Street, Muddy Ruel, and Steve O'Neill.

I THINK THIS GUY HAS LOST SOME VELOCITY ON HIS FASTBALL

68. Joe Cronin, who played 20 years in the major leagues then managed for 15 more, was the American League's President from 1959 until 1973.

69. True. Jackson's best season was in 1969 with the Oakland Athletics when he hit 47 homeruns and drove in 118 RBI's.

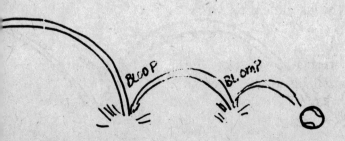

70. Yes, Sandy Koufax held the record with four no-hitters when he retired at the end of the 1966 season. His lifetime accomplishments include a 165-87 record with a 2.76 ERA and 2,396 strikeouts in 2,324.1 innings.

71. No, but he won the American League homerun title twice with 37 homers in 1972 and 32 in 1974, both with the Chicago White Sox. In his career Dick Allen hit a total of 351 homeruns and had a batting average of .292.

72. The Oakland Athletics came from a three games to two Mets lead and won the last two games to win the series.

73. They were the Boston Braves, who became the first modern franchise to move in 1952 when they went to Milwaukee.

74. False. Roger Maris of the New York Yankees set a major league record for homeruns with 61. He was not intentionally walked at all in 1961.

75. The National League has totally dominated the All-Star competition in recent years. The last time the American League won was in 1983 and before that the last time they won was in 1962.

76. In Robinson's 23 years of Major League baseball with the Baltimore Orioles, he won the gold glove award 16 times.

77. The Houston Astro's manager Bill Virdon who led his team to the Western Division Crown in 1980.

78. False. Babe Ruth never won the MVP because they didn't start awarding it until 1931, by that time Ruth was past his prime.

79. False. If you said true look into another sport. Mays hit 51 homeruns in the 1955 season and hit 52 in the 1965 season. He is third on the all-time list with 660 homeruns in 22 seasons.

80. The Los Angeles Dodgers swept the Yankees four straight to win the series. Sandy Koufax win 2 games including a 15 strikeout performance in the first game.

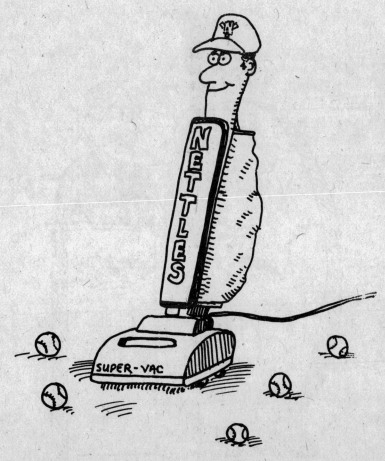

81. Jerry Reuss of the Los Angeles Dodgers no-hit the San Francisco Giants on June 27, 1980 in San Francisco. The score was 8-0.

82. Craig Nettles, who's been playing with the Yankees since 1973, has been one of the top homerun hitters in the American League since 1970 and also a great third baseman as well.

83. If you said the New York Yankees you're wrong. The Boston Red Sox are the only team since 1946 to have hit 100 or more homers except for the shortened 1981 season when they only had 90.

84. False. The only American League team to draw over a million spectators every year since 1964 is the Detroit Tigers.

85. Jon Matlack, who compiled a 15-10 record with a 2.32 ERA in his first full season with the Mets.

86. True. In Stottlemeyer's 11 years with the Yankees he compiled a 164-139 record. The 139 losses are most by any Yankee pitcher in history.

87. False. Mickey Mantle was the first player to hit a homerun in the Astrodome during an exhibition game in 1965.

88. False. The single game attendance record for Yankee Stadium is 74,747 set in a game in 1947.

89. Al Kaline, one of the few players never to play minor league ball, hit .297 in 22 seasons with the Tigers. He is also a member of the 3,000 hit club with a total of 3,007 in his career including 399 homeruns. Kaline wore number 6.

90. John Montefusco, who no-hit the Atlanta Braves in Atlanta on September 29, 1976. The Giants won 9-0

91. Jerry Koosman, who won two games in that series, beat the Orioles 5-3 in the fifth and final game to clinch the World championship for the Miracle Mets.

92. Alan Courtney recorded the very popular song "Joltin Joe Dimaggio", very popular among Yankee fans, that is.

93. Babe Ruth-714, Mickey Mantle-536, Lou Gehrig-493, Reggie Jackson-425, and Rocky Colavite-374.

94. On June 3, 1932, Lou Gehrig hit four homeruns against the Philadelphia Athletics and the Yankees won 20-13. Before Gehrig did it the last player to do it was Ed Delehanty of Philadelphia in 1896.

95. False. Al Downing was the last Yankee pitcher to lead the league in strikeouts with 217 in 1964. He compiled a 13-8 record with a 3.47 ERA that season.

96. False. During those 56 games Dimaggio slammed 15 homers, 16 doubles, 4 triples, 91 hits, scored 56 runs, 55 RBI's, and hit .408.

97. Babe Ruth hit his 60th homerun of the 1927 season off of Washington Senator pitcher Tom Zachary, the homer broke the Babe's 1921 mark of 59. He did it on the next to the last day of the season.

98. Jim Longborg of the Boston Red Sox gave up Mickey Mantle's 536th homerun, the last of his career, in 1968. Mantle retired before the start of the 1969 season.

99. Mickey Mantle led the American League in homeruns four times. He first won it in 1955 when he hit 37, again in 1956 with 52, 1958 with 42, and the last time in 1960 when he hit 40 out for the Bronx Bombers.

100. Mickey Mantle, who played 18 seasons with the Yankees and hit 536 homeruns, third on the all time list when he retired. He also holds the World Series records for homeruns with 18, runs scored-42, RBI's-40, walks-43, and was second in hits with 59.

101. Thurman Munson played only with the Yankees from 1969 until his death on August 2, 1979. He hit 113 homeruns with 701 RBI's and batted .292.

102. Ted Williams, who was the last man to bat over .400 with a .406 mark in 1941. He played 19 years with the Boston Red Sox and hit a total of 521 homeruns.

103. False. Chief Bender was one of the top pitchers in the American League for the Philadelphia Athletics. He had a 210-128 lifetime record with a 2.45 ERA and 1,711 strikeouts. Chief Bender was elected to the Hall of Fame in 1953.

104. False. The Watts Walloper was developed in the late 60's by the California Golden Oaks Products Company in Los Angeles. It was made of California oak that was chemically treated. The bat was being used but the competition was too tough and the company stopped producing it in the middle 70's.

105. No fielder can keep his foot on the bag unless he is making a play.

106. On September 28, 1919, the New York Giants beat the Philadelphia Phillies 6-1 in only 51 minutes.

107. The only three pitchers that are now in the Hall of Fame who threw perfect games are: Cy Young, Addie Joss and Sandy Koufax.

108. In 1980 Mike Squires of the Chicago White Sox, also a first baseman, caught two games. He has not caught in a game since.

109. A pitcher's ERA is calculated by multiplying his total earned runs by nine then dividing the total by the number of innings pitched.

110. Donn Clendonon played for 12 years with various National League teams and struckout a total of 1,140 times while hitting 159 career homeruns. Billy Williams played 18 big league seasons with the Chicago Cubs and Oakland Athletics and struckout a total of 1,046 while pounding out 426 homeruns.

111. True. Mantle is the only person in history to hit 40 or more homeruns and not have 100 RBI's. His totals of that 1960 season were: 40 homeruns, 94 RBI's, 119 runs scored and a .275 batting average.

117. In his 17 seasons of major league ball Joe Adcock never led the league in homeruns. He hit a total of 336 for his career including four in one game in 1954.

118. The record for putouts in a nine-inning game is 22. It is shared by Tom Jones of the St. Louis Browns, Hal Chase of the New York Highlanders (both made this record in 1906) and Ernie Banks of the Chicago Cubs in 1963.

119. False. Robert (Pat) Dillard of the St. Louis Cardinals set the record with nine in a game played way back in 1900.

112. Dick Stuart of the Pirates, Red Sox, Phillies, Mets, Dodgers and Angels. He played 10 seasons and hit a total of 228 homeruns with a league leading 118 RBI's. He received his nickname for poor play in the field.

113. Dave DeBusschere, who pitched for the Chicago White Sox for parts of two seasons in 1962-63. He had a 3-4 lifetime record with a 2.90 ERA.

114. Jay Hanna "Dizzy" Dean and his younger brother, Paul Dee "Daffy" Dean. Dizzy, who was elected into the Hall of Fame in 1953, had a 150-83 career record with a 3.03 ERA. Daffy had a 50-34 career record with a 3.75 ERA.

115. Maury Wills, playing for the Los Angeles Dodgers, stole 104 bases in 1962 to break Ty Cobb's record of 96 set in 1915. Wills threatened to break his own record in 1965 when he stole 94 times.

116. Ted Williams, who was elected into the Hall of Fame in 1966. He ended up with a lifetime batting average of .344 and a slugging average of .634, second only to Babe Ruth.

LOOK PAL, YOUR NAME MAY BE DAFFY, BUT YOU ARE NOT MY BROTHER.

120. Bobby Knoop set the record with 12 in one game in 1966. He also led the American League in triples that year with 11.

121. The record is 11. It was set by Horace (Hod) Ford in 1929 with the Cincinnati Reds and John Cassidy of the Washington Senators in 1904.

122. Jim Bottomley played 16 big league seasons for the Cardinals, Reds and Browns. He played 1,885 games at first base and one game at second. Bottomley had a lifetime .310 average and he led the National League in homers in 1928 with the Cardinals.

123. Boudreau played 15 major league seasons, 13 of which were the Cleveland Indians. He has a lifetime .295 average and was one of the top shortstops in the 40's. A good doubles hitter, he led the American League three times in hitting doubles. Boudreau played his last two seasons with the Red Sox and was elected to the Hall of Fame in 1970.

124. On April 22, 1970 Tom Seaver tied a major league record by striking out 19 and set a record when he set down 10 San Diego Padres in a row on strikes.

125. Melton was 20-9 his first season, thus helping the New York Giants win the pennant in 1937. He had a career record of 86-80 with a 3.42 ERA. In the 1937 World Series against the Yankees Melton lost two games.

NO WONDER I KEEP STRIKING OUT.

126. Cleveland Municipal Stadium has the largest seating capacity of any major league ball park. It can hold 74,000 spectators.

127. Shea Stadium is a National League Park and the home of the New York Mets.

128. Comiskey Park is an American League Park and the home of the Chicago White Sox.

129. The Brooklyn Dodgers moved to Los Angeles and the New York Giants moved to San Franscisco.

130. The Chicago Cubs play their home games at Wrigley Field.

131. Wrigley Field in Chicago. Phil Wrigley, who owned the team and the stadium, thought that baseball should be played during the day so no lights were added for night games.

132. Jimmie Foxx batted .325 with 534 career homeruns and 1,922 RBI's. DiMaggio also batted .325 in his career. He hit 331 homeruns with 1,537 RBI's.

133. Dale Murphy of the Atlanta Braves '82-'83: Mike Schmidt of the Philadelphia Phillies '80-'81; Joe Morgan of the Cincinnati Reds '75-'76; Ernie Banks of the Chicago Cubs '58-'59.

134. True. Ted Llyons never lost a World Series game because he never played in one. He pitched 21 seasons for the Chicago White Sox and during that time they never won the pennant.

135. Sal Maglie, who played 10 years and compiled a 110-62 record with a 3.15 ERA. His last season was in 1951 when he posted a 23-6 record for the New York Giants.

136. False. The record for most major league seasons, 26, was set by Deacon McGuire, who started playing in 1884 and finally retired in 1912. His lifetime batting average is .278 with 45 homeruns and 787 RBI's. McGuire was mainly a catcher, but he was versatile and played every position but second base.

137. Tommy Davis, who had his best years with the Dodgers. At that time he won the RBI title in 1962 with 153 and back to back batting average titles in 1962 and 1963 with averages of .346 and .326 respectively. During his eighteen years he played with the Dodgers, Mets, Astros, Cubs, Athletics, White Sox, Orioles, Pilots, Angels, and Royals.

138. Frank Thomas holds the record for playing with the most teams in one league with 7. During his 16 seasons Thomas played for the Pirates, Reds, Cubs, Braves, Mets, Phillies and Astros. He hit 20 or more homeruns in 9 different seasons and ended up with 286 in his career.

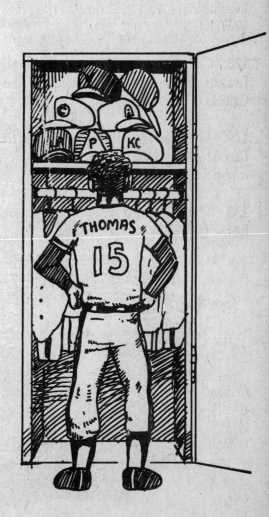

139. Bert Campaneris played all nine positions with the Kansas City Athletics in a 13 inning game on September 8, 1965 and Cesar Tovar became the second player to do so on September 22, 1968 for the Minnesota Twins. Campaneris was the first batter to face Tovar in that game and he struck out.

140. Ty Cobb did that playing for the Detroit Tigers in 1907, 1909-15, 1917-19. His best year was 1911 when he hit .420 and led the league in hits, doubles, triples, runs scored, RBI's stolen bases and slugging average.

146. "Wee" Willie Keeler, who played with the Baltimore Orioles from 1892 to 1910. He had a career average of .345 and once hit in 44 straight games. Keeler was elected to the Hall of Fame in 1939.

147. Tony Oliva played 15 seasons with the Minnesota Twins and had a career batting average of .304. He led the American League in hitting three times. In 1964 (.323), 1965 (.321) and 1971 (.337).

148. Aaron hit his 715th career homerun off the Dodgers' Al Downing to break Babe Ruth's career record in April of 1974. He retired in 1976 with 755 career homeruns.

141. True. From 1920 to 1925 Rogers Hornsby led the National League in batting with his best season in 1924 when he hit .424 for the St. Louis Cardinals. From 1920 to 1925 he averaged 216 hits a year.

142. Honus Wagner of the Pirates, one of the greatest ball players ever to play. During his 21 year career he had an average of .328 with 3,430 hits. He was also a good baserunner and stole successfully 722 times in his career.

143. During his 21 year career Honus Wagner never hit .400. His best season was in 1900 when he hit .381 and led the league in doubles (45), triples (22) and slugging average (.572).

144. Honus Wagner had one brother who played in the major leagues for one season, 1898. His name was Butts Wagner. He batted 261 times and had 59 hits for a .226 average.

145. Ty Cobb never played in the National League. He played 22 seasons with the Detroit Tigers and 2 seasons with the Philadelphia Athletics.

149. False. Nettles was traded to the Yankees before the 1973 season. He played third base and led the league in homeruns with 32 and homerun percentage, 5.5 which reflects the number of homeruns hit per 100 times at bat. In 1976 with the New York Yankees.

150. Yes. Jim Nettles, who played outfield for the Minnesota Twins and Detroit Tigers, batted .225 in his four year career in the major leagues.

151. When Hank Aaron won the MVP in 1957 he was playing in Milwaukee. He led the National League that year in homeruns with 44, runs scored with 118 and RBI's with 132.

152. Yes, Tommie Aaron, who played for seven years with the Braves. He had a lifetime average of .229 with 13 homeruns.

153. In Hank Aaron's 23 years of major league baseball he had a lifetime batting average of .305. He led the league in batting two times, in 1956 with a .328 mark and 1959, with a .355 average. In both those years he also led the league in hits.

154. True. Even though he has hit more homeruns than anybody else in major league history, the most he ever hit in one season was 47 in 1971.

155. Rick Wise hit two homeruns and pitched a no-hitter against the Cincinnati Reds on June 23, 1971 for the Philadelphia Phillies.

156. Denny McLain did that for the Tigers in 1968 and 1969. He was 31-6 with 1.96 ERA in 1968 and won the Cy Young award by a unanimous vote. In 1969 he was 24-9 with a 2.80 ERA and led the league with nine shutouts and shared the award with the Oriole's Mike Cuellar.

157. Christy Mathewson of the New York Giants and Cincinnati Reds. He had a lifetime 373-188 record with an ERA of 2.13 and 83 shutouts. Mathewson won 20 or more games 13 times and 30 or more games 4 times during his career.

158. George Foster, formerly of the Reds, hit 52 homeruns and knocked in 149 runs while hitting .320 in 1977 and won the most valuable player award. He led the league in homeruns again in 1978 with 40.

159. True. In 1909 Ty Cobb hit a league leading 9 homeruns. He also led the leagues in hits with 216, runs scored with 116, RBI's with 115, stolen bases with 76, batting average with a .377 mark and slugging percentage with a .517.

160. Frankie Crosetti, who played shortstop for the New York Yankees for 17 years. He had a career batting average of .245, but he was valuable for his great defensive play. Crosetti played in seven World Series and his team won all seven times.

161. Harry "Jasper" Davis led the American League four straight years with his best season in 1906 when he hit 12 homers with 96 RBI's. In Davis' 22 year career he hit 74 homeruns.

162. Wildfire Schulte of the Chicago Cubs hit 21 homeruns in 1911 and knocked in another 121 and became the first player in the 1900's to hit 20 or more homeruns in one season.

163. Duke Snider who played 18 big league seasons with the Dodgers, Mets, and Giants. He hit 407 lifetime homeruns and hit .295. From 1953 till 1957 Snider hit 40 or more homeruns for the Brooklyn Dodgers. He is fourth on the all-time world series list with 11 homeruns.

164. False. In 1956 Duke Snider led the National League with 43 homeruns and a slugging average(.598). He also led the league that year in walks with 99.

165. Ralph Garr won the 1978 National batting crown with .353 average for the Atlanta Braves. He also led the league in hits with 214, and triples with 17.

166. False. Steve Garvey started his career in 1969 with the Los Angeles Dodgers and has been with them ever since. He is one of the most consistent ballplayers in either league.

167. Carl Furillo who played 15 years with the Brooklyn and Los Angeles Dodgers. He had a lifetime .299 average.

IT'S THE DUKE OF BROOKLYN!

168. Yes. In 1953 Furillo led the National League with a .344 average for the Dodgers. He also hit 21 homeruns and knocked in 92 runs in his best season.

169. The teams in the League's Eastern Division are: The Toronto Blue Jays, New York Yankees, Baltimore Orioles, Cleveland Indians, Detroit Tigers, Milwaukee Brewers, and Boston Red Sox.

170. The teams in the American League's Western Division are: The Texas Rangers, Chicago White Sox, Oakland Athletics, California Angels, Kansas City Royals, Seattle Mariners, and Minnesota Twins.

171. The teams in the National Leagues Western Division are: The Cincinnati Reds, Houston Astros, Atlanta Braves, San Francisco Giants, San Diego Padres, and the Los Angeles Dodgers.

172. The teams in the National League's Eastern Division are: The New York Mets, Chicago Cubs, Pittsburgh Pirates, Montreal Expos, St. Louis Cardinals, and Philadelphia Phillies.

173. Yes, Max Flask of the Chicago Cubs was traded for Clifton Heathcote of the St. Louis Cardinals in between games of a double-header on May 30, 1922.

174. Ty Cobb has the highest career batting of anybody ever to play the game with a .367 average over 24 years of major league play with the Detroit Tigers and Philadelphia Athletics.

398

175. Rogers Hornsby holds the career record for highest batting average by a National Leaguer with a .359 mark playing for the St. Louis Cardinals (1915-26, 1933), New York Giants (1927), and the Chicago Cubs (1929-32). He had an overall .358 mark with 2,930 hits, 302 homeruns, and 1,584 RBI's.

176. True. In 1922 Rogers Hornsby hit 42 homeruns with the Cardinals to lead the National League. He won the title again in 1925 when he hit 39 homeruns again for the Cards. Both years he also won the batting average title with .401 and .403 averages respectively.

177. They both finished their careers with a .344 averages. Speakers had 3,515 hits in his career and Williams had 2,654 lifetime hits. Ted Williams was the more productive homerun hitter with 521 compared to Speaker's 116.

178. False. In Tris Speakers 22 years of major league baseball he never led the league in homeruns. His best season for homeruns was in 1923 when he hit 17 for the Cleveland Indians.

WHERE'D HE GO?

179. True. Ted Williams of the Boston Red Sox led the American League in homeruns in 1941, 42, 47, 49, with his best season in 1949 when he hit 43 out with 159 RBI's also tops in the league.

180. False. Wills led the National League six consecutive seasons from 1960 til 1965. During that span Wills stole 376 bases for an average of almost 63 a season.

186. False. Stan Musial never led the league in strikeouts. He was known as a contact hitter and proved it by having a lifetime .331 average over 22 seasons.

187. Even though his career output was great he never led the league in homeruns. His best season was in 1948 when he hit 39 and would have won the triple crown except that Ralph Kiner and Johnny Mize both hit 40 homers to lead the league.

181. False. Boog Powell never led the league in homeruns even though he had some fine seasons hitting the long ball. His best season was in 1969 when he hit 37 homeruns with 121 RBI's and hit .304 for the Baltimore Orioles. Powell finished his career with 339 homeruns.

182. James "Tip" O'Neill of the old St. Louis Browns of the American Association. He also led the league in hits with 225, doubles-52, triples-19, homeruns-14, runs scored-167, and slugging average .691.

183. Hugh Duffy of the old Boston Beaneaters accomplished this with 236 hits in 539 at bats. He also led the league that year in doubles with 51, homeruns with 18, RBI's with 145, and slugging average with a .688 mark.

184. Cy Young, who played 22 seasons starting in 1890 and ending in 1911. He won a total of 511 games with his best season in 1892 when he won 36 games while losing only 10 and had a league leading ERA of 1.93.

185. Denton True Young who was born on March 29, 1867 in Gilmore, Ohio. He was inducted into the Hall of Fame in 1937 and died on November 4, 1955.

188. Babe Ruth played with the Boston Red Sox from 1914 until 1919. He was mainly a pitcher there and compiled a 89-46 record.

189. True. In 1916 Ruth was 23-12 with a league leading 1.75 ERA and 9 shutouts. He also won a game in that year's World Series. Ruth came right back and won 24 games while losing only 13 in 1917 with an ERA of 2.01.

190. Yes, he was 5-0 from 1920 through 1933. Overall he compiled a lifetime 94-46 record with a 2.28 ERA. In World Series competition he was 3-0 with a 0.87 ERA, not bad for one of the greatest homerun hitters of all-time.

191. Babe Ruth hit a total of 714 home-runs with 2,216 RBI's in 22 major seasons. He had a .342 lifetime batting average and a .690 slugging average.

192. Hal Trosky played first base for the Cleveland Indians from 1933 until 1941 and finished his career with the Chicago White Sox in 1946. Trosky's best season was in 1936 when he hit 42 homeruns and had a league leading 162 RBI's. He also batted .343 that year. He had a career .302 average.

193. Babe Ruth did it twice with 59 homeruns in 1921 and 60 in 1927. Jimmie Foxx hit 58 in 1932, Hank Greenberg hit 58 in 1938, and Roger Maris hit a record 61 in the 1961 season.

194. Rollie Fingers of the Milwaukee Brewers won the 1981 Cy Young award. He led the major leagues in saves with 28. He posted a 6-3 record with a 1.04 earned run average in 47 games and 78 innings.

195. Rollie Fingers holds the major league record in career saves with 301. Fingers also starred in the 1972, 73, and 1974 World Series. He was named the MVP of the 1974 series against the Dodgers.

201. The last time the Dodgers won the World Series was in 1965 when they defeated the Minnesota Twins 4 games to 3. Sandy Koufax was the pitching star winning 2 games and striking out 29 batters in 24 innings.

202. The Tigers came from a 3 games to 1 deficit to beat the St. Louis Cardinals 4 games to 3. Mickey Lolich was the Tigers' pitching star winning three and losing none. The hitting star was Al Kaline, who had 11 hits, 2 doubles, 2 homeruns and 8 RBI's.

196. Sparky Lyle of the New York Yankees won the Cy Young award in 1977 with a 13-5 record, a 2.17 ERA and 26 saves in 72 games.

197. False. The Los Angeles Dodgers beat the Yankees 4 games to 2. The Yankees jumped out to a 2 game to nothing lead but the Dodgers came back and won four straight to take the series.

198. Yankee reliever George Frazier became the first player ever to lose three games in a six game series. He pitched a total of 3 2/3 innings and gave up nine hits, seven earned runs for a 17.18 ERA.

199. Los Angeles Dodgers players Ron Cey, Pedro Guerrero and Steve Yeager all were co-winners of the award. Among the three of them they had 5 homeruns, 17 RBI's on 18 hits and scored seven runs.

200. True. Garvey was 10 for 24 and scored three runs for a .417 batting average. Lou Piniella and Bob Watson led the Yankees with seven hits each.

203. True. Tommy John, then a Dodger, won the first game of the 1978 World Series against the Yankees. He won the second game of the 1981 series for the Yankees against the Dodgers.

204. Bill Madlock of the Pittsburgh Pirates led the National League in hitting with a .341 average to beat out Pete Rose who hit .325 and Dusty Baker who hit .320.

205. Hubie Brooks hit a .307 which placed him ninth in the entire National League. He was the Mets' most consistent hitter in 1981 and led the team in hits with 110.

206. For the second consecutive season Mike Schmidt of the Philadelphia Phillies won the National League homerun title with 31 in the shortened 1981 season. He hit 48 homeruns in 1980 to lead the Major leagues.

207. Yes. He won the homerun title in 1974, 75 and 76. Schmidt has hit 31 or more homeruns seven times out of the last eight seasons.

208. Orlando Cepeda, who hit .325 with 25 homeruns and a league leading 111 RNI's for the Cardinals in 1967. The Cardinals also won the World Series that year beating the Red Sox 4 games to 3.

209. Yes. Cepeda led the National League in homeruns in 1961 with the San Francisco Giants. He hit 46 out and also led the league with 14 RBI's while batting .311. Cepeda was a versatile ball player who played outfield and first base. He hit a total of 379 homeruns in his career.

FOR THE SECOND TIME, I'VE BEEN AT THE RIGHT PLACE WITH THE WRONG TEAM.

211. 1981 homerun leader Mike Schmidt of the Phillies also won the RBI title with 91 beating out George Foster who had 90. Andre Dawson had 64 for the Expos.

212. Tim Raines, who set the rookie record for steals with 71 during the 1981 season. He also batted .304. If it hadn't been for the baseball strike Raines would have had a good opportunity to set a new major league record.

210. Norm Cash was acquired by the Detroit Tigers from the Chicago White Sox before the 1960 season. He played first base for the Tigers for the next 15 years. His best season was in 1961 when he led the American League with a .361 batting average and total hits with 193. Cash also hit 41 homeruns and knocked in 132 runs. Overall he hit .377 lifetime homeruns and batted .271.

213. Cal Ripken Jr., the Baltimore Orioles' shortstop in 1983.

214. True. Schmidt scored 78 runs to lead the National League beating out Pete Rose (73 runs scored) and Andre Dawson (71 runs scored).

215. True. Pete Rose, who is still going strong in his nineteenth major league season, hit .325 with 140 hits in 431 at bats for the Phillies in 1981.

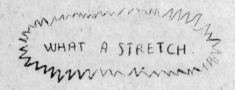

WHAT A STRETCH.

216. Pete Rose, who, at the end of the 1983 season, ranks second in total number of hits with 3,990; first in at-bats with 13,037 and carries a lifetime average of .306.

217. Bill Buckner, the Cubs' first baseman, led the major leagues with 35 doubles in 1981. He also hit .311 with 10 homeruns and 75 RBI's in the shortened 1981 season.

218. Tris Speaker holds the all-time major league record with 793 doubles in 22 years of play. He also had 3,515 hits and batted .344.

219. Gene Richards of the San Diego Padres and Craig Reynolds of the Houston Astros tied for the league lead with 12.

220. Tom Seaver led the Major leagues with a .875 won-lost percentage. He was 14-2 with a 2.54 ERA and 87 strikeouts for the Cincinnati Reds in 1981. Steve Carlton was second in the National League with a 13-4 record for a .765 won-lost percentage.

221. The Philadelphia Phillies led the National League with a .273 team batting average, followed by the Reds (.268) and the Cardinals (.265).

222. The Chicago Cubs had the worst team batting average in the National League in 1981 with an average of only .236. The Braves hit .243 and the Mets had a team average of .249.

223. Dave Concepcion of the Cincinnati Reds hit .308 with 67 RBI's compared to Templeton's .288 average with 33 RBI's and Bowa's .283 average and 31 RBI's.

224. False. Huggins played 13 big league seasons with the Cincinnati Reds and the St. Louis Cardinals. He had a lifetime .265 average. That he was basically a singles hitter is shown by the fact that he had only 205 extra base hits out of his 1,474 total. Huggins was also a good baserunner and stole 324 bases in his career.

225. Dave Kingman played outfield and first base for the New York Mets in 1981. He hit .221 with 22 homeruns and 59 RBI's. In his 12 seasons he has hit a total of 292 homeruns and knocked in 779 runs.

226. Steve Garvey plays first base for the Los Angeles Dodgers. He has never led the league in hitting but is a consistent .300 hitter. He has had six seasons of 200 or more hits in his career. In 1981 he batted .281 with 10 homeruns and 64 RBI's.

227. Fireball Nolan Ryan of the Houston Astros led the National League with a 1.69 ERA in 149 innings in 1981. He had a 11-5 record with 140 strikeouts.

228. Bob Horner plays third base for the Atlanta Braves. He set the NCAA career mark for homeruns with 58 at Arizona State. In 1981 he hit 14 homeruns with 42 RBI's and a .277 batting average. Horner has hit a total of 105 homeruns in his first four years in the major leagues.

229. The teams in the Eastern Division of the National League are: the St. Louis Cardinals, New York Mets, Pittsburgh Pirates, Chicago Cubs, Philadelphia Phillies, and Montreal Expos.

230. The teams in the Western Division of the National League are: Cincinnati Reds, Los Angeles Dodgers, Houston Astros, San Francisco Giants, Atlanta Braves and the San Diego Padres.

231. The New York Yankees, Baltimore Orioles, Boston Red Sox, Milwaukee Brewers, Detroit Tigers, Cleveland Indians, and the Toronto Blue Jays.

232. The Oakland Athletics, Kansas City Royals, Seattle Mariners, Minnesota Twins, California Angels, Texas Rangers, and the Chicago White Sox.

233. The Philadelphia Phillies won the first half of the season with a 34-21 record, 1½ games ahead of the St. Louis Cardinals in 1981.

234. The Los Angeles Dodgers won the first half with a 36-21 record, ½ game ahead of the Cincinnati Reds. The Dodgers went on to win the World Series in 1981.

235. False. The Oakland Athletics won the first half with a 37-23 record, 1½ games ahead of the Texas Rangers. The A's set a record by winning 18 games in April of the 1981 season.

236. The New York Yankees won the first half with a 34-22 record, 2 games ahead of the Baltimore Orioles and 3 games ahead the Brewers. The Yankees went on to lose the World Series to the Dodgers 4 games to 2 in 1981.

237. True. The Expos posted a 30-23 record finishing ½ game ahead of the St. Louis Cardinals in 1981. They finished with a combined 60-48 record.

238. The Houston Astros won the second half with a 33-20 record finishing 1½ games ahead of the Cincinnati Reds. The Astros lost to the Dodgers in the playoffs in 1981.

239. False. The Kansas City Royals won the second half after a horrible first half (20-30 record for the first half) with a 30-23 record to beat out the Oakland A's by 1 game. The Oakland A's then beat the Royals 3 games straight to win the Western Division title.

240. The Milwaukee Brewers won the second half with a 31-22 record finishing 1½ games ahead of the Boston Red Sox and Detroit Tigers. The Brewers lost to the Yankees in the Western Division playoff 3 games to 2.

241. True. The Royals won the second half title in the Western Division but had an overall losing record of 50-53. In the first half of the season they were 20-30, 12 games out of first place.

242. The Cincinnati Reds had the best overall record in major league baseball in 1981 with a 66-42 record compared to Oakland's 64-45 and Los Angeles' 63-47 mark; yet they did not qualify for the play-offs.

243. Pete Vudkovich of the Brewers compiled a 14-4 record, Oriole Dennis Martinez posted a 14-5 mark, and Steve McCatty of the A's had a 14-7 record.

244. Mike Norris pitches for the Oakland Athletics. He posted a 12-9 record with a 3.75 ERA in 1981. His best season was in 1980 when he had a 22-9 record with a 2.54 ERA.

THIS IS WHAT WE GOT FOR HAVING THE BEST RECORD IN BASEBALL IN 1981.

245. The New York Yankees did not win 60 games during the 1981 season. They were 59-48 overall. The Brewers were 62-47 and the Tigers were 60-49.

246. False. Both the Chicago Cubs and the Toronto Blue Jays did not win 40 games in 1981. The Blue Jays had the worst record at 37-69 and the Cubs were second at 38-65.

247. Tom Seaver of the Cincinnati Reds was the only National League pitcher to win 14 games in 1981. He posted a 14-2 mark with a 2.54 ERA and 87 strikeouts in 166 innings pitched.

248. Carney Lansford, who hit a league leading .336 with 134 hits in 399 at bats and 54 RBI's.

249. Eddie Murray of the Baltimore Orioles, Dwight Evans of the Boston Red Sox, Bobby Grich of the California Angeles, and Tony Armas of the Oakland Athletics all hit 22 homeruns each in the shortened 1981 season.

250. Eddie Murray of the Baltimore Orioles knocked in a league leading 78 runs to beat out Oakland's Tony Armas who had 76 RBI's in 1981. Murray also batted .304 and has 133 career homeruns in just seasons.

251. As of the 1983 season Carl Yastrzemski has hit 452 career homeruns with 1,844 RBI's compared to Reggie Jackson's 478 career homeruns and 1,435 RBI's.

252. False. Ricky Henderson of the Oakland Athletics led the American Leagues in steals with 56 in 1981. Jose Cruz of Seattle was second and Leflore was third with 36.

253. False. Ty Cobb's record for stolen bases, 96 in 1915, was broken in 1980 by Oakland A's Rickey Henderson, who stole 100 bases. Henderson set the Major League record in 1981 with 130 swipes.

254. True. Carl Yastrzemski of the Boston Red Sox hit .301 to beat out Danny Cater of the Oakland A's, who hit only .290. It was the lowest average to win a batting title in major league history.

255. Yes, In 1967 Yaz hit a league leading .326 and also led in homeruns with 44 and RBI's with 121. He also led the American League that year with 189 hits, 112 walks, and a .622 slugging average.

ZOOM

BOOF

256. Ricky Henderson of the Oakland Athletics led the American League with 89 runs scored to beat out Red Sox Dwight Evans who scored 84 times.

257. Willie Mays, who played with the Giants and the Mets in his 22 major league season. He hit 660 lifetime homeruns with 3,283 hits and batted .302. Mays also led the National League in homers four times with his best total coming in 1965 when he hit 52.

258. True. Even though Mays is in the top ten lifetime in RBI's he never led the league. In 1962 he knocked in 141 runs but Tommy Davis of the Dodgers led with 153.

259. Bill Mazeroski played second base for the Pittsburgh Pirates for 17 seasons. He started in 1956 and ended in 1972. He batted .260 in his career with 2,016 hits out of 7,755 at bats.

260. False. Ricky Henderson of the Oakland A's led the league with 135 hits to beat out Carney Lansford of the Red Sox who had 134 hits and Willie Wilson who had 133.

261. Lloyd Waner, who played most of his 18 big league seasons with the Pittsburgh Pirates. He had a lifetime .316 batting average and was voted into the Hall of Fame in 1967.

262. Paul Waner brother of Lloyd Waner who played most of his 20 seasons with the Pirates. He led the National League three times in batting and had an overall .333 average. Paul was inducted into the Hall of Fame in 1952.

263. Pete Rose holds the all time record for most 200 hit seasons with 10 compared to Ty Cobb's 9.

264. Yankee great Mickey Mantle hit a career 536 homeruns in 18 years. The switch hitting Mantle was inducted into the Hall of Fame in 1974.

265. True. Cooper led the American League with 34 doubles in 1981 beating out Al Oliver, who had 29. Cooper had a good year in 1981 with 12 homeruns and 60 RBI's while batting .320 for the Brewers.

266. Philadelphia Phillies and Montreal Expos hold the National League record for switch hitters with 158 homeruns in 21 Major League seasons as of the end of the 1983 season.

267. False. John Castino of the Minnesota Twins, who won the 1979 Rookie of the Year award, won the triples title in 1981 with 9. George Brett was second with 7.

268. George Brett of the Kansas City Royals flirted with .400 most of the year and ended up with a .390 average and the Most Valuable Player award. Many consider him the best hitter in modern times.

269. Len Barker of the Cleveland Indians led the American League in strikeouts with 127 in 154 innings pitched. Britt Burns of the White Sox was second with 108 and Guidry of the Yankees was fourth with 104.

270. Jim Palmer has played 18 seasons with the Baltimore Orioles and has compiled a 268-149 record with 2,208 strikeouts and a 2.83 ERA. He won the Cy Young award in 1973, 1975, and 1976. A sure Hall of Famer he is also an underwear model and salesman.

271. Gavvy Cravath led the National League six times in homeruns with the Philadelphia Phillies. He won the homerun title in 1913-15, 1917-19 with his best season in 1915 when he hit 24 homeruns and knocked in 115 runs. Cravath hit a total of 119 homeruns in his 11 year major league career.

272. Ozzie Smith plays shortstop for the St. Louis Cardinals. Though not a great hitter (he hit .243 in 1983) he is one of the league's best shortstops. Smith set the major league mark for assists by a shortstop in 1980 and won the Gold Glove that year.

273. Yes. Carew hit .305 in 1981 for the Angels and has hit over .300 thirteen straight seasons. His best year was in 1977 when he hit .388 with 239 hits for the Minnesota Twins. He was the best hitter in the 70's with a .343 during that decade.

274. True. Singleton was the Mets' first pick in the January draft of 1967 and played his first two seasons with them (1970-71) before going to the Expos. He went to the Orioles in 1975 and had his best season in 1977 when he hit .328 with 24 homeruns and 99 RBI's. Singleton is a lifetime .291 hitter with 208 homers and 868 RBI's.

275. Vida Blue compiled a 24-8 record with 301 strikeouts and a 1.82 ERA in 1971 with the Oakland A's. He has the distinction of starting the All-Star game for both leagues. In 1981 he was 8-6 with a 2.53 ERA and 63 strikeouts.

276. Frank Robinson, who was named the manager of the Cleveland Indians on October 3, 1974. He lasted less than 2½ seasons there and as of 1981 he was managing the San Francisco Giants.

277. If you said Frank Robinson, you are right! He first won the MVP award with the Cincinnati Reds in 1961 when he hit 37 homers and knocked in 124 runs while batting .323. Robinson again won the MVP award in 1966 with the Baltimore Orioles of the American League. He hit 49 homeruns, batted in 122 runs and hit .316 to win not only the MVP but also the triple crown.

278. Yes. In his third season, 1949, Robinson hit a league leading .342 with 203 hits out of 593 at bats. He also led the league in stolen bases that year with 37. He finished his major league career in 1956 with a lifetime .311 average and was elected to the Hall of Fame in 1962.

279. True. In 1920 Ruth set the major league record for slugging average with a .847 mark. He hit 54 homeruns with 36 doubles and 9 triples while batting .376 for the New York Yankees. He also set the single season mark for homerun percentage with a 11.8 mark that same season.

280. George Sisler of the St. Louis Browns set the hit record with 257 in the 1920 season. He also hit .407 that year. Sisler hit a lifetime .340 and was elected to the Hall of Fame in 1939.

281. Earl Webb did that in 1931 with the Boston Red Sox. He set the record with a total of 67 doubles of 196 hits while hitting. 333 that year. That was the only full season that Webb ever played in the major leagues.

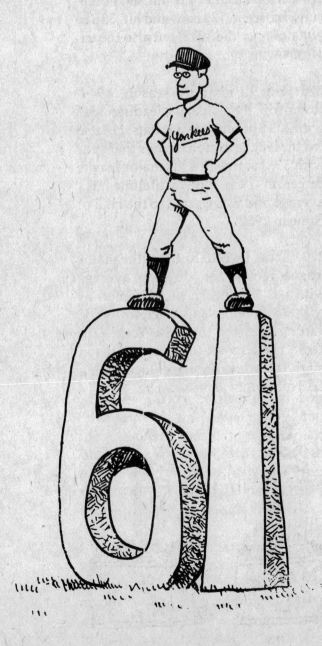

282. True. Owen Wilson set the record with 36 triples in 1912 with the Pittsburgh Pirates. Not a great hitter, he had a knack for hitting triples. He had 12 or more triples for six consecutive seasons from 1909 until 1914.

283. Babe Ruth hit 60 homeruns in 1927 and it seemed a good bet at the time his record would stand forever. But in 1961 Roger Maris hit his sixty first homerun to break the Babe's record. They both played for the New York Yankees and both had the short right field porch to shoot at in Yankee Stadium.

284. Roger Maris hit his record breaking homerun off rookie righthander Tracy Stallard of the Red Sox. He accomplished his feat in the fourth inning of the last game of the season at Yankee Stadium in 1961. For his tremendous season Maris won the most valuable player award.

285. True. In 1921 Babe Ruth had a total of 457 total bases to set a major league record. He had 59 homeruns, 16 triples, 44 doubles, and 85 singles while hitting .378 for the Yankees.

415

286. False. Hack Wilson of the Chicago Cubs set the record with 190 RBI's in the 1930 season. He also hit 56 homeruns and hit .356 that year. Hack wasn't that tall at 5 feet, 6 inches, but he weighed 190 pounds and could hit the ball a long way. From 1926 until 1930 he led the National League in homeruns four times and in RBI's twice.

287. Babe Ruth holds the single season record for walks with 170 in the 1923 season. Ted Williams is second with 162 in 1947 and again in 1949.

288. Lou Brock of the St. Louis Cardinals broke Maury Wills' record by far in 1974 when he stole 118 bases. He also hit .306 that year and scored 105 runs. Rickey Henderson of the Oakland Athletes broke Brock's record in 1982 when he stole 130 bases.

289. True. In 1974 Kranepool was 17 for 35 as a pinch hitter for a .486 batting average which broke the record set by Smead Jolley in 1931. Jolley hit .467. Kranepools' best season was in 1975 when he hit .323 and was 8 for 20 as a pinch hitter.

290. In 1970 Bobby Bonds broke his own major league record for striking out by 2 when he k'ed 189 times with the San Francisco Giants. Bonds is one of the few players to hit over 30 homeruns and steal over 30 bases in one season, something he has done five times in his career.

291. Jack Chesbro of the old New York Highlanders won 41 and lost only 12 in the 1904 season. He also had a 1.82 earned run average pitching in 454.2 innings and striking out 239 batters. Chesbro was elected to the Hall of Fame in 1946.

DON'T THROW IT SO HARD!

294. In 1973 Nolan Ryan struck out 383 batters in 326 innings to break Koufax's record by one. He also won 21 games that year for the California Angels.

295. Nolan Ryan holds the record with five seasons of 300 or more strikeouts. Johnson did it two times and Koufax three times.

296. Walter Johnson, who played with the Washington Senators from 1907 until he retired after the 1927 season. He compiled a 416-279 record with a 2.17 ERA and 3,508 strikeouts. He had the hardest pitch of his time and was elected to the Hall of Fame in 1936.

297. Grover Cleveland Alexander set the major league record in 1916 for shutouts with 16. Playing for the Philadelphia Phillies he also led the league that year with 33 wins, a 1.55 ERA and 167 strikeouts. When he retired in 1930 he had compiled a 373-208 record with 90 shutouts. Alexander was inducted into the Hall of Fame in 1938.

292. Roy Face, who, in 1959 for the Pittsburgh Pirates, went 18-1 for a record .947 winning percentage. His 18 games won all came in relief. He also recorded 10 saves that year. Face was a top reliever in the National League for 16 years. He retired with a 96-82 record in relief with 193 saves.

293. No. In 1914 while playing for the Boston Red Sox, Dutch Leonard had an 18-5 record with a record 1.01 ERA in 222.2 innings. In his 11 year career he went 138-113 with a good 2.77 ERA for the Red Sox and the Tigers.

298. Babe Ruth holds the lifetime major league record with a .690 slugging average compared to Ted Williams' .634, Lou Gehrig's .632 and Willie Mays' .557.

299. True. Aaron had a lifetime total of 6,856 bases. Stan Musial is second with 6,134 and Willie Mays is third with 6,066.

300. Ty Cobb had a total of 5,863 bases in his career to beat out Babe Ruth who had 5,793 total bases in his career.

301. Tom Seaver started his career with the New York Mets in 1967 and is now pitching with the ChicagoWhitesox. He has won 273 games for an average of over 16 victories a season. Steve Carlton started his career with the St. Louis Cardinals in 1965 and is now pitching with the Philadelphia Phillies. He has won 300 games in his career for an average of over 16 victories a season.

302. Steve Carlton has compiled a lifetime 300-200 record with 3,709 strikeouts and an ERA of 3.01. Tom Seaver has compiled a career record of 273-170 with 3,272 strikeouts and a 2.73 ERA. Both have won the Cy Young award three times.

303. Ryne Duren, who for three years was a very effective relief pitcher with the Yankees. He compiled a 12-14 record but had 43 saves and struck out 250 batters in 201.1 innings.

304. Erskine pitched 12 seasons with the Brooklyn and Los Angeles Dodgers and compiled a career 122-78 record. He threw two no-hitters in his career. Erskine no-hit the Chicago Cubs on June 19, 1952 and did the same to the N.Y. Giants on May 16, 1956.

305. The previous record of eight consecutive k's was shared by Max Surkont, Johnny Podres, Jim Mahomey and Don Wilson.

306. Christy Mathewson of the Giants pitched three shutouts during the 1905 World Series against the Philadelphia Athletics who were coached by Connie Mack.

307. Grove started his career in 1925 with the Philadelphia Athletics where he pitched until 1933. In 1934 he joined the Red Sox where he stayed until his retirement at the end of the 1941 season. Grove compiled a 300-140 record with a 3.06 ERA. He led the American League in strikeouts his first seven seasons and he led the league a total of nine times in ERA in his career. Lefty's best season was in 1931 when he also won 2 games in the World Series.

308. True. Toothpick Sam Jones' career highlight was pitching a no-hitter for the Chicago Cubs against the Pittsburgh Pirates on May 12, 1955. He had a career 102-101 record with a 3.59 ERA. He also led the National League three times in strikeouts, once in ERA and once in wins with 21 in 1959.

309. McGinnity had a lifetime 242-142 record in 10 major league seasons averaging over 24 victories a season. He won 32 games in 1903 and 33 more in 1904 with the N.Y. Giants. He continued pitching in the minor leagues after he left the majors until 1925 when he was 54 years old. In McGinnity's first minor league season he won 59 games. The Iron Man was elected to the Hall of Fame in 1946.

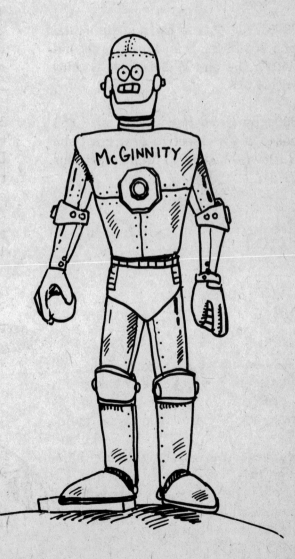

311. Fernando Valenzuela, the rookie sensation of the Los Angeles Dodgers, who compiled a 13-7 record with a league leading 180 strikeouts and an ERA of 2.48.

312. Nolan Ryan, who compiled an 11-5 record with 140 strikeouts and a league leading 1.69 ERA.

313. Yankee rookie pitcher Dave Righetti, who was called up during the season registered an 8-4 record with a 2.05 ERA to lead the AL starting pitchers in that department.

314. Eddie Collins played 25 seasons with the Philadelphia Athletics and Chicago White Sox. He compiled a .333 lifetime batting average of 3,310 hits and when he retired in 1930 he was second to Ty Cobb in stolen bases with 743. Collins was inducted into the Hall of Fame in 1939.

310. Satchel Paige, who, if he had played major league baseball in his prime, could have been as good as they come. He pitched in the major leagues from 1948 until 1953 and pitched a short 3 inning stint with the Kansas City Athletics in 1965. He compiled a 6-1 rookie record with the Indians at the age of 42 and was 12-10 in 1952 at the age of 46.

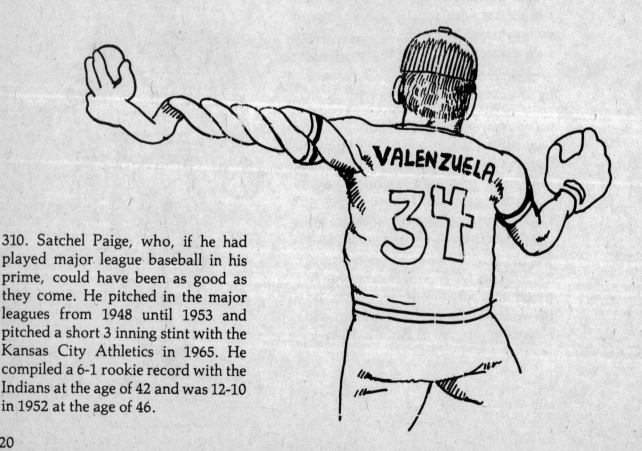

315. Roy Campanella, who for 10 major league seasons was regarded as one of the best catchers in the game. He won the MVP Award in 1951, 1953, and 1955. In his best season, 1953, he hit .312 with 41 homeruns (major league record for a catcher) and drove in a league leading 142 runs.

316. Bill Terry, who played for 14 seasons with the Giants and hit a lifetime .341, second only to Rogers Hornsby in the National League. He hit .401 in 1930 with 254 hits, 23 homeruns and 129 RBI's. Terry was inducted into the Hall of Fame in 1954.

317. Roberto Clemente played 18 seasons with the Pittsburgh Pirates and hit .317 with exactly 3,000 hits. He led the National League four times in batting and won the MVP Award in 1966. Clemente was also a great outfielder with a powerful and accurate throwing arm.

318. Baltimore Oriole Jim Palmer, who has won the Cy Young Award three times, 1973, 75, 76. He has won 20 or more games 8 times. He has a lifetime 2.83 ERA.

319. Duke Snider, who played with the Dodgers from 1947 until 1962 and finished his career in 1964 after one year stints with the Mets and Giants. He hit 40 or more homeruns five consecutive seasons (1953-57) and .407 for his career. In six World Series Duke hit 11 homeruns and drove in 26 runs.

321. False. Cuyler played 18 seasons with the Pirates, Cubs, Reds and Dodgers. He hit a career .321, led the league in stolen bases 4 times, runs scored twice, triples once, and doubles once. His first full season in 1924 with the Pirates Cuyler hit .354 and came right back in 1925 and hit .357.

323. Johnny Vander Meer of the Cincinnati Reds did that in 1938. On June 11 Vander Meer no-hit the Boston Bees 3-0. Four days later, on June 15, Vandy came right back and no-hit the Brooklyn Dodgers 6-0 to establish a Major League record that will be very hard to surpass or equal.

320. Dom Di Maggio, who played 11 years with the Boston Red Sox and who had a lifetime batting average of .298. His best season was in 1950 when he batted .328 and led the league in triples, runs scored and stolen bases. The oldest brother was Vince Di Maggio who played with several teams during his 10 year career. His career average was .249.

324. Although the Giants won 43 games in an unusual fashion in 1916 they could finish no higher in the standing than fourth. The 17 straight victories were all played on the road, the second string of 26 came at home at the Polo Grounds.

325. His own! In 1920 Babe Ruth set the Major League record with 54 homers. In 1921 Ruth broke his own record with 59 round trippers.

326. Maris hit 30 homeruns at Yankee Stadium whereas Babe Ruth hit only 28 at the big ball yard in the south Bronx.

THIS IS THE POLO GROUNDS, RIGHT?

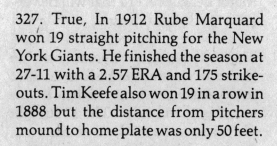

WHAT DO YOU MEAN
"TAKE THE MASK OFF,"
I'M NOT WEARING ONE

327. True, In 1912 Rube Marquard won 19 straight pitching for the New York Giants. He finished the season at 27-11 with a 2.57 ERA and 175 strikeouts. Tim Keefe also won 19 in a row in 1888 but the distance from pitchers mound to home plate was only 50 feet.

328. Bob Gibson who was one of the toughest competitors ever to play the game. In 1968 he posted a 1.12 ERA while leading the league in shutouts with 13, he also struck out 268 batters in 304 innings. Overall he had a 251-174 record with 3,117 strikeouts.

329. Bill Dickey the former Yankee back stop hit .326 in 1936, the highest ever for a catcher. He was a great hitter who also set the American League record for going through a full season without a passed ball in 1931, 125 games. He was inducted into the Hall of Fame in 1954.

330. Lawrence Peter "Yogi" Berra who played on 14 pennant winning Yankee teams in his 17 seasons with the team. He was also voted the most valuable player three times (1951, 54, 55) in the American League. Berra had a lifetime .285 average with 358 homeruns and 1,430 RBI's.

331. Bob Feller who posted a career record of 266-162 including three no-hitters and a record 12 one hitters. He led the league six times in wins, seven times in strikeouts, and five times in shutouts. Bob Feller was inducted in Hall of Fame in 1962.

332. Mike Schmidt who is not only a great fielder but a great hitter as well. He led the league in homeruns in 1974-76, '80, '81, '83 and has hit 389 in 12 seasons in Major Leagues. He once hit four outs in one game in 1976 and seven in five games in 1979.

333. Ernie Lombardi who had a lifetime .306 in 17 seasons with Brooklyn, Cincinnati, Boston and New York in the National League. He was the catcher for Johnny Vander Meer's double no hitters in 1938.

334. Jimmie Foxx who was one of the most feared right handed hitters of all-time. From 1925 to 1945 he hit a total fo 534 homeruns with 1922 RBI's and a .325 batting average. His best season was in 1932 when he hit 58 homeruns with 169 RBI's (both led the league) and .364 batting average.

335. Hank Greenberg of the Detroit Tigers hit 58 homeruns in 1938 to lead the Major Leagues. A great homerun hitter who led the league four times in that department, he also led the league four times in RBI's including a 183 RBI performance in 1937. Greenberg was voted into the Hall of Fame in 1956.

336. Lou Gehrig of the New York Yankees knocked in 100 or more runs 13 consecutive seasons from 1926 until 1938. When he was forced to retire because of an illness which caused his death he was second only to Babe Ruth in homeruns (493) and runs batted in (1,990).

337. False. "Wahoo" Sam Crawford hit 16 homeruns in 1901 with Cincinnati to lead the National League. In 1908 he led the American League with 8 for the Detroit Tigers. Crawford still holds the lifetime record for triples with 312. He was inducted into the Hall of Fame in 1957.

338. Oakland Athletic's manager Billy Martin who won the award for the fourth time tying Casey Stengel. Martin also won it in 1974, 1976, and 1980.

339. Tony Oliva who in 1964 hit .323 good enough to win the American League batting championship. He also led the league in hits with 217 including 32 homeruns and 43 doubles. A severe knee injury hampered Oliva's movement in 1971 and he became a DH after that. He retired in 1976 with a .304 average.

340. George Foster, who led the league in homeruns in 1977 and 1978 with 52 and 40 respectively also led the National League in 1976, 77, and 1978 in RBI's with a three year total of 390, an average of 130 a year for the Reds.

341. True, the first year the award was given Lefty Grove of the Philadelphia Athletics won the MVP with a 31-4 record with a league leading 2.06 earned run average and 175 strikeouts. He also won two games in the World Series that year.

342. Cardinal second baseman Frankie Frisch who led his team to the 1931 World Championship over the Philadelphia Athletics. He hit .311 that year and led the league in stolen bases with 28. A lifetime .316 hitter he was inducted into the Hall of Fame in 1947.

343. Luke Appling of the Chicago White Sox, who played with them for all of his 20 seasons, hit .388 in 1936 for a record for shortstops. He had a lifetime .310 average with 2,749 hits and also hit over .300 16 out of the 20 years he played. Appling was elected to the Hall of Fame in 1964.

344. Ralph Kiner, who led the National League in homeruns from 1946 until 1952 with a total of 294 during that period for an average of 42 a year. In his 10 Major League seasons he hit 369 homeruns. He also hit over 50 homeruns in a season twice with 51 in 1947 and 54 in 1949.

349. Al Simmons who played with various teams in his 20 year Major League career, hit a lifetime .334 with 2,927 hits, 307 of which were homeruns. In his second major league season he had 253 hits and batted .384 for the Athletics. He twice led the American League in hitting with a .381 mark in 1930 and a .390 average in 1931. Simmons was elected into the Hall of Fame in 1953.

350. Carl Hubbell who compiled a 253-154 record in 16 major league seasons and a 2.97 earned run average. From 1933 until 1937 Hubbell had five straight 20 game seasons including a great 26-6 mark in 1936. He led the National League in ERA three times, twice in winning percentage, and once in shutouts with 10 in 1933. He was inducted into the Hall of Fame in 1947.

345. Luis Aparicio of the Chicago White Sox and Baltimore Orioles led the American League a record nine consecutive times from his rookie season in 1956 until 1964. During that span he stole 366 bases for an average of almost 41 a season.

346. Chick Hafey who played for 13 Major League seasons with the Cardinals and Reds hit a career .317. He was known for having the best throwing arm in the league and a very consistent bat.

347. "Smoky" Joe Wood who had one of the best seasons ever for a pitcher in 1912. He struck out 258 and also led the league in shutouts with 10 that year. The year before he no-hit St. Louis. What could have been a great career was cut short because of a severe arm injury. Wood still posted a fine 112-58 record with a 2.03 ERA.

348. Willie Mays first Major League hit was a homerun off Warren Spahn of the Boston Braves. He went on to hit a career 660 which is third on the all-time list.

351. Mathewson pitched for the New York Giants for 17 seasons and he won 372 games with them and one game for the Reds for a total of 373. He had a career 2.13 ERA with 83 shutouts. He won 30 games or more four times, led the league in ERA five times and five times in strikeouts. He was elected to the Hall of Fame in 1936.

352. Tom Seaver was 25-7 with a 2.21 earned run average plus a key victory over the Orioles in the Series in 1969. He also won the Cy Young Award that year. He has the lowest lifetime ERA since the introduction of the liveball (1920) with a 2.73 mark.

353. Three Finger Brown pitched for 14 Major League seasons and posted a 229-131 record with a great 2.06 ERA over that period. His rival of that time was Christy Mathewson. They met 24 times and Brown won 13. His best season, 1906, he was 25-6 with an unbelievable 1.04 ERA. He was inducted into the Hall of Fame in 1949.

354. Sisler mainly played first base but began his career as a pitcher. He hit .407 in 1920 with a record 257 hits and in 1922 he hit .420 with 246 hits. He was considered the greatest first baseman until Lou Gehrig came along. Sisler was elected into the Hall of Fame in 1939.

355. The pride of the Yankees, Lou Gehrig, who holds the record of 2,130 consecutive games played. In all he hit a career 493 homeruns with a .340 average and a record 23 career grandslams. He was inducted into the Hall of Fame in 1939.

356. Hank Greenberg who excited the baseball world in 1938 by hitting 58 homeruns for the Detroit Tigers. In all he hit 331 in his career and batted .313. Greenberg was voted into the Hall of Fame in 1956.

357. Jackie Robinson played 10 seasons with the Brooklyn Dodgers from 1947 until 1956. He batted a lifetime .311 and led the league in 1949 with a .342 average. A great base runner he stole home 19 times during his career, second only to Ty Cobb. He was elected to the Hall of Fame in 1962.

358. True. Willie Stargell led his team, the Pittsburgh Pirates, to the World Championship in 1979 and was voted along with St. Louis Cardinal first baseman Keith Hernandez co-winners of the Most Valuable Player Award in the National League.

359. Ed Walsh who played with the Chicago White Sox from 1904 until 1916 and a four game stint with Boston in 1917. He had a 194-130 lifetime record with a 1.82 earned run average. Walsh also no-hit the Red Sox on August 27, 1911.

360. As of 1983 Nolan Ryan of the Houston Astros has walked 2,022 batters compared to Early Wynn's 1,775 in his 23 year career from 1939 until 1963.

361. If you said Cesar Gutierrez you're right! He did this in 1970 for the Detroit Tigers. The only other time a player had seven consecutive hits in a game was in 1892, when Wilbert Robinson did it for the Baltimore club.

362. Billy Williams did that with the Chicago Cubs. The streak ran up to 1,117 games when it ended in 1970. Only one other player besides Gehrig played more games in succession—Everitt Deacon Scott also of the Yankees with 1,307.

363. Rube Waddell and Sandy Koufax are left handed pitchers.

364. Ron Hunt holds this painful record, having been hit by a pitch 50 times during his major league career.

365. False. Cy Young threw three no-hitters in his career including a perfect game against the Philadelphia Athletics on May 5, 1904 while playing for the Boston Red Sox.

366. In 1956 Dale Long did that for the Pirates and established a major league record in doing so. He ended the season with 27.

367. No, he came close twice. In 1934 and 1936 Gehrig led the American League with 49 homeruns. He hit over 20 homers in 13 seasons, over 30 in 10 seasons, and over 40 in 5 different seasons.

368. Of these three Babe Ruth walked the most with 2,056, Williams walked 2,019 times, and Kiner 1,011 times.

369. Mickey Mantle struck out a total of 1,710 times in 8,102 at bats compared to Babe Ruth who struck out 1,330 times out of 8,399 at bats.

WHAT DO YOU MEAN "STRIKE", HE HASN'T PITCHED IT YET!

370. Eddie Mathews who hit 509 homeruns with the Braves from 1952 until 1967. He joined the Detroit Tigers in his final season, 1968, and hit 3 with them for a career total of 512.

371. Frank Howard, who was known as "The Capitol Punisher" hit 10 homeruns in six consecutive games in 1968 for the Senators. He led the American League that season with 44.

372. False. There is no error given on a base on balls.

373. False. A designated hitter can be pinch hit for. The pinch hitter then becomes the DH, and the original DH can no longer participate in that game.

374. The four ex-Mets in the Hall of Fame are Willie Mays, Duke Snider, Warren Spahn, and Yogi Berra.

375. Tom Tresh won the rookie of the year award with the Yankees in 1962. He hit 20 homeruns and knocked in 93 runs while batting .286 in his freshman season.

376. Fred Lynn who caught the attention of the baseball fans with a great rookie season. He had 21 homeruns, 47 doubles, 103 runs scored, 105 RBI's, and a .331 batting average. He is also an outstanding outfielder.

377. Jim Rice is a right handed power hitting outfielder. In ten seasons he has hit 276 homeruns, 954 RBI's, and a .305 career batting average. Rice won the American League MVP award in 1978 when he hit 46 homeruns and drove in 139 runs to go along with a .315 batting average.

378. False. Agee won the rookie of the year award with the Chicago White Sox in the American League in 1966. He hit .273 with 22 homeruns and 86 RBI's while scoring 98 runs. Agee also stole 44 bases that year finishing third behind Bert Campenaris (52) and Don Buford (51).

379. Herb Score, whose career was so promising before an eye injury in 1957 cut his career short. He led the American League in 1955 and 56 with 245 and 263 strikeouts respectively to go along with a two year record of 36-19. After the injury Score was never again effective going 17-26 and then retired in 1962. His two good seasons were with the Cleveland Indians.

380. Robinson won the 1947 rookie of the year award with the Brooklyn Dodgers. He batted .297 with 31 doubles, 12 homeruns, scored 125 runs, and stole a league leading 24 bases.

381. Bench batted .275 with 40 doubles, 15 homeruns, and 82 runs batted in in 1968 and won the Rookie of the Year Award for his performance. His 1,031 RBI's during the 1970's are the most by any major leaguer in that decade.

382. Richie Allen won the 1964 Rookie of the Year Award with the Philadelphia Phillies. He hit .318 with 29 homeruns and 91 runs batted in. Allen also led the National League with 13 triples and 125 runs scored.

383. Jerry Koosman now of the Chicago Whitesox never won the award.

Trivia Game Player's Madness Strikes!

Whether your specialty is film or sports, astrology or music, there is something for everyone in these over-stuffed, *fun-tastic*, mind-boggling collections of facts, figures and titillating tidbits that will amaze and amuse your game playing partners long after you've packed away your board game and silenced your video!

The Game Player's Book of Complete Trivia

For hours of trivia game playing fun and hundreds of mind-boggling anecdotes, including:

What do bloomers, leotards and guillotines have in common?

Who said "A wide screen makes a bad film twice as bad?"

What was banned from U.S. television in 1971?

The Game Player's Book of Sports Trivia

Features the most recent scores, title holders and record breakers in sports history, guarantees hours of *sport-acular* fun! Including:

Which thoroughbred has won the most money ever?

To whom is the Vardon Trophy awarded annually?

Who was the smallest man ever to play in the major leagues?

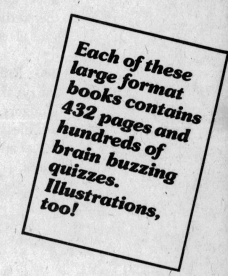

Each of these large format books contains 432 pages and hundreds of brain buzzing quizzes. Illustrations, too!
